D1135185

The Gentle Bonaparte

THE
Gentle Bonaparte

A BIOGRAPHY OF JOSEPH,
NAPOLEON'S ELDER BROTHER

. .
.

OWEN CONNELLY

New York: *The Macmillan Company*

London: *Collier-Macmillan Ltd.*

To my mother

A N D

*To the Empress
and the little King*

ACKNOWLEDGMENTS

THE AUTHOR wishes to express his appreciation for the extraordinary helpfulness of Dr. Whitfield J. Bell, Jr., Librarian of the American Philosophical Society and Mr. Murphy D. Smith, Assistant Librarian, Dr. David C. Mearns, Chief of the Manuscript Division of the Library of Congress, Dr. Herbert C. Schulz, Curator of Manuscripts of the Huntington Library and Art Gallery, Mr. Henry Cadwalader, Executive Director of the Historical Society of Pennsylvania (whose great-great-grandfather was a friend of Joseph Bonaparte), Miss Connie N. Sacco, Senior Reference Librarian of the Yale University Library, Mayor Theodore Rand of Watertown, New York, Mr. Bruce M. King, Curator of the Jefferson County (New York) Historical Society, Mr. Calvin S. Hathaway, R. Wistar Harvey Curator of Decorative Arts of the Philadelphia Museum of Art, and Mr. Kneeland McNulty, Curator of Prints and Drawings, and Madame Guynet-Péchadre, of the Direction des Musées de France. He is grateful also for the assistance of Mrs. Marjorie H. Pray, Genealogist of the Bordentown (New Jersey) Historical Society, Dr. James J. Heslin, Director of the New York Historical Society, Mr. Paul Z. DuBois, Librarian of the New York State Historical Association, Mrs. Lodice M. Grant of the Johns Hopkins University Press, Miss Dorothy W. Greer, Head of the Office of Public Relations of the Henry Francis du Pont Winterthur Museum, Mr. T. W. Webb of the British Museum, Mrs. Elizabeth G. Crouch, Registrar at The White House, Washington, D.C., Mr. R. O. Tudor of the National Gallery, London, Mr. John Sunderland of the Courtauld Institute of Art of the University of London, Señor Alfonso E. Perez Sanchez of the Museo del Prado, Madrid, Monsieur F. Jourdain of the Bibliothèque Nationale, Paris, and Monsieur B. Pannequin of the Musée National de Versailles.

The author is especially indebted to Peter Quennell, Esq., editor of *History Today*, for his encouragement and many favors and to Professor Herbert Rowen of Rutgers University, whose comments on the first draft of the manuscript were invaluable. He also wishes to thank the Research Council of the University of North Carolina at Greensboro, whose generous grants defrayed the cost of producing the manuscript.

The author gratefully acknowledges the permission of the following to reproduce the artworks indicated: The Bibliothèque Nationale de France for the Goya portrait of the Marquise de Montehermoso; the Musée National de Versailles for the Wicar portrait of Joseph Bonaparte and the Lefevre portrait of Julie Clary Bonaparte and her daughter Zénaïde; The Historical Society of Pennsylvania for the Peale portrait of Joseph Bonaparte. He thanks the following for permission to quote from manuscript material: The Archives des Affairs Étrangères, Paris, the Library of Congress, the American Philosophical Society, the Huntington Library and Art Gallery, the Yale University Library, the Jefferson County (New York) Historical Society, The New York Historical Society, and the Historical Society of Pennsylvania. He is indebted to Dr. Frank H. Sommer, of the Winterthur Museum, for leave to quote from the John Fanning Watson material he published in *The Winterthur Newsletter*.

CONTENTS

ILLUSTRATIONS

(following page 176)

Joseph Bonaparte in exile.

Julie Clary Bonaparte and daughter Zénaïde, by Lefevre.

Joseph Bonaparte, King of Spain, by Wicar.

The Marquise de Montehermoso as a young girl, by Goya.

Caroline Charlotte Bonaparte Benton, daughter of Joseph Bonaparte and Annette Savage.

MAPS

❧

The Gentle Bonaparte

CHARMER, novelist, convinced liberal, inveterate do-gooder, spinner of progressive dreams and friend of the common man, Joseph Bonaparte, the elder brother of Napoleon, was one of the most winning personalities of his era. Had the politicians who made Napoleon dictator of France in 1799 been looking for an American-style candidate to run for president (particularly if women had been voting), they might have chosen Joseph instead. "I wish you glory, and for myself your friendship," wrote Madame de Staël to him in 1802, and added, with unaccustomed modesty, "in sharing it, I shall be more fortunate than you." She expressed the feeling of the intellectual elite of the day. Joseph's friendships transcended politics, extending alike to the then royalist Lafayette and the Jacobin Saliceti. As Napoleon's diplomat, he negotiated the first general European peace in ten years, the Concordat with the Pope, and made life-long friends in the process. Lord Cornwallis so impressed his government with Joseph's honesty that when the Peace of Amiens was crumbling, the British would deal with no one else.

Taller, more handsome, more articulate and at ease in society than Napoleon, Joseph had been a successful lawyer and politician when his brother was an obscure lieutenant, and earlier the favorite of the family, his schoolmasters and fellow students. Napoleon loved him, but always envied him. Master of Europe, he blackened with rage when his old nurse said Joseph had been a *joli enfant* while he had not. As Emperor, he put his brother in high places, but seemed determined to prevent the rise of a "rival personality," to use Miot de Melito's words.

As King of Naples, then Spain, Joseph defended "his people" against Napoleon's tyranny, tried to institute constitutional government, and labored at reform and welfare projects. Bernardin de Saint-Pierre called him a philosopher-king. Napoleon ruled him a failure, particularly in Spain, because he refused to devote full time to the war, burn out villages which supported guerrillas, and make bloody examples of captives. "He is too good a man . . . to be a king," the ex-Emperor told Barry O'Meara on Saint Helena. The Count de Toreño, a leader of the rebellion in Spain, demurred: "He would have captivated the Spanish if they had not already been so gravely wounded [by Napoleon] as to honor and pride." When Napoleon said "good," he meant weak, and he continually called Joseph lazy and pleasure-loving, despite abundant evidence that he was neither.

Historians, generally, have accepted Napoleon's judgment. Yet Joseph had most of the qualities we purport to admire in our leaders. No man so beloved of women could have been a saint, but he was an honors student come of age, full of love for his fellowmen, and both a natural aristocrat and democrat. In exile in the United States after 1815, he won the respect and affection of hundreds of Americans. "Franklin and Jefferson," said his friend Charles J. Ingersoll, "were not more sincerely attached to liberty, equality, rational progress, and predominant peace." He was a revolutionary, but a quiet one, who believed men naturally good, capable of improvement by better environment and education, and able to perfect society. These are eighteenth-century propositions, but ones to which Americans are still dedicated.

The appellation "the Great" seems reserved for men of will and force—the conquerors, the spoilers, the wily manipulators of men and nations. Napoleon, who was much more than a soldier, deserves it more than most. But surely Joseph, who was his equal in most things, save ferocity and ambition, and by far his superior in human qualities and adherence to democratic principle, deserves to be remembered.

We celebrate here, therefore, not the Great Bonaparte, before whom all bowed but few loved, but the Gentle Bonaparte, who was loved by all.

The Gentle Bonaparte

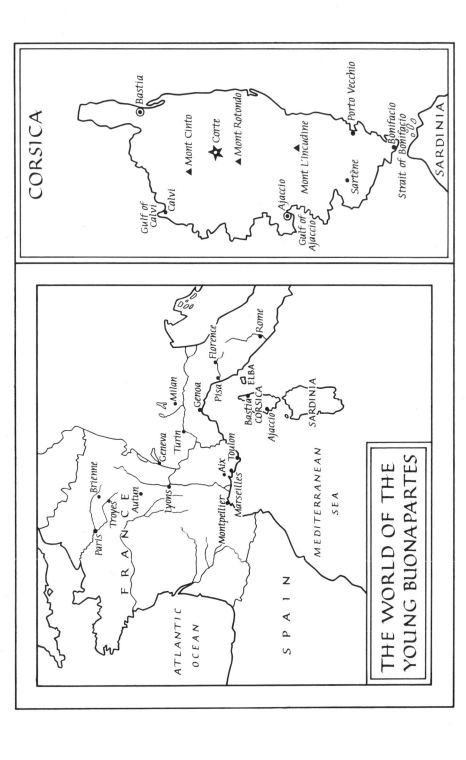

CORSICA

Bastia

▲ Mont Cinto
★ Corte
▲ Mont Rotondo

Porto Vecchio

Bonifacio
Strait of Bonifacio

SARDINIA

Gulf of
Calvi
Calvi

Ajaccio
Gulf of
Ajaccio

▲ Mont L'Incudine

Sartène

ATLANTIC
OCEAN

FRANCE

Paris
Troyes
Brienne
Autun

Lyons

Montpellier
Marseilles
Aix
Toulon

Geneva
Turin
Milan

Genoa
Pisa
Florence
Rome

ELBA

Bastia
CORSICA
Ajaccio

SARDINIA

SPAIN

MEDITERRANEAN
SEA

THE WORLD OF THE
YOUNG BUONAPARTES

⚜

CHAPTER I

The Corsican

GIUSEPPE BUONAPARTE

ON a bitter fall day in 1767, grizzled Corsican rebels in the streets of Corte watched in hushed awe as Letizia Buonaparte, on horseback, rode to the headquarters of Pasquale Paoli, their chief. Madame Buonaparte! *Com'è bella!* A living madonna! *Com'è bella!* Cloaked in black, obviously with child, her face pale with strain, she was still the most beautiful woman they had ever seen. Her head high, she gazed at them out of wide-set velvet eyes, nodding occasionally to an acquaintance (respectable Corsican women did not smile in public; many wore veils). Though only seventeen, she already had the calm dignity which would later impress the courts of Europe. Her poise was unbroken even when her young husband, Count Carlo de Buonaparte, came to lift her down, and she was guided through a guard of huge dogs to meet the elderly Babbo himself.

To reach the ancient capital, in the wild central highlands, she had ridden for days over icy mountain trails, where a missed step might mean death, balanced herself while her horse waded rivers, and wept as the gnarled scrub of the *maquis* whipped at her as she passed, and tore her clothes. Carlo chose to fight for Corsican independence; she saw no choice but to join him. Besides she wanted to be with him when their third child was born. Surely this one would not die like the other two! She had prayed to God *he* would live. Perhaps Carlo was foolish. The Babbo had rebelled against Genoa, and might have won their freedom, but

1

now French troops were pouring in. Rumor had it that Louis XV would buy the island. Could Paoli beat the French? *Se Dio vuole!* All was in the hands of God. Her place was with her husband.

In the rebel stronghold of Corte, Letizia gave birth to her son on 7 January 1768. It was a setting for the birth of a conqueror, this city on its high bluff amid gigantic spires of rock, with its Moorish battlements, populated by some of the fiercest fighting men on earth. But the baby would become the least bellicose, as well as the most charming, of her sons. He was christened Giuseppe, which would be rendered into French as Joseph. From the first he was a quiet and happy child.

HOME TO AJACCIO

Louis XV bought Corsica from Genoa in May of 1768. Defiant as always, Paoli kept the Moor's-head flag of the patriots flying for a year, but he could not win. French numbers and their deadly artillery slowly thinned the ranks of his valiant mountaineers, and crushed their spirit. In June of 1769 what remained of his army was almost annihilated at Ponte Nuovo. The survivors and their families, the Buonapartes among them, gathered in the caves of Monte Rotondo. Should they submit? "My children," said Paoli, "it is for you to think on and decide." There was no real alternative; the Babbo himself soon went into exile, ultimately in England.

Carlo chose to accept the amnesty offered by the French king. Back went the family to Ajaccio, Corsica's capital, major port, and largest city (population 3,000). There on 15 August was born Napoleone (whose name, Carlo would later tell French schoolmasters, had no equivalent in their language). He was, from the first, noisy and troublesome. For the next six years, Joseph and Napoleon had the household's full attention; until 1775 there were no more children who survived.

LETIZIA AND CARLO

Letizia, though perpetually pregnant, ruled Casa Buonaparte with an iron hand, applying Carlo's riding crop to young posteriors when she thought necessary—though hardly ever to Joseph's. Meanwhile she delighted the clergy by attending mass daily, and maintained her reputation as the belle of Corsica. "My mother was as beautiful as love," Napoleon later said. "The elegance of her figure, the radiance of her complexion, the regularity and delicacy of her features, made her a perfect beauty," wrote J. V. Colchen, the Intendant's secretary. She did not go unnoticed by General the Count de Marbeuf, the royal governor, an enlightened and humane administrator, but also a ladies' man. In his middle-fifties, the Count became such a patron of the Buonapartes that some were unkind enough to suggest that Letizia was his mistress. The truth, however, surely, is that he admired Letizia, liked Carlo and respected his ability, and found the connections of both very useful in taming the Corsicans.

Wrote Joseph of his father as he first remembered him: "Always a friend of liberty and of Paoli, whom he idolized, he had however become a good Frenchman, seeing the immense advantages his country gained from union with France." Within the strict conventions of European noble society, Count Carlo was something of an opportunist. He was tall and slender, with aristocratic features, a bright smile, a heavy shock of hair, always carefully powdered and tied into a queue, and huge blue eyes which melted the hearts of women of all ages. It was essential for a man-of-parts, he believed, to cut a *bella figura*; nay, it was a matter of honor. Go hungry if necessary, he told his sons, but never be without a good suit! But he never went hungry, Letizia saw to that. Extravagant he might be, but he was her husband. If money was short (and it usually was) she cut other expenses, not his.

Trained in the law at Pisa, a politician and superb social animal by nature, he made himself useful to Marbeuf. Beginning within his and Letizia's families, he built up a pro-French party, while advising the governor on Corsican law and customs and guiding his policy on pardons. The governor appointed him *procureur du roi* (prosecutor and substitute judge), evidence that Marbeuf did not want justice done severely, for he knew his protégé had little stomach for prosecuting. In 1774 Carlo was on the delegation representing Corsica at the coronation of Louis

XVI, and three years later returned to Versailles as Marbeuf's representative. His title confirmed by the King's *juge d'armes*, he became a French noble. Meanwhile, he had been elected to the Corsican parliament (*états*), and there appointed to a twelve-man delegation which represented the body before the governor.

In 1777, when Carlo was thirty-one and Letizia twenty-seven, they were leading citizens of the island. In the interior, however, they were looked on with suspicion by many, perhaps the majority, of their countrymen. This fact later affected the lives of the whole Buonaparte clan; it deserves explanation.

CORSICA AND CORSICANS

The first Buonaparte had come to Corsica in 1567, the first Ramolino (Letizia's ancestor) about the same time. To the mountaineers, both families were newcomers. Both were originally Florentine and of Italian nobility, though Letizia's had no specific title, and both had remained oriented toward Italy. (Joseph, in his memoirs, takes pains to emphasize that the Buonapartes were not *insulaires*, but cultivated people with European connections.) Moreover, both the Buonapartes and the Ramolinos had served the Genoan government, from the first generation onward. Though they had relatives in the interior, particularly on Letizia's side, they had shown little sympathy for the mountaineers' violent nationalism until the power of Genoa had badly faded. Like most coastal aristocrats, they had prospered as vassals of Genoa. It was easy for them to take service with the French. To the mountaineers this made them almost traitors. Only a man of the stature of Paoli could serve France (as he would later, for a short time) and still be accepted as a true Corsican.

The *insulaires* had seen many conquerors; they wanted *none*. The Moor's-head flag was theirs. It was a curious symbol for a rigidly Catholic people, but apt. Like the Moslem pirates who had sometimes ruled their ports, they defied the world of great nations. Over the centuries, Etruscans, Phoenicians, Greeks, Carthaginians, Romans, Byzantines, Vandals, Goths, and Saracen Turks had held the island. Each new group of conquerors had absorbed a few of the old and pushed the rest into the interior, a land of *maquis*, jagged peaks, deep forested valleys, and gorges laced by roaring, dangerous streams. There, by late medieval times, the progeny of successive waves of warriors had become one people. Corsica, fought over by Italian city-states, occasionally seized by North African deys or pirates, had belonged to Genoa most of the time between 1347 and 1768. But the mountaineers had never truly submitted to anyone.

If the Corsicans could not govern themselves, they ignored the conqueror's law, avoided his taxes, and lived to themselves. Tough, independent, they were disciplined by the customs of their clans and a Christianity which extolled Spartan virtues in men and women, and unquestioning submission in the latter. The French, in one two-year period, recorded 130 murders among them; *one* assassin was punished by the King's courts (which Carlo, and later Joseph, served). "Savage," wrote Miot de Melito of Corsica, "people and mountains uniformly draped in brown." He spoke of the interior, not Ajaccio, Bastia, and the other outposts of Europe.

Some Spartan attitudes rubbed off on the coastal people, but they were not of the fierce mountain breed. The Buonapartes were more Italian than Corsican, and the men, for the most part, had been magistrates, not soldiers. Joseph was more typical of the clan than Napoleon.

When, later, the hard-core Corsicans had a chance to strike for independence, they did. "They returned naturally to their ancient passions," wrote Joseph. The Buonapartes, who remained loyal to France, had to flee the island. For none of them was this a more gigantic event than Joseph, then the clan chief and high in the Corsican government.

JOSEPH AND NAPOLEON: BOYHOOD

"Lazy! At your age I could already beat Joseph," Napoleon once said playfully to his two-year-old son. He did not exaggerate much, but he failed to say that his elder brother seldom fought back. When he did, he could hold his own, but he had to be goaded into it. At heart, he didn't understand why Napoleon wanted to fight, and was always challenging, pushing, and demanding.

Perhaps it was because Joseph was the first child to survive of parents who desperately wanted children. Letizia had coddled him as she never did any of her other children, except perhaps Jérôme, the last, born just before his father's death. He effortlessly got attention from everyone, even his gruff great-uncle, Lucciano Buonaparte, Archdeacon of the Ajaccio cathedral. His paternal grandmother, Maria Saveria, accused Letizia of spoiling him, but so did she, and so did his Aunt Gertruda Paravicini and Great-Aunt Marianna, all of whom lived at Casa Buonaparte. He was a miniature Carlo, down to the wide blue eyes; a beautiful boy, strong, athletic, and full of fun, but understanding of adults, obedient, and good. Everyone protected him; to do Joseph hurt seemed almost a sacrilege, particularly to the women (all his life it would be so). He was the favored, the heir, the future head of the clan, and he always knew it. He grew up the relaxed aristocrat, sure of his title, willing to let the scrambling Napoleon have his small triumphs.

Napoleon was not so handsome as Joseph, and his arrival was no great event. He was cared for by a wet nurse, Camilla Ilari, and a cantankerous servant, Mammuccia Catarina, who was always at odds with Letizia, and seemed for a while to be his only partisan. It quickly became apparent to him that he would have to fight for attention, and he did. Letizia set aside a large room where the boys could do anything they liked. Joseph drew houses, churches, and horses on the walls, looked at pictures, stacked blocks. Napoleon scattered everything, drew soldiers and cannon, assailed Joseph with his wooden sword, and beat his drum with all his might. Later he had to ride the wildest horses, climb the highest trees, and swim when it was stormy, always daring Joseph to do the same. Whereas Joseph, adopting the tastes of Carlo and Great-Uncle Lucciano, loved literature and religious works, Napoleon specialized in mathematics, a mystery to his relatives, the more to amaze and impress them.

Letizia kept the boys out of doors as much as possible. They learned to ride on the family farms at Bocagnano and Bastelica; they explored the rocky coast; they followed the peasants in the fields and the goatherds in the hills, and watched the planting and pruning of mulberry trees (for which Carlo had a royal subsidy). Their health benefitted, and they learned about their father's estates, an essential part of their education.

Corsican aristocrats lived close to the soil; they were not ashamed of muscles and dirty hands. Education, connections, and leadership ability separated them from the people. Their houses might be larger, and boast some furniture and tableware from Europe, but they were scarcely more comfortable than the peasants'. Casa Buonaparte was of stone, four stories high, and had some twenty rooms, but it was drafty and dark, with low ceilings, slits of windows, and bare as a monastery. Letizia later exploded a story that Napoleon had drawn military formations on a rug by snapping "We had no rugs in Corsica!" Food for the family came from the farms, as did wool for cloth-making. Carlo might order suits from France or Italy, but the rest of the family wore mostly homespun, tailored by the women at home.

Joseph developed a deep love of the country. Later, when fabulous palaces were available to him successively in Paris, Naples, and Madrid, he always spent as much time as possible at country places. In exile in the United States, he shunned Philadelphia and New York for an estate in rural New Jersey, where visitors often found him working with his men in the gardens, pruning trees, or laying brick. In 1818, *Niles' Register* reported in some amazement that the ex-King had been observed helping unload furniture for his new home. To those who knew his origins, this would have come as no surprise. As a child, he had been happy walking in the fields and woods, watching things grow, grubbing in the soil, imagining himself overseer of the estates. Napoleon had no such attachment for the soil. The farms were a stage where he could alarm and impress his elders with the risks he took, the family mill a place to astound the miller by calculating its daily capacity. To Joseph the country was a place of pastoral miracles and a refuge from conflict. Involved in it all, but not faced with the daily, grinding work of a peasant, or his perpetual fear of seeing his crops ruined by storms, drought, or plague, he was a rare combination of rustic and romantic. All his life, his one real ambition was to be a gentleman farmer.

SCHOOLING

Joseph and Napoleon, at ages five and four, went to a sort of kindergarten kept by Béguine nuns, then, each when he was six, to the best secondary school available, that of the Abbé Recco. Joseph had made his peace with Napoleon by the time they started school—by letting him have his way in what seemed to him small things. *Noblesse oblige.* Shamed by his easy victories, the little wolf, with his hard, blue-gray eyes, had balanced the account by becoming Joseph's protector. Napoleon never stopped competing, however. He made up for Joseph's advantages in size and looks by ferocity, Joseph's greater charm by flaunting his abilities. (When they were adults, Joseph would still have the same advantages.) Napoleon envied Joseph's grace, gentle qualities, and the easy way he made friends. Joseph, in turn, often wished he could dominate and terrorize like Napoleon. But when the chips were down, Napoleon's affection (and he could be very warm when he had his way) was more important to him than a victory of force or will. Napoleon knew it, and used the fact all their lives, but often hated himself for doing so.

The Abbé Recco, an inventive teacher, once divided the class into Romans and Carthaginians, with the sides sitting facing each other, wooden swords and shields of their nations behind them on the wall. The best scholars each day were to claim a trophy from the other side. Joseph was made a Roman, Napoleon a Carthaginian. No! Shouted the younger Buonaparte. He would not sit with the "losers." But, the good Abbé explained, they were not to have a war, the best scholars would win. No! Joseph, quietly, crossed to the Carthaginian side; Napoleon took his seat with the Romans. The Abbé went on with the class. Napoleon was not proud of his victory, Joseph later recorded: "It required all the authority of our mother to calm him." Probably Napoleon was upset. It is significant, however, that it was Joseph, writing fifty years later, who made a point of it. Undoubtedly Joseph was the more guilt-ridden of the two. All his life, he would find rational reasons for giving in to Napoleon. But he would always wonder if he had been a coward.

Both boys showed a precocious attraction to the opposite sex. The nuns in their first school were charmed to see them walking arm-in-arm with tiny *amies*. Interestingly, however, while Napoleon, moonstruck, pursued little Giocominetta, Joseph's friend sought him out. In their relations with women, the pattern would hold in later years. They never really competed with each other, but Napoleon had always found *the* girl, who noticed him if it were to her advantage; Joseph had women waiting in the wings. Much later, he would cheerfully leave the very young Désirée Clary to Napoleon, who, however, could make little of his opportunity.

CAREERS

Joseph, the Abbé Recco told Letizia after the Roman-Carthaginian incident, was a fine boy—very mature, very Christian. Should he not be trained for the clergy? He was years behind the family in thinking of it. Carlo and the Archdeacon Lucciano had long ago decided to make a bishop of Joseph. They liked to think of Joseph's response to Napoleon's bullying as a display of Christian courage and good sense, though they had their doubts. Both cheered secretly when Joseph occasionally lost his temper and used his greater size and strength to down his little brother, then sighed resignedly when, on next encounter, Napoleon won. Joseph could never stay angry for long; Napoleon was relentless. Everyone agreed that Joseph should go into the Church, and he did not argue. Napoleon made his own choice; the profession of war, either in the army or navy.

For Joseph, Marbeuf secured the patronage of his nephew, the Bishop of Autun, whose diocese boasted the Oratorian *collège d'Autun*. For Napoleon, Carlo petitioned the King for a military scholarship, and one was awarded for Brienne, one of twelve military schools which fed its better scholars to the *école militaire*, in Paris. It was planned for both to go initially to Autun and concentrate on learning French, since neither spoke anything but Italian. When they had mastered the rudiments, Joseph would enter regular classes at Autun and Napoleon go on to Brienne.

Those who think Carlo offered Napoleon's name to the King because he thought Joseph duller are wrong. The attitudes of the Buonapartes were *Italian*, not French, and for Italians, the military was not a preferred career. Like their forbearers in the the Renaissance city-states, they honored semi-amateur, patriot soldiers, but looked on professionals as mercenaries—*condottiere*. Churchmen had much more prestige; moreover, if at all successful, they had better incomes. Even in France, where officers were more highly regarded, few could live on their salaries. Joseph was fully expected to become a bishop. There was scant hope that Napoleon would be a general (or admiral); what chance had an obscure Corsican against the scions of ancient French nobility? Ability was recognized in the army (and navy), but for top positions, credentials were required as well. But for the Revolution, Napoleon might have lived in gentile poverty on obscure posts all his life. As a second lieutenant, we know, he missed meals to save money for books. It was *six years* before he became a first lieutenant, which brought him only twenty percent more pay; he might never have been more than a captain. Joseph could anticipate not only a secure and comfortable life, but a benefice in Corsica, where he could serve as clan chief. It was Joseph, not Napoleon, on whom the family pinned its greatest hopes. It is only in the light of later events that the reverse seems true.

Both boys had made exceptional records at the Abbé Recco's school. Napoleon's reputation as a boy-genius stems from his own dramatizing of his abilities (a talent he never lost) and the influence on memorists of his later career. Most of the stories of his childhood intellectual feats, perforce, came to light after he became Emperor of the French. Letizia, for one, scoffed at most of them. He was a *child*, she kept saying; he liked swords, drums, and soldiers.

The little boys, Joseph, ten, and Napoleon, nine, shepherded by Carlo, left for France in December 1778. Letizia and the royal governor accompanied them to shipside at Bastia. They cried a little, but arm in arm, waved bravely from the rail as their vessel put out to sea. *Coraggio!* (Courage!) was Letizia's last word. She knew she would not see them for years. Already there were three more children at home—Lucien (Lucciano), three, Elisa (Maria Anna), two, and Louis (Luigi), a babe-in-arms. As she doubtless expected, more would come—Pauline (Maria Paola) in 1780, Caroline (Maria Annunziata) in 1782, and Jérôme (Girolamo) in 1784.

It was Joseph his mother missed. Since his father was often

away, she had taken to discussing family problems with him. He had been her little confessor, grave and attentive, full of sympathy, inclined to see the happy side of things. It had made life easier to talk to him. *Coraggio* Giuseppe!

AUTUN

A limpid tributary of the Loire reflected the spires of the ancient town of Autun. With its Roman ruins, magnificent twelfth-century cathedral, and scrubbed, tree-lined streets, it was beautiful, but least so perhaps in January, when Joseph and Napoleon arrived. Black skeletons of trees against a gray sky, the towering Gothic spires of the cathedral, and the mere size of the place were all frightening to little boys from tiny Ajaccio. But the Bishop was benevolent, the principal friendly, and their father stayed for a few days, spreading cheer among the faculty of the *collège* and reassuring his boys. They were soon settled and hard at learning French.

Joseph had to begin by learning to pronounce his name; he would never be Giuseppe again. Napoleone kept his, but was soon keeping the final "e" silent, and would later drop it. Under compulsion to communicate, goaded on by the jibes of schoolmates at the age of maximum barbarism, they progressed rapidly. In three months both were pronounced able to enter classes, and Napoleon had to leave for Brienne.

They parted sadly, Joseph bawling, Napoleon poker-faced with eyes red and wet. "He shed only one tear," the sub-principal told Joseph, "but it proves his pain at leaving you as much as all of yours." It was true. The Abbé saw that Napoleon needed Joseph much more, in fact, than Joseph needed him. Napoleon's extreme pride, his temper, and the Corsican nationalism he had defensively espoused had alienated his schoolmates. Joseph was popular; he would get along. Easygoing, pleasant, determined to be French, generous with what little he had, he already had many of the boys helping him and siding with him. Napoleon was in for lonely years and, in the beginning, outright persecution, at Brienne. Joseph faced happy school years.

The great tragedy of Napoleon's life is that no one ever liked him. He was feared, respected, worshiped, and perhaps loved by some women, but he was never liked. The great glory of Joseph's life is that he was liked by almost everybody, even those who could not respect him. Even Joseph, in later life, preferred to remember the young Napoleon, who "was much different from the way he is represented by authors of memoirs." There was always, however, an unbreakable bond of affection between the two. When Napoleon could trust no one else, he always called on Joseph, and for him, Joseph sometimes undertook the impossible.

Joseph visited Carlo and Letizia in 1782, when they came to the baths at Bourbonne. Otherwise, for five years, he was in contact with his family only by letter. At school, he was relaxed, self-assured, and so organized in his work that some thought him lazy. His record proves to the contrary. In 1783 he was first in his class, had the lead in the school play, and won first prize in *French* for an essay on a tragedy of Corneille. His competence in literature startled everyone except the librarian, who knew he had read almost every novel and play available—secretly, so as to preserve his image of hail-fellow-well-met among his schoolmates. In his *collège*, the principal later told Carlo (he said), there was "neither scientist, nor rhetorician, nor philosopher with such talents as Joseph." High praise indeed, even allowing for a little exaggeration by a proud father.

Joseph was an unqualified success, both as a scholar and human being. His future seemed assured; no one questioned that someday he would be a bishop.

To Serve the King

Napoleon, however, had been exercising his dramatic talents in his letters to Joseph. He was making a fine record at Brienne, but he was a very unhappy boy. Belligerent, introverted, still shouting "Hail Paoli" and swearing Corsica would expel the "tyrants," he had few friends among his French classmates. His letters, however, were full of the glories of military life and the adventures ahead. Joseph was bored. Brienne made Autun seem like a cemetery! And life in the Church! They were fine, the Abbé Chardon, the Abbé Simon, and the others, but did they ever have any fun? And they could *never* touch women. Armed with all the vast knowledge gained in discussions with his teen-aged friends, he decided he wanted no part of the celibate life. No! He must somehow join Napoleon at Brienne. The army was the life for him.

Just when he had made his decision, the Prince de Condé, governor of Burgundy, arrived to distribute the school prizes for 1783. Joseph, a winner and also Autun's most poised student orator, recited poetry in his honor. The Prince was impressed. What will be your career? he asked. The Bishop of Autun, experienced with tongue-tied boys, gently spoke for him: "the Church." To his amazement, Joseph, bowing, had another answer: *Non, Monseigneur le Prince,* "I want to serve the King!" Condé was delighted. Then you shall, my son, you shall.

The next day Joseph wrote Napoleon that he was going into the army—the *artillery.* The future Emperor immediately decided that *he too* would choose the artillery. Until the letter arrived he had been uncertain which arm of service he preferred, and still thought vaguely of a navy career. He then undertook to persuade his father and uncles that his brother was making a mistake. Surely resentment that Joseph, with the world at his feet, had casually decided to invade his domain, motivated him, at least in part.

Napoleon was fourteen, and the letters he wrote have been quoted a hundred times to prove his precocity. "With his [Joseph's] talents he will always come off well in society. But in a battle? . . . He is sure to be a bishop. What advantages for the family!" Undoubtedly, Napoleon was a prodigy, but in this case he was only restating, if exceptionally well, what his elders had said repeatedly in his presence. Moreover, he was not altogether right. In some battles, as we shall note, Joseph came off very well, though Napoleon himself would never admit as much.

One thing is certain: The future Emperor was *not* already dominating the family, as some biographers imply. His father did *not* take his advice. Though much disappointed with Joseph's decision, Carlo let him have his way. Armed with a glowing recommendation of his prize pupil from the principal of Autun, he secured a military scholarship for Joseph, who prepared to enter either Brienne or Metz, a similar school. When Napoleon heard, he begged Carlo to send Joseph to Brienne. Defeated in his attempt to thwart Joseph's plans, the desire to have him near overcame all resentment. Fate, however, now called the turn. Joseph was destined to be neither priest nor soldier.

HEAD OF THE FAMILY

In the spring of 1784, Carlo had visited Paris to petition in Joseph's behalf, arrange for the schooling of Lucien and Elisa, and consult physicians about his own condition. He was plagued with severe stomach pains, fainting spells, and general weakness. Discouraged because the doctors could not help him, and perhaps with a vague premonition of death, he visited Joseph at Autun in June and asked him to return to Corsica for a few months. The vacation would do him good, Carlo said, and they could discuss his future. Perhaps it would be better if Joseph became a lawyer; then he could better care for the family in case of need. Happy at the prospect of seeing his mother and the others again, Joseph agreed.

The homecoming was happy, but Ajaccio struck him as very rustic now, and Casa Buonaparte, which he remembered as large and comfortable, seemed cramped and bare. His Italian brought gales of laughter from the younger children; he had almost forgotten his native tongue. For a while, he was homesick for France, and though that was soon cured, he was firm in his resolve to return to Brienne or Metz. In the fall, he concentrated on learning mathematics for his artillery examination.

Carlo's health, meanwhile, got worse. At the end of the year, he and Joseph set out for Paris, where he hoped to consult the Queen's physician, Monsieur de la Sonde. The voyage weakened him, however, and on making port they went instead to consult the medical faculty at Montpellier. It was too late. There, at the home of a family friend and fellow Corsican, Madame Permon, Carlo died on 24 January 1785; he was thirty-nine. His malady, probably stomach cancer, may have been the same that killed Napoleon at Saint Helena.

Joseph was at his father's bedside constantly until the end, seconded by his uncle, Joseph Fesch, a seminarian at Aix-en-Provence (Letizia's half-brother, he was only twenty-two). The two young men saw to Carlo's interment at Montpellier. Exhausted and emotionally drained, Joseph numbly agreed to accompany Fesch to Aix for a few days' rest.

In the sunny Provençal town, among Corsican friends, he quickly faced up to his new situation. At seventeen, he was the head of the family. For a man of his character, there was no question as to what he must do. He had to return to Corsica, help his mother care for the four children still at home, and manage the estates. The decision made, it seemed his natural destiny. Signing "Joseph, Comte de Buonaparte," he booked passage for Ajaccio, where his weeping mother met him at the dock.

THE YOUNG COUNT

Joseph was like his father in looks, though he soon grew taller; in manner, he was, if anything, more polished, though subject to boyish lapses. Mothers with marriageable daughters beset him at every turn; women threw themselves at him. But in the first years he gave them little encouragement.

He had not returned to Ajaccio for pleasure. Very quickly, he learned enough to unburden Letizia of many business problems, turning to her, and Great Uncle Lucciano, when he needed advice. In off hours, he read law in preparation for eventual examination at Pisa. He also schooled himself in the literature of the enlightenment, which had not been highly regarded at Autun.

Napoleon, meanwhile, had won the privilege of completing his education at the *école militaire* (1784), emerged a sub-lieutenant (1785), and begun service in an artillery regiment. In September 1786, he came home on leave, and managed to stay a year. Never were the brothers closer. Napoleon, unable to afford much of a social life, and still ill at ease in his adopted country, had turned furiously to reading. His biggest trunk was crammed with books, not only professional ones, but the works of Plato, Plutarch, Tacitus, Montaigne, and, to Joseph's delight, French classical drama and the writings of the *philosophes*. For a few months they met happily on common intellectual ground, "declaiming daily" from Racine and Corneille, discussing the "ideal world" of the *philosophes*. Napoleon, wrote Joseph, "was an impassioned admirer of Jean-Jacques [Rousseau]." So were they both; but Napoleon would come to believe that Rousseau meant the "general will" to be interpreted by a select few (or *one*), a view Joseph could never accept. In these happy months, however, they were in general agreement, and discussion was food and wine. If there were meetings in the Elysian fields, Joseph said later, he would want to see Napoleon as he was then. For a little time, Napoleon had shared Joseph's faith both in enlightenment and the common man.

The future Emperor also undertook to "save" the family. The estates, he allowed, were being run in medieval fashion. He wanted to improve the mulberry trees by grafting, introduce French methods of cultivation, and bring in cattle to replace the goats, who destroyed trees and shrubs. "Drive the goats from Corsica?" shouted Great Uncle Lucciano. "So those are your philosophical ideas!" Joseph sympathized with Napoleon, but had to ask where they would get the money for everything. The King! intoned his confident brother, and sent petitions to Versailles. He got no answer. Having stretched his leave to the maximum, spent his pay and money borrowed from Joseph, Napoleon left to join his regiment in September 1787.

THE LAW AND POLITICS

Joseph departed shortly for Pisa "to perfect my Italian, study law, and see to family interests." He managed also to meet Archbishop Loménie de Brienne, one of the most powerful men in France, and through him the Grand Duke of Tuscany, Leopold (later Holy Roman Emperor), famed for his enlightened policies. At nineteen, he displayed a sure talent for ingratiating himself with the mighty, but was still capable of boyish indiscretion. For a short time, more out of hero-worship than anything else, he was associated with Corsican exiles, led by Clement Paoli (the Babbo's brother), and fell under the influence of Christophe

Saliceti, at the time a fiery young proponent of Corsican independence.

Joseph was as much in Florence as Pisa, where, he wrote, "I frequented the University." He had already prepared himself rather thoroughly, however, making use of his father's small but select library. In early 1788 he passed his examinations and became a doctor of laws, *in utroque jure*, certified in both the civil and canon law.

Back in Corsica, Joseph was summoned almost immediately by the mayor of Ajaccio, J. J. Lévie, to be his assistant. Before the year was out he was qualified to plead before the high court of Corsica, at Bastia. His law degree, added to his fluency in French, gave him great advantages. Laurent Giubega, secretary-general of the Corsican parliament, made him his protégé. Madame Giubega began a campaign to marry him to her fetching daughter, Annette, who would soon be of age. The young Count's future seemed bright.

Napoleon returned for a few months during 1788 to complicate Joseph's life. He had changed. Still enamored of Rousseau, he was now an outright revolutionary. At the same time, he was, as ever, a violent Corsican nationalist. The French government was embattled, he said, the King weak and vascillating. What better time to strike for independence? Impatient with the progress of his career, bored with garrison life, he wanted action—a chance to display his talents. Joseph was appalled. He had abandoned island patriotism as impractical and childish after his flirtation with the exiles at Pisa. Drop the French connection? Become *insulaires*? He argued with his brother, but the more he did, the more violent he became. Their Francophile friends began to mutter charges of treason against Napoleon. Joseph, hard put to smooth things over, was relieved when the army refused to extend Napoleon's leave, and he returned to France.

The explosion of the French Revolution in 1789 produced violence in Corsica, which was added to after August by Lieutenant N. Buonaparte, again on leave. His line was the rights of man and freedom from French hirelings—no longer outright independence. Joseph, on the side of moderation, was on a committee which installed municipal guards and worked to reestablish order in Ajaccio. Before anything untoward could happen, however, the French National Assembly resolved that Paoli be invited to return from exile and govern Corsica. Louis XVI assented, and Paoli accepted the appointment, which, astonishingly, carried with it a French general's rank and command of the King's troops on the island.

Corsica celebrated. The extreme Francophiles had their reservations, but could not really object. Joseph was on the delegation which met the Babbo at Marseilles and sailed with him to Bastia, where thousands from all parts of the island had gathered to welcome him. At Marseilles Paoli had taken an immediate liking to Joseph, whom he presented with a signed sketch of himself which Carlo had made, twenty years before, at Corte.

With the sons of Carlo, the Babbo said, he could never have differences. He had not yet gotten acquainted with Napoleon, however.

❧

CHAPTER II

The Republican

THE ARCHDEACON'S PROPHECY

O N the evening of 15 October 1791, the Archdeacon Luc- ciano, patriarch of the Buonaparte clan, lay dying, sur- rounded by his family. Madame Letizia sat by his bed, with Joseph standing quietly behind her, while Napoleon moved about restlessly. Joseph, at twenty-three, had just been elected to the departmental directory, and was one of four men who, under the presidency of Paoli, governed Corsica.* Napoleon, by com- parison, was a failure. After six years as an officer, he had only recently been made a first lieutenant. It was not love of family which had brought him home, but hope of getting higher rank in the Corsican national guard.

Looking up, Great Uncle Lucciano saw that Letizia was fighting back tears. He put a gnarled hand on her arm.

"Don't cry; I die happy. . . . My existence is no longer necessary to Carlo's children. Joseph is at the head of the administration of the country: he can manage the family."

He gazed at the faces around him; all were grave and sorrow- ful—but one. Napoleon's was flushed with anger; his feelings were hurt.

---

* The plan of the French National Assembly called for two Corsican de- partments, Golo, in the north, and Liamone, in the south. Paoli, how- ever, governed the island as one department. The prescribed depart- ments were not established until 1797.

"Tu poi, Napoleone," he said, searching for words. "You, Napoleon, will be a great man!"

Uncounted books have recorded the Archdeacon's words to Napoleon, ignoring the context. Probably what the crusty Lucciano really thought was that if his grandnephew lived to maturity it would be a miracle. He himself was a confirmed noncombatant; in the old days he had stayed in French-occupied Ajaccio and let Paoli and "that fool" Carlo fight the invader. It was Joseph whom he thought destined for success, if not greatness, as did the rest of the family. The young head of the family had barely missed being elected to the French Legislative Assembly in 1791. His directorship was a consolation prize from Paoli. At the next election he might well go to Paris.

In 1791, even Napoleon, though loath to admit it, pinned his hopes on Joseph, who knew island politics, and had influence with Paoli. Napoleon's credit with the Babbo was nil.

THE BROTHERS-POLITICIANS

In 1790, when Paoli arrived, Napoleon had greeted him with a flattering letter, full of revolutionary clichés. "An intriguer," ruled the Babbo, and sent no answer. Joseph then took his brother to see the "Washington of Corsica," who was near Ponte Nuovo, the scene of his defeat in 1769. How, Napoleon asked Paoli, had he disposed his forces on that day? The old general showed him. Napoleon tried to display only interest, but his contempt was ill disguised. Paoli got what he deserved, he said later, and the word got to the general. He could find no place for "that little lieutenant," and Napoleon, his leave running out, returned to France.

Joseph, on the other hand, was greatly favored. In the fall of 1790 he was secretary of the electoral assembly which filled local offices. It gave him a place on the directory of the Ajaccio district. In 1791, his candidacy for the Paris Assembly had been opposed by the Babbo, who had, however, assured his election to the departmental directory. For a man of his age, Joseph had risen fast and far.

Elections were to be held in early 1792 for officers of volunteer battalions. Immediately after the Archdeacon Lucciano's funeral, Napoleon launched a campaign to make himself commander (lieutenant colonel) of the Ajaccio unit. Paoli, however, threw his support to Pozzo di Borgo. Joseph was in a quandary. Pozzo was his friend, and he disliked opposing the Babbo. Napoleon, however, would not give up. He had begun a fight! The honor of the family! Joseph went along with him, and while Letizia grumbled, they kept Casa Buonaparte open at all hours and poured wine by the flagon into potential backers. In the end they made a deal with a third candidate, Quenza. During a stormy four-day election, which ended on 31 March 1792, their supporters combined to make Quenza lieutenant colonel and Napoleon second lieutenant colonel. Napoleon took over the actual command.

Within a week, Joseph was sorry he had gotten involved. Ajaccio had become restive, first over the law requiring priests to take an oath to the Revolutionary government and then over the expulsion of the much beloved Capuchin friars from their monastery. Napoleon, expecting some demonstration on Easter, gathered his whole battalion into the city. Most of his volunteers were mountain men, hostile to the city dwellers. Their very presence invited violence.

On Easter, Napoleon got what he expected, and had almost arranged for. While non-juring priests conducted mass at the Capuchin monastery, a fight broke out in the streets. The volunteers got involved, shots were exchanged, and a lieutenant killed. Napoleon barricaded his men in the Capuchin monastery, the town seminary, and fortified houses. Eight days of violence ensued, during which Napoleon defied demands to withdraw from both the municipal authorities and the French commander of the citadel, Colonel Maillard. His militiamen, their nerves rubbed raw, fired at anyone in the streets, even killing two women as they emerged from the cathedral.

Joseph, all the while, was at Corte, where he had rejoined the directory after Napoleon's election. When the news arrived of the situation in Ajaccio, he recommended that Paoli send representatives to negotiate a settlement, and after they departed, decided to go himself. The delegation wasted no time in ordering Napoleon to take his troops away. He refused. Death before dishonor! Joseph, however, arrived to persuade him it would be death, and he changed his mind.

The Buonaparte brothers had few friends left in Ajaccio; Napoleon had few on the whole island. *"Napoleone e causa di tutto,"* says Georges-Roux, was the general opinion. Maillard thought he deserved a court-martial. Joseph took his brother back to Corte, but said softly: "It seems to me the time for you to go to France." Paoli concurred, promising Napoleon another command later, but telling Joseph he would not give it. On 20 May Napoleon was in Paris, where he found he had been thrown out of the army. France had gone to war in April, however, all Europe was aligning against her, and many trained officers had emigrated, so the war minister was in a generous mood. Lieutenant Buonaparte was reinstated and promoted (July 1792) to captain, but he was not satisfied. Corsica still beckoned.

JOSEPH AND LUCIEN

Napoleon gone, Joseph worked to repair his political fences. In France, meanwhile, the Revolution entered its bloodiest phase when on 10 August 1792 mobs drove the royal family from the Tuileries. While Paris mobs indiscriminately butchered "enemies of liberty" in the streets, nationwide elections were held for the Convention, which would found a republic and try the King.

Joseph was an unsuccessful candidate, but could claim friendship with all six Corsican delegates, including the most radical, Christophe Saliceti, the only one who later voted for the execution of Louis XVI. Whatever the temper of the Convention, Joseph would have had influence there; it was one of his great natural skills to retain the regard even of opponents. As it turned out, Saliceti would be the family's salvation. The fiery Jacobin, even in his happiest moods, was a sinister figure. Tall, cadaverous, he seemed perfect for the part he would later play—master spy and policeman. At this juncture, he had challenged Paoli, whom he thought superannuated, for leadership.

Joseph had moved in his direction, if cautiously, because of the Babbo's lack of energy and disquiet over events in Paris: "Paoli was our President [on the directory] but he didn't attend our meetings. . . . His adherence to the Revolution was not total. The King had . . . written him asking that he protect his Island of Corsica." The young Count de Buonaparte had royalist leanings himself, but he was before all else a Frenchman. Whatever the Convention decided, Joseph would accept as the will of the people, even if it meant shedding his own title.

While he awaited news from France, Lucien was his greatest problem. Now seventeen, he had thrown over a Church career and left the seminary at Aix for home. Joseph got him the post of secretary to Paoli, and was happy to see him take his work seriously. The younger brother, however, craved excitement. Corte seemed a backwater after the cities of France, boiling with movement, the air charged with ideas. Jacobinism attracted him; Saliceti was his idol. He associated himself with the revolutionary clubs, made speeches, and wrote tracts. Joseph urged him to be discreet, but Lucien paid him little heed.

THE BUONAPARTES FLEE

Napoleon, pleading the necessity of escorting his sister Elisa home from the royal school at Saint-Cyr, which was being closed, returned to Ajaccio in October 1792. Actually, he had anticipated getting a command in the expedition, under General Anselme, which was being launched from Corsica against Sardinia. Paoli, anxious to have him out of the way, restored his commission in the national guard. The expedition, which ended in fiasco, returned in March. Paoli dissolved Napoleon's battalion, and he languished in Ajaccio, uncertain what to do next. During the disturbances of 1792, in Paris, he had again thought of promoting Corsican independence, but only if *he* could be a leader. If Paoli would not have him, he was unshakably French.

In the meantime, Paoli heard of the death of Louis XVI at the guillotine. Lucien watched him swell with fury: "They have butchered their King, the best of men!" Crossing himself and repeating *"A saint, a saint, a saint!"* he paced about. "Corsica

wants no more of them. I want no more of them." Then turning
to Lucien: "I am waiting for your brothers. And woe to him who
declares for those brigands!"

Paoli began marshaling the *insulaires* for rebellion. For "we
others, French in heart and opinion," Joseph saw no choice but
to desert him. Lucien left for France. Joseph, in mid-April,
went to Bastia, where Saliceti had landed with a commission from
the Convention, and was made a judge of the district tribunal.
Napoleon soon joined him.

Any hope for a negotiated settlement with Paoli was exploded
by Lucien. At Marseilles and Toulon he addressed the Jacobin
clubs. Overlooking seas of red liberty caps dotted by the excited
faces of pretty women, cheered noisily as an exiled patriot, he
accused Paoli of treason and demanded aid for his countrymen.
On petition from the Toulon club, the Convention ordered the
arrest of Paoli and his chief lieutenant, Pozzo di Borgo. Corsicans
rose *en masse* against the French and their supporters, and the
Babbo called on Admiral Hood's British fleet for help.

At Corte, the island assembly outlawed the Buonapartes. Letizia
fled Ajaccio with her small children, taking to the *maquis* as
she had twenty years before, and guided by a loyal retainer,
reached the coast near Capitello, known to be in friendly hands.
Her signals brought a boat from the fort—with Joseph and
Napoleon on board! They had withdrawn from Bastia with
Saliceti and party, and had been helping Francophiles to safety.

The family united, they went on to Calvi, which still had a
French garrison, and were taken in by Laurent Giubega. His
family received the other outlawed Buonapartes warmly, despite
the danger. For Joseph, the eyes of little Annette shown with love.
Danger made her bold, and for a few days they were close as
they had never dared be before. Calvi had to be evacuated by
the French, however; the Buonapartes sailed for Toulon, where
they landed on 13 June 1793.

Behind them, in Corsica, the mountaineers of Paoli sacked the
Buonaparte properties; in Ajaccio, the citizens joined in, taking
revenge for Napoleon's Eastertime depredations of the year before. While Joseph had few personal enemies on the island,
Napoleon had many, none more implacable than Pozzo di Borgo,

who, for over twenty years, kept a vendetta alive, serving the British and later Russians, until Napoleon was defeated and exiled.

TOULON

It was the year of the Terror. Count Joseph de Buonaparte became Citizen Joseph Buonaparte—impoverished citizen. The penniless refugees, their few clothes becoming shabbier by the day, were in no danger of attack as aristocrats. He settled his mother and the five younger children in a run-down house at La Valette, near Toulon, where for some months, Letizia became a household drudge, with no time even to learn French. Elisa (sixteen) was some help, though Saint-Cyr had not taught her how to haggle with grocers and tradesmen, and Louis (fifteen) was stable and cheerful (not the neurotic he would become). The others, Pauline (thirteen), Caroline (eleven), and Jérôme (nine) ran wild. Pauline, already a startling beauty, one minute flirting outrageously with passing men, the next bounding over walls and running like a frolicsome kitten, drove her mother to distraction.

While Napoleon returned to French service, and he and Lucien advertised their Jacobin sympathies, Joseph had to play the father. He was too busy for politics, and it was just as well. The France of Robespierre (in full power by the fall) hardly struck him as the fulfillment of the dreams of the *philosophes*. The inspired words of Rousseau swelled from every platform—to justify tyranny! How could they? But there were mouths to feed. Swallowing his pride, he went to Paris and petitioned the Convention for relief. Saliceti certified the Buonapartes patriot exiles, and Casabianca, a more conservative deputy, pled their case out of friendship for Joseph; the funds were granted. They did not go far, but Saliceti put Joseph on salary as his secretary, got him an allowance as a future commissioner to Corsica, and finally, in September, a contract as an army supplier. Still the family lived hand-to-mouth.

Then, suddenly, Napoleon was a hero, and in December 1793, a general, able for the first time to contribute to the support of the family. Fate and Saliceti had been his benefactors. In July, the British, with help from local conservatives, had seized Toulon. A French army moved in to lay siege to the city, and with the military came Saliceti and the younger Robespierre as representatives-on-mission. Just when the artillery commander was wounded, Napoleon happened to be nearby on another assignment. Saliceti gave him the artillery, which, after capturing key heights, he emplaced so as to outgun the British fleet. The battle over, Saliceti further made sure that Lazare Carnot, the "architect of victory" who was reshaping the French armies, heard of Captain Buonaparte's performance. Promotion and an assignment in Paris were his reward.

Napoleon could help Letizia and the children, and did. For some years more, however, they had to depend largely on Joseph. The fortunes of the Buonapartes were not yet tied to the fate of their *condottiere*. They wished him more success, but for Letizia, surely, finding a wife with a fat dowry for Joseph seemed more important.

DÉSIRÉE AND JULIE

The family moved to better quarters in Marseilles. The city, like Toulon, had risen against Jacobin rule and been whipped into line. One of those arrested in the aftermath was Étienne Clary, son of the millionaire merchant and soapmaker, François Clary. His wife went frantically to plead for his life before the *Conventionnel*, Albitte, taking with her Étienne's sixteen-year-old sister, Désirée. Obtaining an order for his parole, she rushed off to have him released, leaving Désirée to find her way home. Joseph, who had been to see Albitte, found her peering timidly into the street. How did *you* get here, Mademoiselle? he asked smiling. She told him. Ah! Your brother is safe. "A little *demoiselle* like you should not go on the streets alone with night coming. I will take you home." Without a thought, she agreed. By the time they reached her door, Désirée wrote much later, "we had become *tout à fait* good friends." She invited him to visit soon, and, smiling, asked if she might know her protector's name. "Joseph Bonaparte came the next day and did not hesitate to come again and again."

The Buonapartes became friends of the Clarys. Joseph became their advocate, and managed to get all charges against the brothers, Nicolas and Étienne, dropped. He was constantly with Désirée, a pretty, dark-eyed sprite, scatterbrained, charming, full of laughter and nonsense, who romped with his sisters when he bored her. Letizia, however, eyeing the Clary fortune, thought Joseph should marry, and favored Désirée's plain and mannerly sister, Marie Julie, twenty-two. The Clarys were amenable, and offered equal dowries for the two sisters, but touted Julie's solid qualities while hinting that Désirée would never grow up. Napoleon, entering the scene, urged marriage with Julie in the family interest. *He*, if anyone, could control Désirée, he said. Joseph, laughing, agreed. His mother had already persuaded him to propose to Julie. He was not in love with Désirée, and he knew that Napoleon was, though he considered her a child. Désirée was enjoying a triumph over the little general. She had him climbing walls, playing children's games, and generally making a fool of himself. Napoleon could command troops, but women—never.

Julie needed no persuading; she was in love with Joseph, and always would be. They were married in August 1794, at Cuges, near Marseilles. Julie was not greatly endowed with either face or figure, we are told by the Duchess d'Abrantès, but was "an angel" and a "rare and perfect person," and, we may be sure, considering the remarks, no competition for the beautiful Laure. Still, she was not unattractive. Small, always slender, with huge black eyes, soft, dark hair, and a tiny oval face, she retained a girlish appeal even when middle-aged. Shy, retiring, and not too strong, she shrank from public life. Her dearest wish, in later years, was that Joseph could somehow retire and live in the country with her and their daughters, Zénaïde and Charlotte, born in 1801 and 1802. Joseph yearned for the country too, but when he occasionally joined her there, quickly found her company suffocating. After the first years, by mutual consent, she maintained a home while he pursued his career in far places alone. Nevertheless, Joseph cherished and respected Julie, appreciated her wifely virtues, and loved their children dearly. In times of stress his thoughts always turned to his family, and his letters to Julie multiplied.

BUSINESSMAN

Joseph's marriage was the one happy event of 1794. He spent the early part of the year helping prepare an expedition to re-cover Corsica, promoted it with speeches and articles, and sailed with it in June, only to see it chased back into port by the British navy. In July, Robespierre fell, the Thermidorian reaction began, Napoleon and Lucien were thrown into prison, and Joseph found himself under surveillance. Joseph had conservative con-nections, however, both in the Convention and locally, and was soon cleared. Napoleon and Lucien were saved by Jacobins, in-cluding Saliceti, who, in the nick of time, had turned against Robespierre. But the futures of Napoleon and Lucien, who for months remained under suspicion, seemed very unpromising. Joseph, for a while, appeared to have come off unscathed, but in March 1795, after the failure of another expedition to Corsica, he lost his contract with the army.

For a time, Joseph had to draw on Julie's dowry (150,000 francs) to meet expenses, but Nicolas Clary soon took him into the family business. They moved to Genoa, where trade with the Middle East was easier (French ports were under British block-ade), taking Julie and Désirée with them. Julie's inheritance from her father, who died in 1795, soon made them rich, and Joseph, who knew Italy and Italians and took naturally to negotiating, added to the fortune rapidly.

Napoleon, meanwhile, refused an assignment to fight rebels in the Vendée, lost his commission, then had it restored, and labored at a desk job in Paris. He wrote Joseph that he might take service in Turkey, and complained of his poverty, at the same time pretending to be enjoying the "center of sciences, pleasures, arts, and civil liberty," while, by implication, Joseph was going to seed in the provinces. He complained bitterly that Désirée did not write: "My compliments to Julie . . . and the silent one." In September 1795, he asked Joseph to tell Désirée they were finished. They had never been very close. She later regretted it, apparently, though she and her husband, Marshal Bernadotte, had a throne in Sweden after Napoleon had disappeared; her descendents still reign there.

In October, the Convention, meeting in the Tuileries Palace, was threatened by mobs, now under royalist leadership. Barras, charged with defending the body, cast about frantically for an officer cold-blooded enough to stop the people, and settled on Napoleon. On 5 October the Corsican's cannon belched grapeshot, scrap, and rusty nails point-blank into the oncoming horde. The Convention was saved and the war ministry again smiled on Napoleon. "We conquered," he wrote Joseph, "all is forgiven."

Joseph, meanwhile, had made himself useful to the French government. Through refugees in Genoa and visitors from Corsica, he established contact with Francophiles on the island. Also, taking advantage of the free port, he procured needed commodities which could not reach France directly. His services earned him the post of French consul in Genoa (February 1796). A private success already, the assignment added little to his distinction, but he liked the work. He saw himself contributing, as he would more importantly later, to ultimate peace. Nothing pleased him more. But sadly, Napoleon loved conflict as much as Joseph did peace.

Encounter with Josephine

In March 1796, Napoleon married Josephine de Beauharnais, whose husband, the Viscount Alexandre, had gone to the guillotine during the Terror. She was five years the little general's senior, the mother of two children, and a socialite without visible means of support, whose latest lover, by all reports, had been Barras, now a director. Immediately after the marriage, Napoleon was given command of the French army of Italy, and, en route to his headquarters, began signing his name "Bonaparte." To his family, his marriage was a disaster, his command possibly a dishonorable by-product, and the name change a denial of his ancestry. But they did not desert him, and since Joseph had discovered that some of their Italian progenitors had used "Bona-parte," accepted the new spelling.

Napoleon called on Joseph to help supply his ragged troops, which, in cooperation with Saliceti, he did with speed and energy. The army slammed through Piedmont and into Lombardy, winning victories over the Austrians and their allies. Joseph conferred with Napoleon at Albenga in April, then set off for Paris to explain peace negotiations with the Italian states to the Directory and bring back Josephine, whom he had not met.

Dealing with the Directors proved easy; Josephine presented problems. No stranger to women, Joseph realized from the instant of encounter that she would seduce him if she could. Napoleon's wife! He drew back; the thought of it left him cold. We must be off for Italy, Madame! How soon can you be ready? She laughed. Italy? Whatever for? It was almost two months before he could drag her away from Paris. He had found, meanwhile, that she was not only beautiful (except for bad teeth), but gentle, kind, happy, charming, and most intelligent. It was easy to see why Napoleon fell in love with her. But was he blind? In her society everyone seemed to be sleeping with everyone else, and "Rose," as they called Josephine, was more notorious than the breathtaking Thérése Tallien, with whom she competed for honors in nudity beneath diaphanous evening wear. It was common knowledge that General Murat had shared Rose's bed a month earlier. Barras still visited her. The perfumed Hippolyte Charles, who titillated the *raffiné* ladies by playing the squeaky-voiced marionette, all but lived with her. Joseph was no Puritan, but it was too much. Napoleon's letters made it worse: "I am in despair, my wife, all I love in the world, is ill [I am told]. I have lost my head. Reassure me. . . . I love her to frenzy!" Joseph begged Josephine to go to her husband.

Very well, said Josephine finally, she would go to Italy if Hippolyte could go. Impossible, ruled Joseph, but after thinking it over, he agreed. Why not let her advertise her sins? He had long since decided he could not afford to come between Josephine and her intimates, or tell Napoleon what he knew about her. He knew that Napoleon, when in love, could be led by the woman like a lamb on a string. His brother would hate whoever crossed Josephine or "lied" about her. Getting Monsieur Charles organized took time, but in late May they at last departed. The lovers traveled in one coach, Joseph in another; at overnight stops Rose and Hippolyte had adjoining bedrooms. Joseph ignored them and spent his time writing.

NOVELIST

Deeply saddened by the sight of maimed, mutilated, and blinded soldiers on the roads, he began a novel condemning war. He abhorred conflict of any sort, and war, to him, was the ultimate insanity. Battles did not frighten him; he had been under fire. As a supplier at Toulon, he had taken the same risks as staff officers, and sustained a slight wound. Though he had a commission as major (*chef de Battalion*) in the Corsican volunteers, he had not put on a uniform. He preferred to serve as a noncombatant.

His book, finished two years later and published in 1799, was called *Moïna, ou la religieuse de Mont-Cenis.** The heroine, a young shepherdess, sees her fiancé dragged off to serve in the army of Italy (Napoleon's!), and her idyllic valley senselessly pillaged by troops of both sides. She waits in the shambles for her lover, who returns, only to die in her arms. Everything she loves destroyed, she becomes a nun. Romantic, from a present-day viewpoint saccharine, it nevertheless depicted the horrors of war with shocking realism, and rang with compassion for its victims. Bernardin de Saint-Pierre, France's most famous living novelist, found it moving, and was flattered that it owed something to his *Paul et Virginie*. In later years he would call Joseph "that *philosophe* so worthy of a throne." Madame de Staël was transported, though perhaps as much by the author as his work.

Many took *Moïna* as a renunciation of Napoleon's policies. To Joseph, however, it was a "philosophic" work, nothing more. But it revealed a deep-set humanitarianism which Napoleon would never share, and makes predictable many of their conflicts.

---

* The second edition (1814) was titled *Moïna, ou la villageoise de Mont-Cenis.*

RETURN TO CORSICA

Joseph delivered Josephine to Napoleon in Milan on 13 July 1796. She was hardly grateful: "I am bored to death here . . . I miss my friends. . . . My husband doesn't love me any more, he adores me, I think he has gone mad," she wrote Thérése Tallien. No matter, she was going to Brescia—where she would be nearer Hippolyte. While Napoleon returned to the campaign, Joseph watched over her for a while, as best he could.

Meanwhile a request came from General Gentili that Joseph return to Corsica, where a French expedition had finally gotten ashore. He and Saliceti were to organize the administration pending the arrival of the Directory's representative, François Miot (later Count de Melito). When Joseph arrived, in October, "the tricolor was already floating over the citadel of Ajaccio." He could proceed with the sort of work he loved—restoration and reconciliation. He determinedly forgave his enemies. "I saw no sign of ill will toward my family," he recorded. Actually he refused to see any. Casa Buonaparte had to be refurbished from basement to roof, but he asked no indemnity. He had money; Ajaccio was poor. His neighbors responded well to his gestures.

Miot arrived at Bastia in January 1797 and crossed the mountains to Ajaccio "along paths where the only animals you can trust are the Corsican horse or mule." The journey was hairraising, and to the sheltered bureaucrat, the people as frightening as their country. At Ajaccio, however, the sight of his host reassured him:

A party of inhabitants, all on horseback . . . came out to receive me. Among them was Joseph Bonaparte . . . I was more than happy to see him. A gentle and distinguished figure, his manners engaging, his speech polished, everything about him disposed me in his favor.

Joseph became Miot's chief adviser. He and Saliceti had already divided the island into two departments, with capitals at Ajaccio and Bastia. Miot confirmed the officials in office, and with their help selected others. Joseph's candidates, however, he notes, always got "public approbation," whereas Saliceti's, almost invariably former exiles of Jacobin leanings, did not, so that he generally favored Joseph's men. "I had no cause but to congratulate myself in that regard." The government installed, he called an electoral assembly which elected Joseph a member of the lower house of the French legislature (the *cinq cents*, Council of Five Hundred).

In April, under cover of a storm, which reduced their fear of capture by the ubiquitous British fleet, Joseph and Miot sailed for Italy. Thanks to hurricane winds, they were in Livorno (Leghorn) in four hours. Diplomatic assignments awaited them both.

THE DUPHOT AFFAIR

Assigned as minister to Parma, Joseph had barely unpacked his bags when he was ordered off to Rome. Napoleon's campaign over, Italy at his feet and Austria suing for peace, the Vatican had reluctantly agreed to establish diplomatic relations with the despised French Republic. The Directors, aware of difficulties facing the first ambassador, singled out Joseph, a *ci-devant* Italian aristocrat who spoke the language, had the right personality, Church training—and a surname which would keep Rome reminded of French power. His task would be first to convince the Pope, Pius VI, that the Republic was not run by infidels, then to try to induce him to discourage the royalist and church-led rebels in the French Vendée and Brittany, recognize French "constitutional" clergy, and forego claim to confiscated Church property.

Joseph arrived in Rome in August 1797, accompanied by Julie, his sister Caroline, and a large suite of civilian and military subordinates. He began well. His knowledge of traditional forms and protocol, his obviously sincere piety, and his undisguised good will won over the papal secretary, Cardinal Doria. At his audience with the Pope, the old man's "my son," uttered with stiff formality at the beginning, was at the end soft and fatherly. Presents came the next day—six horses from His Holiness, two from the Cardinal. The new ambassador rented the Corsini palace, where he entertained lavishly, democratically issuing invitations to Cardinals, Roman aristocrats, businessmen, artists, and potential revolutionaries alike. Désirée and her mother shortly arrived, giving him an oversupply of charming hostesses.

There were those who thought Joseph had orders to foment revolution in Rome and the Papal States. His behavior, however, gave them the lie, as did the presence of four ladies whom he surely would not have put in danger. In fact, Talleyrand, the French foreign minister, had given him what Lucien calls "pacific instructions." He tried to carry them out, and but for Napoleon's interference, might have had some success.

Napoleon cared little for the policies of the Directors. He had dictated peace to former enemy powers as he saw fit. Eager to build a seat of personal power in Italy, he had brought into being the Cisalpine Republic in the north, and encouraged revolutionaries everywhere. To the "Citizen Ambassador" in Rome (he no longer used Joseph's name) he urged that an uprising begin upon the death of the aged Pope, if not sooner. Joseph gave Roman revolutionaries no encouragement, but Napoleon's disciples, strong in the embassy, goaded them on. Among these was General Duphot, twenty-seven, recently engaged to Désirée.

On 27 December three revolutionary leaders presented themselves to Joseph. A revolution was planned, they told him. Would he advise them? Would he, if necessary, give them protection? "I told them that as an impartial spectator, I would report to my government on whatever happened; that I was unable to say more at the moment." They went ahead with their plans anyway, on the same night. By some reports the handsome Duphot attended one meeting and loudly promised General Bonaparte's aid amid toasts to the Roman and French Republics. The revolutionaries, however, were few, led by gross amateurs, and had in their ranks government spies who gave away their every move. By morning papal troops seemed to have crushed the insurrection. Joseph secured the release of French citizens and Roman employees of his embassy who had been arrested and prepared to forget the matter.

On the afternoon of the 28th, however, a small crowd gathered before the embassy gate, shouting "Long live the Republic! Long live the Roman people!" and demanding admittance. A representative was let in, one of the visitors of the day before, an artist, wild eyed with excitement. "We are free!" he shouted. "We come to demand the support of France." Joseph ordered him out. The crowd grew larger and noisier. Joseph put on his uniform of office and started out to speak to the mob.

Before he could reach the gate, papal cavalry appeared and charged the people. In panic, they broke down the barriers and fled across the grounds and into the embassy, the cavalry in pursuit. Foot soldiers entered the building, shooting down refugees as they came. Joseph, flanked by Generals Duphot and Sherloch, met them in the central foyer. They stopped. Where is your chief? He would not show himself. You are on French territory! Withdraw at once! They did, exchanging fire with refugees as they went, but appeared to be regrouping outside. Sword drawn, Joseph advanced again, demanding they leave. Duphot, tired of talk, and perhaps conscious that Désirée might be watching from her apartment, rallied armed refugees some distance away and attacked the invaders. Joseph, horrified, suddenly saw him wading into a line of bayonets, sword flailing. He and Sherloch tried to reach Duphot, but he hacked his way into the mass, leaving a trail of enemy dead, until, shot and stabbed repeatedly, he fell dead. Young officers managed to recover Duphot's body. Joseph barricaded his people in one wing of the palace, and there they remained until ten in the evening, receiving desultory fire. The Tuscan and Spanish ambassadors arrived to carry out protests, but no Roman official.

Finally, the Cardinal Secretary sent Joseph a guard of forty men, but no apology or explanation for the outrage. The honor of France, Joseph decided, required that he leave Rome. He demanded his passports, and departed at six the next morning with his staff, family, and the grief-stricken Désirée.

On 30 December he reported to Talleyrand from Florence. The minister approved his behavior:

Despite the care which you took to omit anything personal about that horrible day, you could not conceal from me that you displayed the highest degree of courage, *sang-froid*, and an intelligence which misses nothing, and that you sustained with magnanimity the honor of the French name.

After Joseph's departure, a French army occupied Rome, and the short-lived Roman Republic was established. No intrigue of Joseph's had prepared the ground for these events, however. He had vainly tried to establish an accommodation with the Pope, a task to which he would happily return four years later.

BRUMAIRE

In late January 1798, Joseph was in Paris, where the Directors received him warmly and offered to make him ambassador to Berlin. He declined, preferring to take the seat in the Council of Five Hundred, to which he had been elected while in Corsica. Napoleon was busy promoting his scheme to conquer Egypt, a means of striking at Britain (by interdicting land routes to India, and disrupting her trade with the Orient). He sailed with his army in May.

Before he left, Napoleon confided to Joseph that he had lost faith in the Directory. It was still strong, he said, but France would gradually realize that it was a poor government. Meanwhile, it was best that he be in the field. His name would remain associated with glory, and not with the failures of the "lawyers" of the Directory. When France needed him, the public would support him; he could found a strong government. "Our dreams of a republic were the illusions of youth."

Joseph could not agree that republican government, in general, was impossible; he suspected Napoleon would oppose any government he could not control. But he agreed that the Directory had its flaws. The main problem was that the constitution was not observed. Duly elected members of the chambers were excluded arbitrarily, and Directors changed by *coup d'état.* He agreed to watch developments and keep Napoleon informed.

He determined, however, that he would join no party, but allow his judgment and conscience to guide his vote in all cases. This he thought proper for a representative, and it would enable him to keep friends who could not separate their personal and political feelings. Moreover, for Napoleon's sake, he felt it essential to stay on good terms with the Directors, all five, if possible, whatever their political leanings. After all, General Bonaparte would perish if supplies and reenforcements were withheld. Egypt was not Italy; he could not live off the land and thumb his nose at the world.

Lucien, who was elected to the Five Hundred in the spring, was no man for caution. With ever-increasing vehemence, he opposed the government on the one hand the Jacobins in the Assembly on the other. He rejected the Directory as feeble, but purported to fear a return of the Terror. In his soberer moments, he admitted that many of the leading Jacobins, so called, were not Terrorists, but democrats who favored universal manhood suffrage and legislative supremacy. They included Generals Jourdan and Bernadotte (just married to Désirée). Perhaps principally because he thought their day was past, he aligned himself with Talleyrand, Sieyès, and Roederer—the constitutional "revisionists," who favored a stronger executive.

If the Directory was weak, its foreign policy came off as aggressive. The creation of the Roman Republic, promotion of revolutions in Holland and Naples, Napoleon's expedition, and other moves provoked general war. Austria, Russia, Turkey, and a host of minor powers joined England against France. During the winter of 1798–99 the French were expelled from Italy, and barely held their own in the Rhineland and Switzerland. Napoleon's invasion of Syria had failed miserably; Nelson had long since stranded the army in Egypt by burning its fleet. Opposition to the Directory mounted. "It vegetated more than it governed," Lucien said later. "The Republic was about to perish on the Tartar pikes of Suvarov [the Russian commander in Switzerland]." Joseph and Lucien finally reached agreement in principle: "The present composition of the executive power held no hope for the Republic."

Joseph became a revisionist, therefore, but he continued to maintain a wide personal influence in all parties. The Jacobins, including Saliceti, lion of the Club du Manége, were welcomed at his *soirées* along with royalists. There also were *ideologues* like Benjamin Constant and Madame de Staël, who carried the Paris intelligentsia into the revisionist camp. At a later stage, Madame de Staël worked for Napoleon with the devotion of a lover. She saw him as a Joseph-in-armor, and only much later would learn the sad truth. Joseph had the trust of an astonishing variety of people, many of whom, in a crisis, would listen to his advice, and more who, because they knew him, would give his brother the benefit of doubts. In the spring of 1799, he left the Five Hundred, which facilitated his chosen role.

Lucien, meanwhile, became President of the Five Hundred, and participated in unconstitutional maneuvers designed to produce, in effect, a Directory which would resign on cue, making way for a new government. In the end, the panel included two revisionists, Sieyès and Roger-Ducos, who would resign, two Jacobins, Moulin and Gohier, who would not, and Barras, who could probably be intimidated. The Five Hundred remained a problem; Lucien could lead it—but not when it came to revision. It was hoped Jacobin members could be kept away when a test came. The upper house, the *anciens*, seemed safe.

For several years Sieyès had been looking for a general to support his projects—one he could control. Napoleon, initially, was not on his list. His favorite, General Joubert, had been killed; the next candidate, Hoche, had died; Jourdan and Bernadotte had disappointed him by becoming active Jacobins, and so it went. He finally settled on General Bonaparte. None of the other active conspirators—Talleyrand, Cambacérès, Fouché, and Lucien—were enthusiastic. Lucien, no partisan of military dictatorship, thought his brother "dangerous," and would later return to that opinion; he was too much like Napoleon to trust him. Once the choice was made, however, he gave his all.

In late summer, 1799, Joseph advised Napoleon to return to France. His letter was carried to Egypt by a Greek retainer, Bourbaki, in a hollowed-out cane. In October, Napoleon arrived in Fréjus. Nothing is more indicative of Joseph's position than that Gohier, a Jacobin Director, notified him of his brother's arrival. Joseph and Lucien went to meet Napoleon and traveled with him to Paris. Once there, events moved swiftly.

On 18 *Brumaire* (9 November) Sieyès, Roger-Ducos, and, belatedly, Barras resigned. The Jacobin Directors wavered, and were put under guard. The Council of Ancients was notified of a Jacobin conspiracy. To protect against it they voted to make Napoleon commandant of the troops at Paris and to assemble the chambers (Ancients and Five Hundred) at Saint-Cloud, in the suburbs, the next day.

The story of 19 *Brumaire* has often been told: Napoleon, successful in the *anciens*, howled down in the Five Hundred, almost crushed by an angry crowd at the tribune, carried out in a faint —Lucien trying to calm the deputies, shouted down—Sieyès and Talleyrand about to flee—the appeal to force—Lucien among the troops, pledging to thrust his sword into Napoleon if he betrayed the Republic—the expulsion of the Five Hundred from the Orangerie—triumph and midnight proclamation of a new order—Napoleon the dominant of three consuls.

Joseph had remained in the background, conferring with the leaders, working to win over or neutralize opponents. He induced Augereau, among others, to *talk* to Napoleon. The general, troop commander in a previous coup which remade the Directory, might have ruined everything, but he agreed to stand aside. With Désirée's help, Joseph had persuaded Bernadotte not to come to Saint-Cloud at all. This was no small matter. "Belle-Jambe," a dandy but a soldier's soldier with an immense following in the army, might have rallied the troops to the Jacobins. Joseph had also induced Jourdan to stay away. His influence on the intelligentsia is beyond question. Madame de Staël had Benjamin Constant at Saint-Cloud, sending her reports on developments. "There is no doubt that all high-minded people . . . wanted Bonaparte to triumph," she recorded later.

For all that he had supported the coup, Joseph was overcome with guilt and shame at the sight of deputies, encumbered by their long togas, fleeing into the gardens and woods before grenadiers with fixed bayonets. Convinced that the Directory had to be replaced by a strong constitutional government to prevent a recurrence of the Terror, he had hoped it could be done by parliamentary means—at least nominally so. The violence shocked him; worse, it had ruined all pretense that the procedures were legal. Napoleon was a usurper, pure and simple.

The victors parleyed; no one seemed to know what to do. Recall the Five Hundred, Joseph insisted; it is the only thing to do. Assemble all who can be found. By nine in the evening fifty were brought together. A quorum declared, they authorized the three Consuls to produce a new constitution. The rump of the *anciens* concurred in the action. It was a sorry substitute for majority approval, even if secured under threat, but it proved adequate.

Joseph's conscience always troubled him when he thought of *Brumaire*. In his memoirs he said much of the background, but very little of the events. Nevertheless, at the time, he thought the outcome good for France. His first efforts were in behalf of men Napoleon wanted to deport. Among others, he saved Bernadotte, Jourdan, and the Bonapartes' old benefactor, Saliceti.

In truth, the Republic Joseph had hoped to save was dead. For him, however, the greatest years of his life, in terms of public service, lay just ahead.

✣

CHAPTER III

The Peacemaker Undone

THE GOOD YEARS

Few historians—left, right, or center—have much adverse to say about the first years of the Consulate, 1800 through 1802. It is no accident that this was the period of Joseph's greatest influence over Napoleon. His proclivity for peace counterbalanced the First Consul's will-to-power and his democratic liberalism his brother's authoritarian variety. If Napoleon's political-tactical sense dictated that he listen to Joseph, it is nevertheless true that he did.

After quick victories in 1800, Napoleon sued for general peace. In France, reform, progress, conciliation, and revitalization were the order of the day. The First Consul delivered a constitution which created legislative bodies of reasonable strength (considering conditions) and gave every man the vote. He reformed the administration and the courts, began a codification of the law, and much else. Freedom of speech and of the press, if not total, were granted in degree extraordinary for France. The intelligentsia and scientific community extolled the new regime.

Since 1793, Joseph had held that the Revolution could end only when the *émigrés* were brought back, and a government created which would utilize the talents of all Frenchmen—aristocrats and ex-Jacobins alike. Napoleon made the concept his own. "Careers open to talent" became his rule. "Where is the revolutionary . . . who would not have confidence in an order of things where Fouché [a notorious Terrorist] will be minister [of police]?

What gentleman, if he is still French, cannot hope to make a life in a country where a Périgord [Talleyrand de Périgord] will have power?" A new society of astonishing harmony arose.

Declining a cabinet post, Joseph became a councillor of state at large, and devoted himself to keeping Napoleon informed on current attitudes and opinions. He wanted the government "to reflect the enlightened will of the nation." To this end he spent much time touring the provinces, talking with officials, businessmen, intellectuals, priests, and peasants, and carried on a heavy correspondence. "How many times have I not been consulted, regarding a legislative or administrative measure, as to what the opinion was of such and such a person of good sense, of such and such a class of society, in Paris, in Lyons, in Marseilles!"

To the same end (and because he loved it), Joseph cultivated the widest possible circle of friends. Hundreds trooped to his country estate, Mortefontaine (which he and Julie bought with their own money). There Madame de Staël read freshly penned pages of her latest work and Chateaubriand from the manuscripts of *Atala*, *René*, and *Génie du Christianisme*, Benjamin Constant mouthed boring profundities, the Marquis de Lafayette, "Hero of Two Worlds," conversed politely, avoiding his political ideas, unchanged since 1789, Bernardin de Saint-Pierre sat sipping wine and being adored, Arnaud and Fontanes read their poetry, Denon and David clashed over the merits of the master painters, Laplace described the universe emerging from explosions of molten matter (a topic fascinating to the ladies, curiously enough), politicians and generals furiously made small talk, Pierre Louis Roederer, politician and journalist, diplomat and writer, took skin off everybody with his sarcasms, the great Talma showed his offstage personality, and the gentlemen vied for the attention of Mademoiselles Cantat and Devienne of the Théâtre Français.

There was frivolity, but the air was alive with ideas and opinions, which Joseph stored up for Napoleon's guidance. For a while, his brother listened to him. British intelligence referred to Joseph as *l'Influent*—*the* influential man. Increasingly, however, Napoleon did not like what he heard—too much love of peace in the countryside—too much democratic maundering among the intellectuals. He slowly brought the free society which Joseph cherished under discipline.

In the first years, Joseph was Napoleon's chief diplomat. Step by step, he negotiated what he believed would be a lasting peace. Full of hope, signing treaties in good faith, he was incapable of suspecting that Napoleon was using him, and would respect agreements only so long as it suited him.

THE AMERICAN DELEGATION

In early 1800, while Napoleon won victories in Italy, Joseph undertook to end an undeclared naval war with the United States. That country had declined to join France against Britain in 1793, despite a treaty of alliance which dated from the American Revolution (1778). The French had accepted President Washington's neutrality proclamation calmly, nevertheless. The United States was too weak to help much, and as a belligerent would merely be blockaded by the British; as a neutral she could ship supplies and unofficially furnish bases for the French. Washington, however, had expelled the French Minister, Edmond Genêt, for equipping privateers in American ports, and allowed John Jay to settle differences with the British. Americans were no more happy than the French: "Damn John Jay!! damn every one that won't damn John Jay! damn every one that won't put lights in his windows and sit up all night damning John Jay!!!" But the French had begun attacking American merchantmen, sunk or captured hundreds, and provoked Congress into authorizing United States ships to fight back. An American delegation, sent to treat with the Directory, left in a huff after anonymous agents ("X, Y, Z," and a beautiful lady) asked for a bribe, a huge loan, and apologies from President Adams. By the time of *Brumaire*, Americans were wild for an alliance with Britain, but Adams decided to give the new French government a chance.

The President's representatives, William Vans Murray, Oliver Ellsworth, and William R. Davie, were guarded and hostile at the start. They coldly demanded an indemnity for American losses and apologies from France. Joseph could give neither; the Consulate would not suffer for the sins of the Directory. Should not the sister republics make a fresh start? Why not mutually repudiate the Treaty of 1778 and make a joint agreement defining and pledging to respect the rights of neutrals? It took months, since the Americans had to consult with their government, but they finally agreed. What the infant United States needed most was peace in which to develop her strength. Joseph meanwhile had made fast friends of the delegates. He talked straight, stood on no ceremony, and obviously wanted a settlement. He showed them Paris, brought them together with Lafayette and other heroes of the American Revolution, introduced them to the circle at Mortefontaine, walked their legs off showing them his estate. He had, they told each other, much in common with American country gentlemen. He quizzed them for hours about the United States, laughing at his own ignorance. General Davie—should he not call him *gouverneur?*—had he really founded the first state university? *Parbleu!* In France there are, one might say, no other kind! Was the Congress generous with funds? What? Not a national university! Incredible!

The signing of the Franco-American convention (30 September 1800) was followed by a celebration at Mortefontaine. The Americans already knew the large but unspectacular country house, with its park, well-pruned woodlands, and glassy lakes. They had enjoyed hunting, riding, boating, and just sitting quietly by the water, watching the swans glide by. It was purchased, noted William Vans Murray, "of the heirs of the late M. Morfontaine [*sic*] who died quietly in his bed!" Joseph, typically, had wanted it known that he had not taken the property of a victim of the guillotine.

Murray wrote twenty-four pages in his diary during the three-day fête. He and Mrs. Murray, accompanied by Lafayette, were greeted by Julie and Joseph. "His wife—a small delicate woman —a little jealous. . . . M[onsieur] J. B. has a mild disposition— tranquil—a little lazy—guarded—but not reserved—a pleasing countenance—loves the chase [hunting] & his country estate. . . . He has an easy flow of literary knowledge w^h issues from him like insensible perspiration without his seeming to know it—he is very unaffected & w^{h}out pretense—the bane of the French clever men [which make most clever Frenchmen offensive]." The Murrays met Lucien, Secretary of the Interior, and Colonel Louis Bonaparte, Guardsman Jérôme, sixteen, Caroline and Pauline, wives of Generals Murat and Leclerc. (Only Elisa, married to Count Bacciochi, was absent.) Napoleon and Josephine "dashed into the court with a coach and six white horses—guards before & behind." Letizia presided grandly throughout: "Mother of that singular family—a lady who looks as young as the Consul's wife." He found Josephine pleasant, however; she asked him to send flower bulbs from America! Napoleon, whom he had not met before, was so affable that he thought him like Joseph: "He . . . is too generous . . . generosity was Caesar's foible and his ruin."

At Joseph's request, Lafayette and La Rochefoucauld had invited all the Americans in Paris. At that they were almost lost among the hundreds of Frenchmen, foreign diplomats, and their ladies. Everyone was there: the Consuls Cambacérès and Lebrun, Sieyès, now demoted to senator, the ministers, including Fouché and Talleyrand, and droves of lesser officials, generals, legislators, *litterateurs*, artists, and scientists.

The first day ended with a dinner and concert. The next there was a hunt, a larger dinner, and a fireworks display on the lake before the chateau (it ended with gigantic bursts of color from which emerged a small flotilla flying the flags of France and the United States). This was followed by a performance by the company of the *Théâtre Français* in the park. "Genl. D-e [Davie] and I clapped the songs," wrote Murray. Mr. Ellsworth, sated with entertainment, had withdrawn—"indisposed." The other two stayed until the end, mightily impressed, especially with Mademoiselle Devienne. "After the play we retired to bed—at 3½!!" The festivities ended on the third day with a ball for twelve hundred. It lasted much past "3½."

The Americans departed happy. Relations between France and the United States would remain excellent—until Napoleon initiated his Continental System, which violated the rights of neutrals which Joseph (and he) had guaranteed.

Joseph was already involved in negotiations with Austria which resulted in the Treaty of Lunéville (9 February 1801). The rolypoly Count Cobenzl became so fond of Mortefontaine that it was hard to get rid of him. The treaty involved losses of territory for Austria, but not humiliating ones, such as would later make her Napoleon's implacable enemy.

THE CONCORDAT

Next came the Concordat of 1801 with the papacy, which was signed at Joseph's town house in Paris. The document was put in final form by Cardinal Consalvi, representing Pius VII, and Joseph, seconded by the Abbé Bernier. Napoleon made excitement and hastened negotiations by threatening to declare France Protestant, a move recommended by the majority of his council of state, though impractical. In the end Catholicism was recognized as the religion of the majority, but not the state religion; the government could pursue a policy of toleration. The distinction between constitutional and non-constitutional clergy was eliminated; peace among Catholics was restored after a decade of strife. Napoleon almost immediately gave the Concordat questionable interpretation. His relations with the Vatican were destined to deteriorate apace until in 1809 he made the Pope his prisoner. Nevertheless, the Concordat remained the working agreement between France and the Holy See for *one hundred and four years.*

THE PEACE OF AMIENS

Meanwhile, Pitt had fallen from power in Britain. The new Prime Minister, Addington, agreed to talk peace. At the end of 1801, after six months of preliminary parleys, Lord Cornwallis arrived in Paris to negotiate a treaty. Though in America his name was synonymous with Yorktown, that defeat was the only notable failure in a long public career which had included terms as governor general of India and viceroy of Ireland. No British statesman, save Pitt, commanded more respect; his government set a high value on peace, or he would not have been there. Again, Napoleon asked Joseph to represent France.

Cornwallis abhorred Talleyrand, master of "chicanery and intrigue," reputed to take bribes—no man of honor. Napoleon, he thought, acted too much like a king, and always had the foreign minister at his side. He and Joseph hit it off immediately, however; neither doubted the other's good intentions. "I hope we will throw off reserve," said Cornwallis, "[and] work not as diplomats, but as men who sincerely want to serve our governments, and arrive quickly at a solid peace." He chided Joseph for not inviting Lafayette (his enemy at Yorktown) to meet him. "We English recognize only two species of men, good and bad; M. de Lafayette is one of us." He suggested they confer at Amiens—away from Napoleon and Talleyrand. Joseph agreed.

Kindly and open as he was, Lord Cornwallis, tall, distinguished, erect and soldierly at sixty-seven, was the personification of *Milord Anglais*. Determined to observe all the formalities at Amiens, Joseph did "fastidious research" into diplomatic etiquette and protocol. He need not have worried. Cornwallis met his carriage, opened the door, and before Joseph could say a word, seized him under the arms and lifted him down. "I hope *that* is the way we will work," he said smiling, "all our etiquette must not delay the peace one hour."

A pact was framed in record time: mutual restoration of conquests with minor exceptions; evacuation of Malta and Elba by the British, withdrawal of French troops from Naples. The atmosphere was cordial, entertainments frequent. When none were scheduled, wrote Méneval, Joseph's secretary (later Napoleon's), "After dinner Lord Cornwallis and Captain Nightingale used to retire to his lordship's chamber, and spend the rest of the evening drinking, after the English custom." Joseph, as might have been expected, was lodged at the home of the city's most beautiful woman, Madame de Folleville.

With negotiations complete, the British government demanded that Cornwallis ask more money in connection with prisoner exchange. He flatly refused. He had given his word to Joseph; to break it was unthinkable. London let him have his way, and the treaty was signed without further ado on 25 March 1802. Joseph never forgot the English stateman's gesture. *"Quel noble caractère que celui de lord Cornwallis!"* he wrote in his memoirs thirty years later.

Joseph, returning to Paris the night of the signing, found

Napoleon at the Opera. The First Consul introduced the peacemaker from his box, and he was wildly cheered. Congratulations poured in from all quarters. "The peace with England is a joy to the world," gushed Madame de Staël. "The First Consul should be grateful . . . you serve him . . . your excellent goodness makes all hearts wish you success." Joseph shortly became a grand officer of the newly created Legion of Honor, a distinction he had truly earned, and thereby a senator *ex-officio*.

On Easter Day, 1802, a *Te Deum* was sung at Notre Dame to celebrate the conclusion of the Concordat and the Peace of Amiens. Huge crowds cheered the procession to the cathedral. For the first time in ten years all Europe was at peace. France, beset two years before by enemies and in domestic chaos, was orderly, prosperous, and content. Never, avowed Talleyrand, had she had greater prestige, power, or glory. In all of this Joseph had played a proud part. Yet when Napoleon asked him to ride in a state coach with eight horses, and take a place of honor in the cathedral, he refused. Instead he rode and sat with the other councillors of state.

He disliked Napoleon's unrepublican conduct, and he was beginning to wonder if, having accomplished all any ruler could dream of, his brother's ambitions were not going to ruin it.

PRESIDENT OF ITALY?

During his campaign of 1796–97, Napoleon had sponsored the creation of the Cisalpine Republic in northern Italy. Overrun by the Austrians in 1799, it was freed by Napoleon in 1800, and reconstituted as the Republic of Italy. Under the careful supervision of Murat, commanding French troops in Italy, delegates were elected to a *consulta* which met at Lyons (in France, where Napoleon could better control it) during the winter of 1801–02. It was to approve a new constitution, which increased the power of the executive, and name a President.

Napoleon determined to engineer the election of Joseph to the presidency. Joseph was interested. But would Italians accept him? He consulted his friend Count Melzi d'Eril, a suave Milanese ex-diplomat, art connoisseur, gourmet, and linguist, who, nevertheless, was a left-wing republican, Ferdinando Marescalchi, the

Italian ambassador in Paris, and others. They were enthusiastic. Yes. The *consulta* would elect Joseph. Privately, they knew they would have to select someone Napoleon approved. Why not Joseph? He was a good candidate on his own merits—liberal, honest, experienced, and in many ways Italian—and he was close to the First Consul.

Joseph returned to Napoleon. Very well, he would stand for election. But, if he became President, French troops must withdraw from the Republic immediately. Murat, he said, was bullying the civilian leaders. Italy must be truly independent. He would not be a "political mannequin." Moreover, he demanded the Piedmont (under French occupation) be annexed to Italy and that she be given access to more ports—both to make her economically more viable.

Napoleon, furious, told Joseph to forget the whole matter. He had himself named President of Italy. European capitals were aghast. In mid-year he became Consul for life. What next?

RUPTURE OF THE PEACE

As 1802 progressed, relations with Great Britain deteriorated apace. Napoleon's schemes for reviving the French Empire in Louisiana and the West Indies caused minor alarms, but nothing compared to his other moves. He denied the British markets in France, limited those in Spain and the Dutch Republic and their colonies, menaced those in Portugal, Germany, and the Baltic area. When the British left Elba, he annexed it to France, along with Piedmont. He brought Genoa under French control, put a French administrator in Parma-Piacenza, converted Tuscany into a puppet kingdom. French garrisons in the north Italian states were strengthened; Naples was threatened and pressed to ally with France. Napoleon's agents induced Turkey to open the straits to France, and worked feverishly in Egypt, Greece, the Balkans, and the Ionian Islands. Allied with the Spanish Bourbons and favored by the Ottoman Sultan, in control of the major Italian ports, Elba, and Corsica, able to enter Naples at will, Napoleon was poised to take control of the Mediterranean—if the British evacuated Malta.

Not surprisingly, the British kept Malta, in violation of the

Treaty of Amiens. Napoleon had kept to the letter of the pact, but he had violated its spirit a hundred times over. In December 1802, Lord Whitworth came to Paris to try for a new agreement to preserve the peace. He wanted to negotiate with Joseph, however, not anyone else, and positively not Talleyrand, who, he did not mind saying, could be approached only "money in hand."

Joseph met with Whitworth and tried to find a solution. He was torn, in the beginning, by conflicting feelings. From a strictly legal standpoint, the British had no case. Napoleon kept shouting about Malta, and as a brother, Joseph wanted to support him. Yet in his heart he knew who was destroying the peace. As the months dragged by, he became convinced that Napoleon wanted no settlement. In April he was sure. Napoleon suddenly announced he would sell the immense Louisiana territory to the United States—for a paltry $15,000,000. Joseph objected violently. Why? The answer was evident. Napoleon expected war. Louisiana would be vulnerable to conquest by Britain, with her superior navy, or the United States, which urgently needed the port of New Orleans. Why not dispose of a liability, curry favor with the Americans, and let *them* defend Louisiana against the British?

Whitworth, unable to make terms, publicly insulted by the First Consul, departed in May 1803, and Britain declared war on France. Napoleon responded by seizing Hanover (property of the English crown). French troops now occupied northern Germany to the Elbe as well as northern Italy. Already the whole map of Germany had been remade, in two years of conferences, according to the Treaty of Lunéville. The Continental powers, restive, secretly applauded the British and waited apprehensively for Napoleon's next move. "He is again going to cover Europe with blood," Joseph told Miot angrily.

THE REPUBLIC CRUMBLES

In 1802, Joseph had watched in dismay while the senate docilely accepted the Constitution of the Year X, not so much because it made Napoleon a virtual king (Consul for life, able to name his successor), but because it totally subjected the parliamentary bodies—senate, tribunate, and *corps legislatif*—to his will. In 1803 he was appalled at the facileness with which the senators rewarded themselves with extra incomes and property (at Napoleon's suggestion). "I have no more illusions about republicanism in France," Joseph told Miot, "it exists no more. Not a member of the senate opened his mouth against the measures. . . . The most republican took pencils to calculate what each would get."

Napoleon pushed rapidly toward the creation of the Empire. Even at the end of 1802, Miot observed, "The Tuileries and Saint Cloud were no longer . . . the seat of a government and the residences of the chief magistrate of a republic, but the court of a sovereign." The repressions of monarchy reappeared also. Jourdan mourned the death of the Republic in print; the police seized his pamphlet. Benjamin Constant was banished from France. In 1803 Napoleon reorganized the Institut so as to exclude the *ideologues*. Joseph tried to reconcile the First Consul with those who remained in the country, but he wanted war. "Who is the most superior woman of antiquity and of our time?" Germaine de Staël asked sweetly. "That of either who has had the most children!" snarled Napoleon. She was not pretty any more; her feminism no longer charmed him. And he was thinking about monarchy, heredity, children. He had none. Who would succeed him?

Joseph went into semi-retirement at Mortefontaine. At first outraged at Napoleon's monarchal ambitions, he was slowly won over. He was attached to the Republic, but neither the people nor their legislators seemed to be. France had benefited greatly from Napoleon's administration, and as it was, his death could mean the end of his system and the return of chaos. There had already been a number of attempts on his life. The French might not accept a successor named by the First Consul, but despite the Revolution, they were emotionally disposed to accept a monarch's heir. Centuries of tradition made it seem "right." Perhaps only a monarchy could give France a stable, permanent government. Napoleon would be Emperor of the French, not king and successor to the Bourbons. The new nobility would be one of service, not feudal privilege; it would be open to all men of talent. Establishing an empire, moreover, might help quell the hostility of European monarchs, to whom "French Republic" meant government by guillotine and Jacobin armies on the march.

Unable to oppose the Empire, as such, Joseph did his best for the cause of liberty, defiantly speaking out and remaining loyal to his friends, whether Napoleon approved or not. He continued to see Jourdan, the *ideologues*, Fouché (temporarily ousted from the ministry); he cultivated friendship of Lafayette, whom Napoleon had found mule-headed and now ignored. Napoleon had to listen to his lectures against censorship and the *cabinet noir*, which opened letters in the mail. He jumped to defend anyone he thought persecuted. In early 1804, when General Moreau was arrested for complicity in a Bourbon plot, Joseph decided he was innocent, visited him in jail, got Lafayette in to see him, carried him letters from all and sundry, helped his family, and worked to save his life. Moreau was allowed to emigrate to the United States.

Joseph's resistance was one of gestures, but he could not do more. Napoleon was his *brother*. And who could govern France better? To try to destroy him would be evil; to moderate his policies was enough. Then there was the *family*. An *imperial family*! The idea was irresistible. An imperial family had status exclusive of its reigning member; it would be freed from Napoleon, in a sense. He, Joseph, would be a prince. The prospect appealed to him. To whom would it not appeal?

The Duke d'Enghien

As plans for the Empire became known, Bourbonist plots multiplied. Across the Rhine were droves of *émigrés*, agitating, writing, sending agents into France, forming regiments to fight for the "rightful" King, Louis XVIII. Among them was the Duke d'Enghien, sole heir of the Prince of Condé, first prince of the blood. He was at Ettenheim, in Baden, just a few miles from French territory. In March 1804, Napoleon sent troops into Germany who seized the Duke and brought him to Vincennes. He was ordered tried for treason. Rumor had it he would be shot—a warning to the Bourbons and their supporters.

Joseph found Napoleon at Malmaison. "I reminded him of his political principles, which put him above all factions. . . . I recalled to him the circumstances under which he entered the artillery after the encouragement given me by the Prince of Condé . . . in 1783, at the collège d'Autun." He reminded him of their teacher's poem: "Condé! such a name! the universe reveres it." Napoleon was taken aback. He sat silent, making nervous movements, avoiding Joseph's eyes. The Duke is no leader of a movement, Joseph told him; his father and grandfather are alive! Napoleon showed impatience. "His pardon is in my heart," he said, "since I have the power to pardon. But that is not enough for me; I want the grandson of the Great Condé to serve in our armies; I feel strongly about that."

Joseph returned jubilantly to Mortefontaine. Enghien is saved! he told his dinner guests. "Ah! That's better!" breathed Madame de Staël, "otherwise we would never see Mathieu again!" Laughing, she looked at Mathieu de Montmorency, an aristocrat of ancient title, related to the Bourbons. Bah! shouted another noble. "The First Consul is fooled if he thinks the nobility . . . cares about the Bourbons!" Look how they treated some of us! "Tonnerre! Tonnerre!" he bawled, referring to Joseph's confidant Clermont-Tonnerre. They argued away happily, all assuming that the young Duke was safe. Next morning, however, Joseph learned that Enghien had been executed during the night.

He hurried to Malmaison. Réal is the culprit! said Napoleon, livid with rage. I will not have that Terrorist in my government! He had orders to delay the execution! The Count Réal, in charge of police in the Paris *arrondissement*, admitted a dispatch had arrived during the night—not from Napoleon but a state secretary. Since he had retired, his servant held it until morning. Too late! Napoleon seemed inconsolable. "It would have been *beau* to have the grandson of the great Condé for an aide-de-camp." Joseph was taken in by the act. He did not even think it amiss when Napoleon forgave Réal, and ruled Enghien victim of a "strange fatality."

At the time, Napoleon, as head of state, did not publicly deny responsibility. At Saint-Helena, he blamed the execution on Talleyrand, who called him a liar. It was a case of pot-and-kettle by grand masters of prevarication. Both were guilty; the Duke had been captured to be shot.

The courts of Europe were horrified. Jacobinism! Shades of the Terror! Even the hardened Parisians were shocked. Condé! It was a name of heroes, unsullied in any generation. The Duke had been young and handsome—and an only son. Who was so callous as not to share his father's pain? Only the most soulless Jacobins were happy. "I am enchanted," said one, "Bonaparte has joined the Convention." The intellectual community was shaken to its foundations. Madame de Staël fled to Switzerland. Chateaubriand, who had accepted a diplomatic post, followed her example, as did many others.

The Succession

Two days after the Duke's execution, the senate resolved to "modify the institutions" of the government. On 18 May 1804, a *senatus consultum* made Napoleon the Emperor of the French; the people voted overwhelmingly for the change. For months before the senate action, a violent conflict raged between Napoleon and his brothers over the succession. It has been depicted as a petty, ridiculous squabble by many historians. To Joseph it was not.

A great reason for creating the Empire was to provide for hereditary succession, thus securing the permanence of the government. The senate, initially, favored primogeniture—the standard European rule. Unless Napoleon fathered a legitimate male child, Joseph would have succeeded him, then, unless Joseph had a son, Lucien, and so on. Napoleon, however, announced that he wanted to adopt an heir, for which there was no precedent later than Roman times. Joseph was furious. "I am fed up with his tyranny!" He can appoint a successor now! Why create an Empire? "No heredity, no family, no intermediary caste! No obstacle to the ambitions of military chiefs . . . who can hope to [replace him]. . . . No resistance in the legislative bodies!" Was *no one*, not even his family, to share power with Napoleon? He angrily threatened to join with "patriots and friends of liberty to destroy such tyranny!"

Joseph, thought Miot, was motivated by ambition, which "he disguised from himself." Perhaps he was, in part. Pride of family was more in evidence. Napoleon's position, he felt, was an insult to them all. Were they not good enough to be a real imperial family? Whom would he adopt? What if it were Eugène de Beauharnais, son of that slut Josephine. Eugène was a fine boy, but no Bonaparte. Of course Napoleon talked of adopting the son of Louis and Hortense de Beauharnais (Josephine's daughter). But Louis had been forced into the marriage, and though Hortense was blond, beautiful, full of life, and the soul of virtue, he hated her. He stayed away from home perpetually, with his regiment or at the baths, dosing himself; he had become melancholy and sickly. Rumor had it the child was Napoleon's. It wasn't true, but the choice would strengthen rumors. Joseph made clear to Napoleon that *he* did not want to be Emperor. Why not divorce Josephine, he asked his brother, and marry a princess who can give you children? He got an angry response.

Lucien complicated matters by marrying Madame de Joubèrthon, a woman of uncertain reputation and with children. Napoleon demanded he divorce her. NO! Lucien fled to Rome. Jérôme made a similar blunder. An officer in the French navy, he had jumped ship in the West Indies and gone to the United States, where he had married Elizabeth Patterson of Baltimore. Joseph urged Napoleon to accept her. After all, the Catholic Bishop of Baltimore had officiated. No, said Napoleon. "It seems," Joseph told Miot, "that destiny has blinded us and may, by our own faults, one day return France to her old masters."

More men than Joseph thought the hereditary principle worth defending. Faced with surprisingly stiff resistance in his Council of State and the legislative bodies, Napoleon compromised. The succession was fixed in his natural and adoptive line, then Joseph and Louis's natural lines. Lucien and Jérôme were excluded.* Unofficially, Napoleon named Louis's son, Napoleon Charles, the heir-designate.† The child, however, was only two, and could

---

* Lucien did not serve Napoleon again until 1815, during the "Hundred Days." Between 1809 and 1815 he was in exile in England. Jérôme returned in 1805, and, under threat of courtmartial, agreed to an annulment of his marriage. He ultimately became King of Westphalia.

† Napoleon Charles died in 1807. A second son, Napoleon Louis, died before the Second Empire was established. The third son, Louis Napoleon, became Napoleon III.

not be adopted until he was eighteen. Meanwhile, Joseph was the heir apparent.

PRINCE ÉGALITÉ

Not fully satisfied with the arrangements, but pleased to see that Napoleon's power still had some limits, Joseph cooperated with his brother. He was named Prince and grand elector, and since Napoleon insisted that *militaires* must be in the succession, became a colonel of the fourth infantry regiment and spent the summer of 1804 with it at Boulogne. The Emperor was delighted. "At least he will know what it is. Epaulettes won't scare him anymore; he can get on a horse and command like anybody else. He must stay in the profession." That Joseph would not do. The "instincts of my whole life" mitigated against it. In August 1804, he returned to Paris.

The army at Boulogne was poised, supposedly, to invade England. But Napoleon seemed determined to provoke war in Europe. "What I have done up to now," he told Joseph and others, ". . . is nothing. Europe will not be at peace until she has a single chief, an emperor who has kings for officers." For his coronation (2 December 1804) he had persuaded the Pope to come to Paris, but he meant to crown himself. He had ordered the presumed sword and regalia of Charlemagne brought from Aix-la-Chapelle (Aachen) for the ceremony. The successor of Charlemagne, first Holy Roman Emperor! And what of the present Holy Roman Emperor, Francis of Austria? Napoleon cared not. Joseph could not help being appalled at the monster he had helped create, but he was tied to him by clan loyalty and affection for the brother of his youth, of whom he was reminded often by a gesture or a sudden happy smile.

He refused, however, as always, to give up his friends. "I have reached the point," Napoleon complained, "where kings write to me as 'my brother . . .' and Joseph . . . passes his time writing philosophical letters to Regnault and to Jourdan. To Jourdan!" Occasionally Joseph could not help puncturing Napoleon's ego. Asked about coronation robes before a roomful of people, he said he'd as soon wear the same as his attendants. "I remember

only that the same persons were born my equals and friends."
Of course, he said, the "chief magistrate" should stand out.
"Dites donc *souverain!*" snapped Napoleon.

Joseph threatened not to attend the coronation. He had better,
his imperial brother told him testily. "You will have to come to
the Tuileries: I will see you and call out *bonjour Prince Égalité!*
—and that word will kill you." He deserved no comparison to the
Prince Égalité of the Terror, but an equalitarian—in the sense
that Washington and Jefferson were—he would ever be.

Joseph did appear at the coronation. As he and Napoleon
entered Notre Dame there came suddenly one of those moments
when Napoleon was his boyhood self. "Oh! If our father could
see us now!" he said. It was such things that kept Joseph tied
to the terror of Europe.

⚜

CHAPTER IV

King of Naples

WAR IN EUROPE

IN 1805, Napoleon lashed Europe toward war at a breakneck pace. The Austrian Emperor, affronted by his imperial presumptions, was further shaken when he made himself King of Italy (the former Republic), giving hereditary control of one-third of the peninsula to the new French dynasty, and usurping a ceremonial title which traditionally had belonged to a Habsburg.* For his Italian coronation, at Milan, Napoleon had brought from Monza the Iron Crown of the ancient Lombard Kings, and assumed their style. *Napoleo Rex Totius Italiae* read the commemorative medal he ordered struck—Napoleon King of All Italy. To the remaining independent rulers on the peninsula, the gesture was ominous.

The Pope, who had already lost part of his territory, anxiously pursued a policy of non-involvement and passive resistance. Queen Marie Caroline of Naples secretly begged the British and Russians to protect her from "that Corsican bastard, that parvenu, that dog!" Simultaneously, she responded to long-standing offers from Talleyrand and in the fall signed an alliance with France.

---

* Joseph had declined to accept the crown. Napoleon refused to give him a free hand, and insisted that he renounce his rights in the imperial succession. Louis declined for similar reasons, and Lucien refused the condition that he divorce his wife. Angry with his brothers, Napoleon made Josephine's son, Eugène de Beauharnais, an experienced soldier of twenty-three, his viceroy.

THE KINGDOM OF NAPLES

1. The divisions shown are the ancient territories, each of which comprised several provinces (a total of fourteen).
2. Sicily plus numerous small islands, like Ischia and Capri (shown), remained under Bourbon rule and served as British bases. Capri was captured after Joseph's departure.
3. Pontecorvo and Benevento were Imperial fiefs.

PAPAL STATES

Ancona

ABRUZZI

Corfinium
Sulmona

Rome
Albano

MOLISE

ADRIATIC SEA

Pontecorvo

Terracina

CAMPANIA

Gaeta

Volturno R.
Capua
Benevento

APULIA

Bari

Caserta
Naples
Lakes Patria and Lucrino

Ischia
Pompeii
Sorrento
Capri

Salerno

Brindisi

LUCANIA

Taranto

Otranto

TYRRHENIAN SEA

Lagonegro

Cassano
Cosenza

CALABRIA

Stuart's landing

Santa Eufemia
Maida

Messina

Scilla
Reggio

Palermo

Strait of Messina

SICILY

MEDITERRANEAN SEA

But no one expected her to respect it if any advantage lay in doing otherwise.

Russia meanwhile had allied with Britain (April 1805). Austria hesitated, awaiting Napoleon's next move, which came swiftly. En route from his coronation at Milan to Paris, he visited Genoa and received the city fathers, who, rehearsed in advance by Talleyrand, asked that the city-state be annexed to France. The Emperor benevolently consented. Austria, pressed to the limit, cast her lot with Britain and Russia in August 1805.

For two years Napoleon had maintained a huge concentration of troops at Boulogne, poised for a highly advertised invasion of England. Surely, however, by the beginning of 1805, he had abandoned the plan; with his enemies multiplying in Europe, to have pursued it would have been suicide. In Italy, he had inspected the forts of the Quadrilateral, which guarded the kingdom against Austria in the north. At Paris and Boulogne in August, he had all too publicly proclaimed that his expedition would sail whenever Admiral Villeneuve's fleet appeared to guard the channel. But before he knew that Villeneuve had been repulsed by the British, his troops were already marching for Germany.

Taken in by Napoleon's show at Boulogne, the Austrians expected to crush his forces in Germany before he could arrive. His 200,000 French, however, were in the Rhineland by the end of September, and were reenforced by 100,000 troops of his German allies. Rolling eastward, the Grande Armée surrounded and captured Mack at Augsburg, sent other Austrian armies into confused retreat before the Russians could support them, and in November captured Vienna. An Austrian army under the Archduke Charles, sent against Italy, withdrew north to try to repair the situation, but too late. At Austerlitz, on 2 December 1805, the anniversary of his coronation, Napoleon crushed a Russo-Austrian force under the Czar Alexander and the Continental war was over.

MARIE CAROLINE ERRS

At Naples, Marie Caroline, encouraged by initial successes of the Austrians in northern Italy, allowed an Anglo-Russian army to land in November 1805. Hardly were they ashore, however, when the news of Austerlitz arrived; they hastily withdrew. Damning the Allies for deserting her, she instructed her diplomats to tell the French that the expedition had forced itself on her. Cardinal Ruffo went to Rome to plead with the French ambassador, Cardinal Fesch, Napoleon's uncle; he was then to go on to Paris, but Talleyrand had him turned back. The Queen told her ambassador in Paris, Gallo, to beg the "Emperor of all Europe" for peace. And swallowing her pride, she wrote Napoleon herself, but he was unreceptive to her entreaties. "I will finally punish that whore," he had already written Talleyrand.

Anticipating Marie Caroline's treachery, Napoleon had ordered preparations for an invasion of Naples as early as August. In December an army of 40,000, under Marshal Masséna, was on the march. "The Dynasty of Naples has ceased to reign," proclaimed the Emperor from Schönbrunn. Until 1805, his Mediterranean policy had involved using the Spanish Bourbons, nominally his staunch allies, to bring the Neapolitan Bourbons to his side, putting an east-west squeeze on the British. Now he intended to achieve his purpose by seizing Naples. This most important kingdom, he determined, would be ruled by Joseph, a brother he could depend on, even if he had to cater somewhat to his soft-headed ideas.

JOSEPH, CONQUEROR

At Paris, Joseph had supervised the civil administration in Napoleon's absence. He was startled to receive, on 7 January 1806, orders to take command of the French army of Naples. "If my presence were not necessary in Paris," Napoleon wrote, "I would march on Naples in person." Leave within forty hours, he commanded. In *forty-eight hours*, Joseph replied, but he left in forty. His brother's proffer of special trust was irresistible, especially since a letter in the same packet notified him that the Emperor was detained at Munich on family business—the marriage of Eugène to Princess Augusta of Bavaria and talks regarding a bride for Jérôme from the royal family of Württemberg.

Joseph overtook Masséna at Rome on 23 January, and helped

complete arrangements for passage of the army through the Papal States. Pius VII received him warmly, much reassured by his presence (as Napoleon intended). Assuming command of the army, he moved on to Albano, where on 28 January he learned that there was more to his mission.

"I will place on [the Neopolitan] throne a prince of my family, preferably you," wrote Napoleon, ". . . if that doesn't suit you, someone else." The terms were made known separately—Joseph's rights in the French succession unimpaired, a Neapolitan army, a free hand. Having made the concessions which he knew Joseph would demand, Napoleon assumed an angry air of command. "Tell him that surely that [at] the least hesitation [to accept the crown], he is lost entirely," the Emperor told Miot. "I recognize as relatives only those who serve me. . . . He must win glory! He must get himself wounded! Then I will respect him. He must renounce all his old ideas!"

Joseph could not remake his character, nor did he care to, but he accepted the throne. He was encouraged by general indifference to the overthrow of the Bourbons. The Duke de San Teodoro, sent to Albano by Marie Caroline in late January, abandoned the Bourbon interest, and engaged to deliver the forts protecting the capital. The Queen, in a desperate attempt to rally the lower classes against the French in the name of religion, paraded with her children to the Church of Saint Anne of Chiaia. The lazzaroni watched unmoved; they had helped her overthrow the Republic in 1799, and been rewarded by vicious repression. On 11 February she sailed for Sicily, where King Ferdinand had been for some weeks.

The government of Naples was taken over by a regency council—the Princes of Aragon and Canosa and the jurist Cianciulli. They approved Teodoro's "armistice," and notified Joseph to march at all speed for the capital. Their great fear was that the lazzaroni would run wild and destroy property before the French arrived.

The campaign became, in Rambaud's words, a *"promenade militaire,"* his troops in high spirits, swinging along, loaves of bread skewered on their bayonets, accepting drinks of wine from peasant onlookers, joking with the girls. On 15 February, when

Joseph reached the city of Naples, he was escorted through an arch of triumph in the Largo San Dominico. Bourbon troops remained in the south, the fortress of Gaeta had been bypassed, and some guerrilla bands were operating, but the effortless seizure of the capital, the only city of any importance in Naples, seemed to forecast a short campaign.

On 16 February, Joseph attended a *Te Deum* in the Cathedral of San Gennario (Saint January), Naples' patron saint, presented a necklace of diamonds to the saint, and received the good wishes of the Neapolitan clergy, led by Cardinal Ruffo di Scilla.* Later, over the protests of his military advisers, he went incognito into the streets. Recognized, he harangued the people in Italian on his plans to help them, drew cheers, and was escorted back to the palace by amazed and happy *lazzaroni*.

This was conquest after Joseph's own heart.

His quick success made Napoleon uneasy. "I congratulate you on your reconciliation with Saint January," he wrote sarcastically, "but . . . I hope you have also occupied the forts . . . and disarmed the city." Wrote Joseph: "Death from starvation is common here. . . . Surely something can be done about it." Napoleon had other thoughts: "I have not heard that you have had a single one of the *lazzaroni* shot. . . . If you don't make them fear you from the start, you will have trouble."

PACIFICATION

Joseph had taken necessary precautions, but he did not consider the capital likely to explode, and his estimate proved correct; the city never saw so much as a serious riot during his entire reign. Elsewhere pacification proceeded rapidly, though the summer brought some excitement. On the east coast Reynier's corps fought its way to the tip of the boot and captured the fortress of Reggio on 20 March. On the opposite coast Gouvion Saint-Cyr and Lechi marched south almost unopposed, installing garrisons as they went. In April, Joseph made bold to tour Calabria, in the extreme south, the most recently conquered

---

* Not Marie Caroline's diplomat; that Cardinal Ruffo remained in Rome.

province, bandit-ridden and dangerous even in peacetime. A brave one! the mountaineers said. They flocked to see him, cheered his promises of peace and prosperity, told him of their problems. Over the pained objections of the stiff-necked Reynier, he granted pardons left and right to prisoners, military and civilian.

Napoleon meanwhile had officially designated him King of Naples, with the title Joseph-Napoleon I (Giuseppe-Napoleone). On 11 May he made his first royal entry into Naples, was received by the municipal senators, the nobility, and the clergy, and attended another solemn *Te Deum*. The British marked the occasion by bombarding the forts of the city and capturing the Isle of Capri, just offshore. A few days later Vesuvius erupted briefly. Some Neapolitans took it as a bad omen, but they were wrong. Joseph's reign would be glorious. The eruption did announce a summer of troubles, however.

Gaeta, on the coast north of Naples, continued to hold, thanks largely to the skill of its commander, a little pot-bellied man with a drooping cavalry moustache who looked like anything but a soldier—the Prince of Hesse-Philippsthal, a noble German soldier of fortune. Next to food and wine, which he consumed in elephantine quantities, he loved battle; stern but full of humor, absolutely fearless, he made soldiers even of the lackluster hirelings of the Bourbons. "Gaeta is not Ulm! Hesse is not Mack!" he howled at the French from the ramparts. In June, Masséna had before Gaeta 10,000 men, backed by over one hundred cannon; Joseph appeared to initiate an around-the-clock bombardment. Even so, it was not until mid-July, when Hesse was wounded and carried off to Sicily, that the garrison surrendered.

Meanwhile, taking advantage of Hesse's resistance, the British landed a five-hundred-man expedition under Sir John Stuart on the southern coast. Reynier assembled an equal force and rode to the attack—too impetuously. He was defeated. Joseph positioned his reserve to protect the capital. To his surprise, however, Stuart moved south, and after a few weeks, withdrew to Sicily.

The British had hoped to promote a popular uprising, and though guerrillas did appear, they showed more zeal for looting than fighting the French. Neapolitans, whatever they thought of Joseph, did not want the Bourbons back, and the British were unprepared to sponsor anyone else. Stuart left garrisons at Reggio, Scilla, and elsewhere, which it took months to expel. But his experience had convinced the British that Napoleon could be attacked more profitably elsewhere. Neither during Joseph's reign, nor that of Murat, which followed, did they seriously attempt to invade the mainland, and the Bourbons could do nothing without them.

Joseph had refrained from assuming detailed control of military operations; he had good commanders, and he let them function. Throughout the campaign, however, he had shown energy and good judgment, and had taken more risks than the generals expected. His attention to the needs of the troops—their food, clothing, medical care, about which he was continually asking them questions—won him a solid popularity. His prohibition against looting and insistence on humane treatment of the population, though sometimes flagrantly violated, brought dividends as peace returned.

After the British withdrawal, only guerrillas remained to be dealt with, and without support, the bands dwindled. Many of the leaders, such as the ferocious Baroness Laura Fava, fled to Sicily. The most famous, Fra Diavolo, was captured and executed. Dashing, wily, a man of many disguises—the most usual that of a friar, though he was no churchman—Diavolo had once talked a French general into letting him cross the lines into Gaeta, from which he somehow extricated recruits for his band brought from Sicily. Joseph sought some excuse to save him, but could find none.

The brutalities of his generals gave Joseph much concern. Masséna, a heavy-handed professional with the face of a debauched boxer, provoked an angry encounter with the King by executing the Marquis di Rodio, captured in uniform. Rodio had, however, been commissioned to lead the guerrillas. Reynier, a haughty Swiss, took vengeance on whole villages in the south. But it was soon over. Joseph proclaimed amnesty for all guerrillas who would take an oath to him; he was free with pardons for those captured in action. Some banditry continued, principally in Calabria, where centuries of the most grinding poverty and predatory government had produced a hard and cynical people who took easily to violence. Generally, however, the country was at peace by the end of 1806.

Napoleon had meanwhile placed Louis on the throne of Holland, created the Confederation of the Rhine, and provoked a war with Prussia and Russia. "Your Majesty may smile that I speak of [capturing] Fra Diavolo," Joseph wrote him in November. "When he receives this letter he will probably be in Berlin." Napoleon was in Berlin. In the spring he would defeat the Russians at Friedland, and at Tilsit make an ally of the Czar and create a German kingdom, Westphalia, for Jérôme.

From the first, Joseph's main interest had been in domestic reform and reorganization; after 1806, he was able to devote almost his full time to these tasks.

REMAKING SOCIETY

Joseph knew full well that he was the King of the upper classes, who had made him welcome because he safeguarded their property. "The grand seigneurs of the kingdom, who are the richest proprietors, are decidedly for the new government," he wrote Napoleon; "most of the other proprietors are for me too. . . . But unfortunately the number of proprietors is small, and almost all the others [are hostile to them]." Joseph's problem was to remake society. No government could hope for permanence which did not. The Republic of 1799 had fallen because the leaders, oddly enough, were rich nobles and burghers. The Bourbons had recovered control with the help of the masses, whom they had betrayed when once again in power.

Talleyrand had advised Joseph not to "disturb the nobility or institutions of the country." Naples, he thought, with essentially only upper and lower classes, and nothing between, could be ruled no other way. Napoleon considered the Neapolitans depraved, controlled by passion, without principle, governable only by the whip—like Egyptians, he said. He had little faith even in the nobility, whom he thought would bow to anyone in power and turn on anyone who showed weakness. "Disarm, disarm the

Neapolitans!" he instructed. "Believe that you will never win popular support in that country." Joseph disarmed them; and with heavy heart he allowed the execution of die-hard guerrillas. But he would have none of the cynicism of Napoleon and Talleyrand. He was determined to rebuild society and make a *nation* of his feudal kingdom.

If, however, he attacked the upper classes frontally, he would alienate virtually all educated Neapolitans. He would then have to establish an all-French government—a foreign dictatorship—which would rule until a new generation was educated to leadership.

Joseph chose to propitiate the upper classes, enlist their support, and then push and persuade them to accept reforms. His plans included the gradual abolition of feudalism, land redistribution with compensation to owners and government loans to peasant buyers, the breaking of control of industry and commerce by vested interests, revamping the tax system to shift the burden from the lower classes, and the use of crown and Church property for the public good. He hoped to restyle the courts on the French model, enforce equality before the law, and ultimately introduce the Code Napoléon. He intended to start people voting in local elections immediately, and eventually to have national elections, a constitution, and a parliament. Meanwhile, he meant to develop a civil service where selection and promotion were based on talent, and destroy the deeply inbred feeling among Neapolitans that offices were *rewards* rather than trusts. Similarly, he hoped to use the armed forces as a training ground for patriots—from all classes. Promotion would be on merit, service to the nation pictured as a privilege, not a punishment, and soldiering honorable—not a business for mercenaries. Basic to everything was the improvement of education. Joseph envisioned a complete system of public schools, open to all without cost, with crown scholarships to support university and professional training for the best qualified graduates.

By Miot's testimony, Joseph worked "day and night" during the hectic first months. His schedule was always rigorous, as became apparent to Napoleon from the immense volume of reports and correspondence which reached him. The Emperor's reaction was interesting. Wrote he in December 1806: "Go out in society and animate the country; it is necessary for the city and for you. You should have a grand circle, and *not live too seriously.*" It was the Napoleon who "knew" Joseph speaking, the cadet of Brienne, pontificating about his brother's character, fearful that he would become a competitor. "How dare you not be yourself!" he seemed to be saying. After 1808, when Joseph became King of Spain, Napoleon seemed positively determined to deny his successes, and even *make* him fail. More than one memoirist noted that the Emperor seemed most unhappy when his brother scored a triumph.

While Joseph was in Naples, however, Napoleon was too much occupied with war and reorganizing Europe to interfere with his activity. The imperial neglect was undoubtedly salutary. Considering that the reign lasted little more than two years, Joseph was incredibly successful in setting Naples on the road to modernity. If she later strayed from it, it was not his fault.

THE MINISTRY

Ultimately, Joseph was determined to have an all-native government. To set the machine in motion, however, he induced Napoleon to send him a number of men chosen for their special talents. Four of these he made ministers: François Miot (interior) and Pierre Louis Roederer (finance), both French; Ferri-Pisani (minister secretary of state) and Christophe Saliceti (police and war), both Corsicans. The other three ministers were Neapolitans: the Marquis di Gallo (foreign affairs), the Prince di Pignatelli-Cerchiara (marine), and Michelangelo Cianciulli (justice). The key men were Miot, Roederer, and Cianciulli, who were charged with carrying through the bulk of Joseph's reforms, which we shall treat in detail below.

Miot, small, sharp-faced, and studiedly aristocratic, was, in fact, a self-made man. Beginning as a minor bureaucrat in the service of Louis XVI, he had advanced steadily under the various governments of the Republic. He was a worker, not a politician, though liberal, progressive, and like Joseph, a constitutionalist. He founded an entirely new ministry—interior—the like of which

Naples had never had. Joseph rewarded his truly remarkable services with the title Count de Melito. As Miot de Melito, he became one of the most famous memoirists of the period.

Roederer, son of a lawyer of Metz, had been a rabble-rouser in the early days of the Revolution, inciting the workers against the bourgeoisie, "parasites who feed on the public body." The Terror had sobered him, however; he had helped bring Napoleon to power, and shared his authoritarian liberalism, if not his penchant for war. Humorless, precise, honest, and demanding, Roederer was the perfect finance minister, though Joseph had to soothe the feelings of his associates on occasion. Irascible and caustic, some believed Napoleon had exiled him to Naples. Actually Joseph had exerted himself mightily to get the Emperor to send him Roederer. He performed prodigies at Naples.

Cianciulli was a wise and gentle jurist of international reputation. Joseph chose him to be minister of justice because of his liberalism and great influence in the Neapolitan legal profession. Reforming the courts and modernizing the law in Naples required exceptional knowledge and finesse. The judges, especially, many with hereditary offices and noble titles, were determined to defend their privileges, and were past masters of deviousness. Progressive ministers in Naples had always been met with smiling acceptance of reforms, which, in fact, were negated by interpretation and procedural maneuvers. Joseph expected Cianciulli to move slowly, but achieve real results; the King's faith was justified.

Ferri-Pisani's task was one of coordination and record-keeping, for which the bright young bureaucrat was eminently qualified. Gallo, ex-ambassador of the Bourbons to Paris, a thorough Neapolitan but one who believed his country's future lay in cooperation with France, could sing harmony to Napoleon's foreign policy with conviction; he was perfect for his job. Pignatelli administered an almost non-existent navy—the Bourbons had taken all the seaworthy ships with them to Sicily—but his name was an ornament, and he proved a surprisingly adept ally of Miot in fostering harbor and internal waterway improvements.

Saliceti was a necessary evil. The old Jacobin, who but for Joseph would have been in exile in the French West Indies, or some worse place, brought his family to Naples, and took up permanent residence (he died there in 1809). He lived in style, and had become an art collector, but had lost neither his air of mystery nor his nose for intrigue and criminality. He had been involved in so many plots that he could spot an amateur across a ballroom. With unerring instinct, he smashed every group contemplating violence against the regime before it could act. More than once, his police greeted assassins sent after Joseph from Sicily the moment their feet touched shore. The most celebrated was Agostino Mosca, who carried a lock of Marie Caroline's hair next to his heart. Saliceti reformed the capital police, established a gendarmarie in the provinces, and organized secret police. An army of spies and informers did his bidding, including the trusted mistress of Colonel Hudson Lowe, who directed British espionage from Capri. Saliceti's ruthlessness often appalled Joseph, but his services were indispensable.

Saliceti's ministry of war was actually run by Marshall Jourdan, "exiled" by Napoleon to serve Joseph as commandant of the city of Naples. Tall, bulky, and blond, with a round, boyish face, he seemed at first brush too young to be the victor of Fleurus, the hero of the Republic in 1794, when Napoleon was still a nobody. He was, however, old in spirit; his enthusiasm had died with the destruction of his beloved Republic. Subsequently, Napoleon's well-advertised distrust had made the army regard him as an honorary marshal. Nevertheless, he was a competent professional; in Naples, where he had Joseph's full trust and backing, he served well. Later, in Spain, when Napoleon undermined Joseph's prestige, Jourdan found it impossible to command obedience.

Despite the preponderance of foreigners in the ministry, the government as a whole was more Neapolitan than it had been under the Bourbons, who, after all, were not natives either, and had never concerned themselves greatly about the nationality of their minions. Joseph populated his council of state and household almost exclusively with Neapolitans, including the Princes di San Teodoro and Colonna di Stigliano and the Duke di Cassano-Serra. Similarly, secondary posts in the government, and the whole administration and judiciary, were manned largely by nationals. French advisers abounded at all levels, but no one who knew Joseph doubted that he intended for Neapolitans, eventually, to govern themselves.

Approach to Popular Government

On Miot's recommendation, Joseph left the fourteen traditional provinces intact, but divided them into uniform districts, "governments," and municipalities. The King appointed provincial intendants, district sub-intendants, and mayors (the "governments" were electoral districts). As soon as the system was instituted, citizens who paid a certain yearly tax (in most areas twenty-four ducats, or about $22) and all professional people, were given the vote. In the municipalities they met yearly to select a list of persons from which the King (or for small towns the intendant), selected the mayor and city council. In the governments they again made lists from which the King chose councils to advise the intendants and sub-intendants. The voters were few, since the tax requirement, by Neapolitan standards, was high. Their votes restricted the King's appointive power, but, except for mayors, only over advisory officials. Even this feeble concession to the popular will, however, was made over the objection of Napoleon.

It was 1808 before the Emperor would allow Joseph to issue a constitution. It provided for a one-house parliament appointed by the King, two-fifths from lists drawn by electors, one-fifth from nominations of the university, academies, and courts, and two-fifths from clergy and nobles. It revealed, wrote Miot, "that aversion which [Napoleon] no longer disguised for all that would affirm the liberty of peoples and the political independence of peoples."

Joseph was not proud of his voting laws or constitution. Certainly if he had remained at Naples, he would have worked constantly to improve them. During his short reign, however, he could not overrule Napoleon on such major matters. "I have a right to command a little where I have 40,000 troops," the Emperor asserted. He did command—less than he wanted to, but more than a little.

ASSAULT ON FEUDALISM; LAND REFORM

For weeks in the summer of 1806, Joseph's council of state debated his decree abolishing feudalism, suggesting dozens of amendments. Convinced they were trying to emasculate the law, the King rose, blazing with anger. "Do you believe . . . I will support privileges here? Are we to destroy gothic institutions, the remains of barbarism, only to revive them in other forms? . . . No! The people have groaned too long under the weight of intolerable abuses; they shall be delivered, and if obstacles appear, never doubt, I shall know how to smash them."

The upper class advisers got Joseph's message. If they wanted a share in the government they must support reform. He was King of all the people. In August 1806, Joseph decreed feudalism abolished.

Proprietors were guaranteed a crown indemnity for monetary losses entailed. They lost, however, without compensation, all personal, juridical, and prohibitive rights. The latter had enabled them to forbid peasants to grow certain crops, improve buildings, use new methods, and the like, and were a major obstacle to progress. Lords could no longer judge their tenants, or harass them by requiring a hundred traditional deferences and emoluments. Water courses were freed, and the mills utilizing them. Common lands, pastures, and forests were ordered divided among users. Implementation took time; royal commissioners labored at assessing indemnities and dividing lands well into the reign of Murat. The impact of the moves was obscured by delays and the fact that municipalities replaced the lords in control of some common facilities (for example, mills), so that the peasants continued to pay fees. Nevertheless, a giant step toward freeing the common farmer had been taken.

To broaden peasant freedom, Joseph offered government loans to peasants who wanted to become landowners. As an example to proprietors, he encouraged peasants on crown and confiscated properties to buy the land they cultivated, sending agents to explain to them how it could be done for small yearly payments. To increase pressure on landlords, who lived high and were perpetually in debt, he abolished entail and perpetual trust (legal arrangements under which an heir could not sell his inheritance, which accounted for the survival of many large estates). In addition, he opened, on assurance from French experts that they could produce crops, many previously uncultivated areas (for instance the Tavogliere of Apulia). The land was offered to peasants at extremely low rent, applicable (less five percent interest) for the first five years to the purchase price. New land, made available by draining swamps and marshes, was offered on the same terms.

Miot, Roederer, and Cianciulli all had a part in producing these plans. Murat continued their implementation. If subsequent governments had done so the effect would have been truly revolutionary.

THE COURTS AND THE LAW

Feudal and Church courts were abolished in 1806. Familiarizing the judges and people with the change and regulating the transfer of cases to the proper royal courts took a year. In 1807, a decree outlining a new court system was promulgated, and again time was required to prepare for the abolition of the old courts and the smooth removal of business to the new. Careful attention had to be given, perforce, to the appointment of judges. The new system required fewer, which allowed for the retirement of conservatives; but to avoid alienating whole families and provoking general opposition, many had to be eased into ceremonial officers, awarded titles, and the like.

The preliminaries completed, Joseph ordered the new courts to begin operating on 1 November 1808. A tangle of tribunals with a hundred varieties of jurisdiction and an uncertain chain of appeal were replaced by a simple, orderly system which began with justices of the peace in the municipalities, and proceeded through intermediate civil or criminal courts in the provinces to a court of cassation at Naples. Despite the chronic leisureness and venality of the Neapolitan lawyers, justice was done more speedily and at less expense to litigants.

The transformation of the law began immediately on Joseph's arrival, with an order to the courts to apply the principles of equality before the law, equality of punishment, and civil liberty. Cianciulli labored continually to bring procedures in line with French practice, and kept a battery of experts at work on translations of the French codes and production of explanatory material. When Joseph was ordered to Spain (May 1808), the work was sufficiently advanced to allow him to proclaim most of a new penal code in effect and order the Code Napoléon (civil code) instituted on 1 January 1809.

Though the Neapolitan legal profession, backed by the Church and popular sentiment, staunchly ignored the civil code's provision for civil marriage and divorce, its other provisions went into effect. Even the requirement for equal division of inheritances, so unpalatable to the landed class, was generally observed. While Napoleonic rulers remained in Naples, the people had the advantage of the same legal rights and safeguards against arbitrary imprisonment, torture, and the like as the French.

The Church

No European economy, save perhaps that of Spain, was so burdened by the Church as that of Naples. One adult male in every ten was a churchman; two-thirds of these were monks. So numerous were monastics that although the orders had a combined income of 5,000,000 ducats (22,000,000 francs) a year, most of them lived in shocking poverty. Their condition did not encourage spirituality, and so hard pressed were the monasteries to support their idle hundreds that many were not performing the educational and charitable tasks which had once justified their existence.

Napoleon ordered all the orders abolished. Joseph chose to save the Franciscans, however, and got his way. The rest were suppressed, beginning in 1806 with the Jesuits (the Pope had disbanded the order in 1773, but the Bourbons had ignored the fact). Convents were consolidated to drastically reduce the number. There had been thirty-eight in the capital alone; many, with very lax rules, served as refuges for noblewomen, and hardly deserved religious sponsorship.

The monks and friars were treated gently. They had the choice of either entering the secular clergy or accepting pensions and becoming laymen. In some areas there were disturbances attending the confiscation of the monasteries, but in most cases the problem was safeguarding property from looters.

The government took over lands, buildings, furnishings, artworks, and treasures, which, after the return to the Church of really sacred objects, were valued at some 30,000,000 ducats (132,000,000 francs). This wealth was added to the "National Properties," for use or liquidation in the public interest. The government, however, assumed responsibility for homes for orphans and the aged, hospitals, asylums, and the like, and many schools formerly run by monastic orders. The institutions were expanded and improved and new ones added. In the balance, they received more in property and money from the National Properties than the monasteries had contributed.

Out of hostility to Napoleon, the Pope never recognized Joseph, but he advised the Neapolitan clergy to cooperate with him. Generally, the admonition was obeyed. If, at the time, the majority of the churchmen thought Joseph's policies smacked of brimstone, they made no trouble. Religious peace prevailed throughout the reign.

FINANCES

Roederer descended upon the sleepy Neapolitan chambers of finance like a demon. "He has many enemies," Joseph explained to Napoleon, "because he has true probity, true attachment to me; *he will not let them steal*, he is inflexible. . . . Roederer . . . has voluntarily made himself the *bête noire* of everybody, to serve me."

The minister put all the banks out of business but one, the Bank of Saint James (San Giacomo), which he equipped to function like the Bank of France. He appointed directors-general of direct and indirect taxes and treasures-general of receipts and disbursements and pruned and reordered the provincial bureaucracies working under them. Accounts in multiple sets had to balance each day or lights burned through the night.

Separate treasuries were set up to handle the national debt and National Properties.

The collection of direct taxes was brought quickly under the purview of salaried officials. The contracts of tax farmers, who had collected most indirect taxes, were systematically bought back, and their functions handed to civil servants. The most powerful of the "farmers" were the holders of *arrendamenti,* which gave them the right to collect taxes in perpetuity and keep the proceeds. They were compensated with government bonds worth 48,000,000 ducats, on which the government had to pay 2,400,000 interest annually, but the gain in revenues was 6,000,000 ducats a year.

For twenty-three direct taxes of the old order, Roederer substituted a single land and industrial tax. The indirect tax system was similarly simplified, though the need for immediate revenues prevented a total revision. Half the internal tariffs were removed, and the rest slated for elimination. An attempt was made to dispense with crown monopolies on salt but prices soared and they had to be restored.

The National Properties, comprising 200,000,000 ducats in crown holdings, 30,000,000 from the Church, some 10,000,000 confiscated from individual Bourbonists, were carefully managed. Resisting the inclination to dispose of them wholesale to fill the empty treasury, Roederer retained most of them, and applied the incomes to the support of charity, education, and public works. Some were made collateral for forced loans.

Sales were held at intervals to obtain cash to meet current expenses or to reduce the public debt. Cash buyers paid one-quarter or one-fifth immediately, the rest in installments. The government's creditors were offered the alternatives of reregistering their claims and receiving an annual interest at five percent, or being paid in National Properties. If they elected to be paid, they were issued certificates in the amount of their claims. They then bid on properties at public auctions and paid in the certificates.

By use of the National Properties, the debt was reduced from 100,000,000 ducats to 50,000,000 in two years. Moreover, the certificates did not cause inflation, as had the similar *assignats* of the French Revolution. Inevitably, some did circulate as paper money, but issues were kept in line with the real value of the property they represented, and those turned in were not recirculated.

Joseph and Roederer had hoped that the sale of National Properties would serve to increase the number of small property holders. Unhappily this did not occur. However, much land, which had been all but unused, was transferred to enterprisers who put it under cultivation.

Roederer was not able to balance the budget. For one thing Joseph's progressive projects, in the short run, were too expensive, and the King somewhat too generous to his supporters. Deficit spending, however, had delivered many positive benefits, and the system Roederer had introduced proved basically sound. Murat's budget balanced at the end of 1809 and the next year he had a surplus. Considering that Joseph and Roederer had begun with an absolutely empty treasury, their achievement was spectacular.

THE ECONOMY

Naples was almost wholly an agricultural country, which is why Joseph gave priority to breaking feudalism and land reform. His work benefited the economy markedly after 1808, but during his reign, enterprisers, peasant and otherwise, were discouraged by factors beyond his control. The British blockade tightened after 1806, and the self-blockade called the Continental System made things worse. Naples had much to sell to France and northern Europe, and might have been unfazed, but she had always shipped by sea—even her domestic traffic had depended on coastal shipping. Roads and internal waterways were poor, and ran to the ports; those bearing northward were not adequate to carry the traffic. In 1807 and 1808 goods needed in France, like grain and wool, rotted in warehouses. Joseph decreed a suspension of rents, and dropped tariffs on the most affected commodities, but these were temporary measures.

Utilizing French army engineers and idle soldiers of all branches to reenforce Neapolitan builders, he attacked the communications problem frontally. Lakes Patria and Lucrino were made navigable and linked with the waterways system. The ancient canal of Corfinium at Sulmona was restored. The highways to Rome via Terracina and Caprano were improved. Calabria was virtually given a new road system, including metalled thoroughfares connecting Lagonegro with Reggio and Cassano. Naples was linked to Brindisi via Benevento. In the Molise, hit hard by an earthquake in 1805, roads and bridges were repaired and new ones added. A new bridge was built over the Garigliano on the highway to Rome, and another over the Noce near Lagonegro.

The chronic problems of usury, scarcity of hard money, banditry, and disease were also attacked. Money-lending was placed under regulation. Forced loans quickly spent, and money from France, wrung from an irate Napoleon by Joseph's refusal to pay French troops, put more coin in circulation. Police, gendarmes, and troops, French and Neapolitan, worked at the slow process of making banditry unprofitable. Miot's ministry endeavored to introduce new medical techniques and medicines; Joseph ordered the entire population vaccinated for smallpox, and enlisted native physicians, French military surgeons, and the medical faculty of the university to help. The clergy was urged to help break superstitious resistance.

Agriculture, meanwhile, slowly adjusted to the needs of the Empire. Joseph rejected Napoleon's proposal to make Naples a sort of tropic colony, and hoped to develop a balanced economy. Nevertheless, cotton and sugar, especially, promised large profits, and the King gave production his support. Cotton farms were established near Castellammare, Torre Dell'Annunziata, Salerno, and Otranto which by 1809 could furnish three-sevenths of French needs and satisfy the local market. Less successfully, sugar beets, and some sugarcane, were grown. Exportation of raw silk and grain increased as the roads were improved, as did that of olive oil, though ships were required to move large quantities.

Experts secured from France by Joseph and dispatched with interpreters and staffs by Miot labored to improve farming methods. The peasants knew nothing of fertilizing, deep plowing, efficient harvesting and storage. Grain was of poor quality and full of waste, dirt, weeds, and mold. Cotton was often taken before maturity; grapes were usually picked too late, and made sour wine. Animals, left in the open to fend for themselves and given no food supplements, were small and few. The peasants, tradition-bound and inclined to take a safe bad crop rather than experiment as the foreigners suggested, were hard to convert. Progress, however, was made.

Industry expanded little. Joseph favored private enterprise (the unquestioned progressive thing in his day), while opposing corporative privilege, including that of municipalities and guilds, and strictures on the production and movement of goods. In this spirit he had consolidated the banks, which had not served all equally, reduced internal tariffs and adjusted national ones, re-formed the tax system, and brought the law in line with the Code Napoléon. Naples, however, lacked industrial management and skilled labor; native capital favored agriculture or commerce; foreign capital avoided Naples because of bad past experiences. The King used government capital to open a new tobacco plant in Naples, new iron mines in Calabria, and to expand the crown foundaries, but resisted doing more, preferring to use his limited resources for broader purposes. Europe did not want the low quality wool, cotton, and silk cloth which Neapolitan plants produced for the domestic market, or most of the gloves, hats, soaps, and perfumes which the capital produced. Europe did want agricultural products, and so Joseph and Miot exerted themselves to foster their production and get them to market.

The value of Joseph's work really became apparent during the reign of Murat, when general prosperity prevailed. By 1808, however, Naples was already moving her usual exports, and had begun selling "colonial" goods to France which she had pre-viously had to buy herself. The economy was expanding, and therein lay great promise for social and political advances, which, if Joseph had remained, he and his successors might have seen fulfilled.

EDUCATION

Acting through Miot's ministry, Joseph founded 1500 public primary schools, and left plans for a thousand more. He established two *collèges* in the capital and three in the provinces, and intended to have ten more. In a country where the Church had always had complete control of education below university level, and schooling had been largely for the rich, this was a shattering change. If churchmen took the program calmly, it was because most of the qualified teachers were clerics, or defrocked monks, friars, and nuns. Nevertheless, they knew something revolutionary had occurred. One part of the original program they did oppose, adamantly and successfully—a system of grammar schools for girls. The King opened a model institution in the capital, but few but French girls attended and it was closed.

Miot reorganized the administration of the university, at Salerno, began an expansion of its library, and brought in new faculty from other Italian states. The student body was enlarged by the liberal granting of royal scholarships. The medical school, which had been famous as early as the thirteenth century, but had declined in recent decades, got new laboratories and advice from French experts. The government also sponsored the writing of textbooks, which were lacking for many courses.

A School of Art and Design was created under the direction of the French painter J. B. Wicar. Joseph was liberal with scholarships for talented youngsters—in fact sought them out in the provinces. Some of them he sent on to Rome, Florence, or Venice for further training.

The two great Neapolitan conservatories, Santa Maria di Loreto and Pietà dei Turchini, were consolidated. The resulting Royal Conservatory boasted two of the most renowned composers of the day, Finaroli and Paisiello. The crown furnished scholarships, expanded the faculty, and granted pensions to artists who performed or instructed occasionally. A furor resulted when Joseph banned the time-honored practice of castrating young boys to preserve their soprano voices. But the King stood his ground, even against bishops and cathedral deans who predicted the destruction of their great choirs, and he prevailed.

If Joseph did not accomplish all he hoped in education, he made strong beginnings, and set, for feudal Naples, revolutionary precedents.

LITERATURE, SCIENCE, AND THE ARTS

Joseph collected paintings, sculpture, ancient *objets d'art* and books on all subjects; he was constantly at the theater and opera. Miot shared his interests; Saliceti was a connoisseur of art, Roederer, a member of the French Institut, Cianciulli, a literary talent and musician. Louis Reynier, who served as royal commissioner in Calabria, was later internationally known as an archaeologist and historian. Count Stanislas Girardin, Joseph's equerry, son of King Stanislas of Poland, the protector of Rousseau, was both soldier and poet. So it went. It is not strange that the government smiled on the intelligentsia.

The King pensioned Naples' leading sculptor, Raffaele Morghen, commissioned frescoes by Giuseppe Cammarano, her most famous painter, and sponsored the work of dozens of lesser lights. In addition to Wicar, the court painter, who probably did the best portraits ever of Joseph (see photo insert), he brought Simon Denis from France. His landscapes graced the royal palace, and some of them, later, Joseph's home near Bordentown, New Jersey. As an adjunct to the School of Art and Design, a gallery was founded where the public could enjoy, and students study, the artworks from the confiscated monasteries and convents. The King added to the collection from the canvases and objects in the royal palaces at Capodimonte and Caserta. (The Bourbons had removed almost everything from the palace in Naples.) Objects discovered at Pompeii or Baia were brought there as well.

Miot's ministry took over Pompeii, and continued excavations. Exportation of artifacts and artworks uncovered were forbidden. Some were, perforce, smuggled out, but except for the regulatory precedent set by Joseph, the ancient city would not be the attraction it is today. The Temple of Serapis, unearthed at Pozzuoli, and the Roman baths at Baia, and other ruins, were given similar protection.

Joseph brought from Milan Vincenzo Monti, Italy's most distinguished poet, for extended stay. The court turned out *en gala* for the premier of his *Pythagoreans*, with music by Naples' Paisiello. A friend of the King was Gabriele Rossetti, later a leader of the Carbonari, an exile in England (1820), and father of a family of British authors and artists. Joseph made a shrine of the home of Tasso, at Sorrento, and built a monument before it; he considered that the sixteenth-century poet had deepened his own compassion for the innocent and influenced his writing style. He intended to collect all of Tasso's writings and deposit them at Sorrento, but there was too little time.

Vincenzo Cuoco, who had made his reputation at Milan after being exiled from Naples in 1799, had the pleasure of seeing his history of the Neapolitan revolution republished under royal auspices, together with the final volume of his *Platone in Italia*, which would later inspire Italian nationalists. Also published were works banned by the Bourbons (who had not even allowed the Code Napoléon to be printed) such as Mario Pagano's book on penal reform, an essay comparable to that of the *philosophe* Beccaria.

Scientists were few in Naples, but Joseph gave offices and honors to those he found. The rector of the university, Cotugno, was one of the royal physicians. Miglietta, a member of the medical faculty, became director of vaccinations; the surgeon Amantea became a consultant to the King's physician, Paroisse. Close relations developed between Neapolitan medical men and French military surgeons, such as Paroisse, Mangin, and Chavassieu d'Audebert. The King granted pensions to the geologist-priest Savaresi, the agronomists Cagnazzi and Tupputi, and many others.

To honor the *illuminati*, Joseph constituted the Royal Academy, with branches for history and antiquity, *belles lettres*, and fine arts, and designated "Royal" the Society for the Encouragement of Natural and Economic Science, founded during the reign by Augusto Ricci.

Napoleon worried that the intellectuals would gain too much influence. "I look on scholars and spiritual men as I do coquettes," he wrote Joseph, "one must see them, talk with them, but no more take them for wives than the others for ministers." Joseph, who remembered how Napoleon had once scrambled frantically to get nominated for the Institut, ignored him.

THE ARMY

Napoleon thought the Neapolitans too corrupt to be soldiers. "As to the idea of having . . . Neapolitan troops as good as mine, I don't believe you will live . . . to see that miracle." He proposed a sort of Neapolitan Legion, officered by Frenchmen and foreigners. Joseph insisted on a national army, however. He wanted French troops to leave. Until they did, he believed, he would never be fully accepted as a Neapolitan or be able to develop national pride in his people.

He appointed a military board to screen the records of former officers, and recommissioned those deemed best. In addition, he took some French officers into Neapolitan service, notably Generals Dedon, d'Arcambal, and Campredon, to assist, respectively, in modernizing the artillery, ordnance, and engineers.

Two young sons of the Prince Colonna were among Joseph's first volunteers. Their earnestness moved him almost to tears. "I want, before I die, to revive the glory of the name Italian," he wrote Napoleon, ". . . then I will have been a success. They are more susceptible to generous and noble sentiments than any other nation." He hoped other young men from the upper classes would come forward. Many did, especially to enter the Military Polytechnic School or Artillery School, both Joseph's creations. If they came merely to be educated, or ingratiate their parents with the King, they developed new attitudes. Many of them would be nationalist leaders in succeeding decades.

Joseph failed to develop an army, however. Though he had some 13,000 troops in 1808, only 4,000 of them were Neapolitans; the rest had been transferred to his service from the French army. The reasons were simple: He had too little time. His draft requirement was too light (one man per year per thousand, as compared to eight per thousand under the Bourbons). Finally, Napoleon proved more than half right about the Neapolitans. They saw no glory in soldiering. Of some 4,400 conscripted in 1807, 1,600 deserted; to train them, Joseph had to ship them to the fortresses of northern Italy.

Still, Joseph's faith in his people was not misplaced. On his beginnings, Murat was able to develop an army of considerable spirit.

Joseph's navy in 1808 consisted of some fifty gunboats—a shallow-draft fleet to guard the coast. Since he knew he could do little to challenge British seapower, he had elected to use his resources otherwise.

COURT AND SOCIETY

"You have to deal with a woman [Naples] who is crime personified," Napoleon lectured his brother. Joseph did not believe it. He threw himself into the affair with his kingdom with a happier image in mind, and almost made his beloved live up to it. He gave love, as was his nature, expecting it to be returned, and in great degree it was. If the nobles and their ladies adhered to him initially because he protected their property and feared that Napoleon himself might take the crown if they rejected Joseph, they nevertheless developed a genuine attachment to him. If the *lazzaroni* did not appreciate all his plans, they knew that he never let them go hungry, that there was more room in hospitals for their sick, and that the children of some, who had been bold enough to present them, were in school. But most of all, they liked him. He was a *bella figura*—not like "The Nose," King Ferdinand, fat and sleepy. The face! the eyes! the women said. A fool can see he is a good man! They also saw he was a *man*. If it was the men who rushed to talk to him in the streets, the windows above were always crowded with women, tittering happily.

In the countryside it was the same. If, in the remote areas, bandit-guerrillas never altogether stopped lashing out at the French and their affluent collaborators, Joseph seemed to ride in the center of an area of calm wherever he went. Crowds met him, priests and mayors made speeches, and the people warmed to his presence. If, generally, conscription, French army requisitions, and perhaps the departure of revered monks from the village obscured in their minds the value of land reform and the retreat of feudalism, when Joseph appeared they believed that authority was on their side. And they were not wrong. For all Joseph's penchant for gradualism, they were not wrong.

"From the Duke de Ascoli . . . to the last Neapolitan, Fra Diavolo included, I have them all," Joseph wrote Napoleon in May 1806. After the violence of the summer that followed, Napoleon never let him forget that he had been overoptimistic. Yet it seems that he might have "had them all" if his reign had been longer—or if all Naples could have seen and heard him on television.

The administrator and commander who worked night and day in the first months later found time for relaxation. The social life of the capital was brighter than it had been for decades. The King set the example with lavish balls and receptions, and hunting parties at Capodimonte and Caserta. The country, he assured Napoleon, who hinted he might visit in late 1807, was incomparable for hunting: "If it was renowned in the time of Augustus, sung of by Horace, it has lost nothing in the ruggedness of its mountains or the abundance of its game." And on Joseph's hunts, as he did not add, beautiful women were a necessity, as they were at all his city functions. Even the dark and fiery nymph, La Fineschi, toast of the opera of Naples, took to horse to be with Joseph (and later turned up in Spain).

The King's one serious affair, however, was with a more subdued and ladylike beauty, the Duchess d'Atri, who was with him constantly during the last year. As his hostess she governed palace functions with a sure sense of tradition, quietly dominating the half-dozen princes who were ceremonial officials, and disposing the absent Queen's aristocratic ladies-in-waiting. Joseph created something of a scandal on his departure by giving her an estate from the royal domains valued at 2,000,000 francs.

Flaunting Napoleon, Madame de Staël traveled from Switzerland to visit Joseph, passing over Neapolitan society like a thunderstorm, bulky, chattering, and to the disciplined Italian ladies, totally unbelievable. The former Madame Tallien, now the Countess de Caraman, visited also, leaving the men murmuring appreciatively and the women livid at her revealing costumes.

Life was never dull in the capital, and the city itself, hugging the shore of the incredibly blue Bay of Naples, was one of the most beautiful in the world. Joseph loved Naples, and left her more beautiful than he found her. His Corso Napoleone ran from the Royal Palace, high above the shore, through the city to Capodimonte and connected with the highway to Rome, sweeping enroute over the Sanita gorge, never before bridged, and through a tunnel in solid rock. The Foro Napoleone, finished by Murat, was begun by Joseph. He personally supervised the laying in of the walks and gardens of the Loggetta a Mare, near the palace, and opened them to the public. He straightened and widened the Strada di Chiaia, and many other streets. Along Naples' streets more than seventeen hundred oil lamps with parabolic reflectors were installed. A city lit before only by occasional flickering tapers before madonnas glowed at night, more beautiful and safer for travel.

Joseph was content. His government was successful, his finances improving, his kingdom generally peaceful, his personal life pleasant. In early 1808 he was looking forward to many happy years in Naples. But it was not to be.

Napoleon's Plans

"Naples deprives me of an army and costs me a lot of money," Napoleon growled. Joseph had adamantly refused to pay French troops in his kingdom; the imperial treasury had been forced to do so—to the tune of 7,500,000 francs in two years. His people would not pay *tribute*, as if conquered, he said. At the same time he had reduced taxes, which, at the start, had been much below the average in France. Instead of paying French troops, Joseph paid the national debt, interest, compensation for feudal rights, and offered loans to peasants! Napoleon didn't like it—or the gentle handling of the monastics, or Joseph's gradualism, or his semi-independent economic policies, and much more. He had become a Neapolitan! the Emperor charged, a nationalist! a veritable traitor to France!

While Napoleon complained bitterly about Joseph's behavior, he was secretly pleased that the King had won a measure of popularity and improved his reputation as an enlightened liberal. The Emperor needed a front man for his seizure of Spain, a man who would appeal to the Spanish liberals, one whom they would believe could protect Spain's independence while giving her needed reforms. Joseph was just the man. Napoleon did not intend, however, that he have the free hand he had exercised in Naples. That Joseph would not realize until it was too late.

THE CROWN OF SPAIN

Joseph reacted almost with alarm when, in December 1807, Napoleon summoned him to Venice and offered him the crown of Spain. What of the present king, Charles IV? Was he not an ally? Not a good ally, said Napoleon. It was the Mediterranean policy again; Spain was not serving him properly. The French could now menace the British from Corfu (acquired at Tilsit); Naples was no longer so important. He wanted Joseph in Spain. It was the "second kingdom of Europe," Napoleon argued, appropriate for the elder brother of the Emperor. Joseph refused to go.

The Emperor turned to Louis. "The climate of Holland doesn't suit you. Besides Holland will never emerge from her [economic] ruins." One kingdom had been enough for Louis, however. His struggles with Napoleon had pushed him to the edge of paranoia. "I am no provincial governor . . ." he replied. "I took an oath to Holland." Lucien, contacted by Joseph for Napoleon, refused again to abandon his wife. Joseph tacitly appoved of the sentiments of both. But who in the family could now "help" Napoleon but him? Joseph's acute sense of obligation made him vulnerable.

In the spring of 1808, Napoleon was at Bayonne, on the Spanish border, arranging the demise of the Spanish Bourbons. His letters to Joseph were very persuasive. Spain ached for liberal reform, he said. The dynasty was corrupt and loathed by the people. He was surrounded at Bayonne by Spanish grandees ready to do his bidding. French troops had occupied Madrid without firing a shot; there would be no fighting. To hurry Joseph's decision, Napoleon dispatched the prudish Queen Julie to Naples. Something of a pall fell over the court. When, in May, the Emperor ordered Joseph to Bayonne, he went.

As parting gestures, Joseph approved a constitution for Naples, made the Code Napoléon the law as of 1 January 1809, nominated his most useful courtiers for knighthood and Naples' leading *savants,* plus selected foreigners, for membership in the new Academy of Science and Literature. He also distributed to those who had served him properties valued at some eleven million francs.

Joseph wanted to be well remembered, and he would be. Naples had prospered under his administration. The groundwork had been laid for further progress under his successors, Marshall Murat and Caroline Bonaparte. Fifty years later, Italy's great unifier, Camillo di Cavour, paid tribute to his work, which, he said, had "very serious results."

Confident that Napoleon was telling him the truth about conditions in Spain, Joseph hoped to repeat his success there.

⚜

CHAPTER V

Napoleon and Spain

THE SPANISH ALLY

CHARLES IV of Spain had allied his country with France in 1796, and maintained the relationship continuously. In 1808 he was a doddering old man—mild, trusting, a lover of the countryside, and given to spells of insanity. The Queen, Maria Luisa, broad-shouldered, strong, and self-willed, had always dominated her husband. Once, lusty Bourbon kings had taken their pleasures widely, while queens took their solace in religion. Maria Luisa had reversed the tables. No words can tell her character better than Goya's portrait, a startlingly unflattering piece of work. Her face, lax, lined, brutally imperious, has not a trace of softness.

The real ruler of Spain was His Serene Highness Don Manuel de Godoy y Alvarez de Faria, Prince of the Peace (with France, 1795), Grand Admiral of the Navies, Generalissimo of the Armies, Grand Chancellor, etc., etc. As a young officer of the palace guard, his slim good looks had caught the Queen's eye. Beginning as her creature, he had in twenty years come to dominate her, and control the government. That Maria Luisa was Godoy's mistress none could doubt; the youngest *infante*, Don Francisco, strikingly resembled the Prince of the Peace.

The Crown Prince, Ferdinand, was consumed with hatred for his mother and Godoy, and intrigued endlessly to overthrow his father, whom he despised. He had a considerable popularity, mostly because his accession would mean the end of Godoy. But also he had a certain affability, and, since the public regarded his grotesque, jutting jaw as a mark of royalty, was considered handsome. It was generally ignored that he was devious and cowardly. Put under house arrest in 1807 (his mother said he had tried to poison her), he had betrayed all his followers, including the respected Duke d'Infantado. He maintained communication with the British, and simultaneously begged Napoleon for the hand of a Bonaparte princess.

Personally unsavory, Godoy was also held responsible for Spain's pitiable condition, for which her alliance with France was heavily responsible. Because of it, the British had blockaded her ports, cut off communication with the colonies, and staunched the still vital flow of American treasure into her coffers. Her coastal cities were kept alive only by illegal commerce, and were wracked by unemployment, hunger, and violence. The inaccessibility of normal markets for manufactured goods had caused similar difficulties in her inland cities. Since Napoleon's rise to power she had been forced to give over Louisiana in return for territory in Italy, which had later been annexed to France. Her navy had been all but destroyed at Trafalgar. She paid an annual tribute to France, and furnished her troops. The Spanish government was in truth bankrupt, and had been driven by increasing unrest to repressive measures, which, among other things, had elevated the Inquisition to power unknown for a century.

From Napoleon's point of view, however, Spain was merely a poor ally. Since 1801 she had disappointed him at every turn. Directed to keep the Portuguese from trading with the British, she had failed miserably; moreover, taking feeble precautions to cloak the fact, she traded with them herself. The Spanish Bourbons had been ineffective in inducing their Neapolitan relatives to follow a pro-French policy. In 1803 Charles IV had promised Napoleon a war subsidy of 6,000,000 francs a year, which he had not paid. In 1805 he had furnished the Emperor thirty ships, mostly rotten relics with inept crews, which had been shot to splinters at Trafalgar—together with the pride of the French fleet. The few troops furnished the imperial armies had proved unreliable.

Napoleon was certain, moreover, that if he ever seemed vulnerable, Godoy, with scavenger instinct, would turn on him. This feeling was confirmed in 1806. In October, as Napoleon maneuvered to close with the Prussians in central Germany, with the Russians already in the field and rumors rife that the Austrians would soon join them, Godoy issued a war proclamation. Vague and grandiose, it called on the Spanish to defend crown and religion against "the Enemy" (unnamed). Simultaneously the Spanish army began campaign preparations. Then, in late October, news of French victories at Jena and Auerstadt reached Madrid. Godoy cancelled his orders to the army, and with magnificent *sang froid*, told the French ambassador that *Portugal* had been the enemy referred to in his proclamation.

Napoleon's correspondence shows no concern over Godoy's behavior. Nevertheless the Emperor surely determined in 1806 (if he had not decided earlier) to bring Spain and Portugal under his direct control. Neither was strong, but either might invite the British to land on the Peninsula; both traded with the enemy; Iberia was rich, but he was getting little from it; Iberia fouled his system and offended his sense of order. The Portuguese were too few to concern him. As for the Spanish, why should they not be grateful if he removed their sick and ineffective rulers?

Early in 1807 Napoleon demanded that 14,000 Spanish troops (one-third of the regular forces) be sent to Germany. A few months after their arrival he isolated them on the Danish islands. Peace made with Russia (Tilsit, July 1807), and the map of Germany redrawn, the Emperor turned in earnest to the problem of the Peninsula.

GODOY OPENS THE GATES

Godoy was the key to easy conquest. He was aging; with the death of Charles IV his career (and perhaps his life) would end. Napoleon secretly offered him a kingdom, Lusitania (southern Portugal), to be guaranteed by the Empire.* Godoy accepted, and in the Treaty of Fontainebleau (27 October 1807) agreed to

---

* The ancient kingdom of Lusitania had comprised most of Portugal and part of Spain; Godoy was to get much less.

allow Napoleon to send troops (28,000) through Spain to Portugal, and to establish a reserve at Bayonne. The reserve, as Godoy well knew, was the advance guard of the French army of Spain.

Portugal had to be subdued first; it was the most convenient landing place for British troops. Before the Treaty of Fontainebleau was signed, a French army of invasion was on the march. Commanding was General Andoche Junot, soon to be Duke d'Abrantès. At Toulon, in 1793, a turning point in the career of the then Sergeant Junot had come while he took dictation from Captain N. Buonaparte. A British shell kicked dirt over his papers; he dusted them off and continued to write. Napoleon marked him for advancement. Junot's army met no real resistance; he entered Lisbon on 29 November 1807, just as the Portuguese royal family departed unceremoniously aboard a British battleship. In unhurried fashion, the general set about organizing a civil administration. His troops established garrison routine and amused themselves. The easy conquest had made Junot overconfident. He was right in assuming that the Portuguese would give him no trouble, but as it proved, the British had surprises in store for him.

While Junot was still on the march, troops from Bayonne began to inch south. The corps of Moncey, Dupont, and Verdier entered Spain, followed by Bessières with divisions of the Imperial Guard. In February 1808 the French occupied the fortress of Pamplona. On the opposite coast, Duhesme's corps marched on Barcelona. Godoy made objection to the movements of these "friendly" troops. The populace was confused, as were the officers of the Spanish army, who generally gave over fortresses without a fight. Within a few weeks there were almost 100,000 French troops in Spain.*

In March Marshal Murat, "Lieutenant of the Emperor in Spain," joined the main army of 40,000 which was marching on Madrid. In 1795 an unknown Major Murat had rolled up the

* LOCATION	COMMANDER	NUMBER
Bayonne-Burgos route	Bessières	22,000
Catalonia	Duhesme	20,000
Aragon	Verdier	16,000
Nearing Madrid	Murat (Dupont, Moncey)	40,000

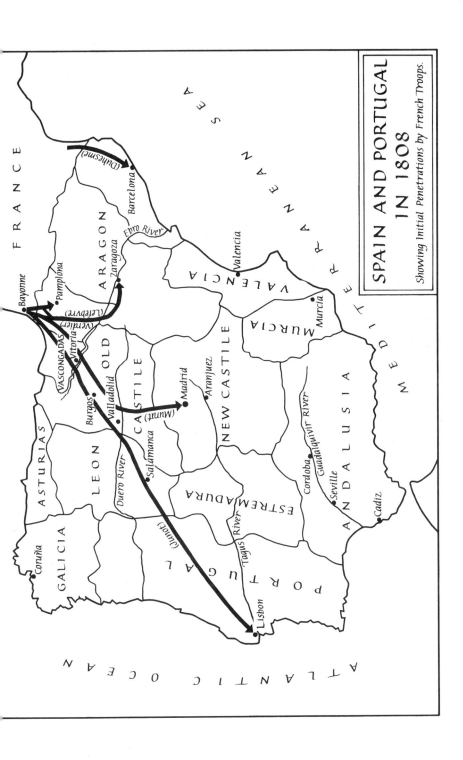

SPAIN AND PORTUGAL
IN 1808

Showing Initial Penetrations by French Troops.

guns which delivered Napoleon's "whiff of grapeshot" and saved the Convention. Honors and titles had since come his way, together with the hand of Napoleon's sister Caroline. Already Grande Duke of Berg (in the Rhineland), he hoped to be made King of Spain, though Napoleon had made him no promises. As he traveled toward Madrid he wrote the Emperor inquiring as to his "wishes." What was to be done in Madrid? The intentions of the Emperor, Napoleon replied, would be kept secret, which, he added slyly, should not be difficult—"I don't know what they are myself."

BOURBON AGAINST BOURBON

It was true that events at the Spanish court had complicated matters. In March the royal family, considering flight to the colonies, had moved to Aranjuez, their summer residence. There, on 17 March, partisans of the Crown Prince incited a mob to storm Godoy's palace. The Prince of the Peace fled to his attic and hid by rolling himself in a rug. The rioters moved on to the royal palace, and as they swirled about the courtyard, the Crown Prince forced his father to abdicate and proclaimed himself Ferdinand VII. Godoy, flushed from his rug by thirst after thirty-six hours, was seized by the mob, which would have torn him to bits had it not been for Ferdinand, who personally intervened and had him clapped in prison. The new King hoped his rescue of the Prince would please Napoleon, without whose approval his crown was in jeopardy.

Ferdinand had the enthusiastic backing of the French Ambassador, François de Beauharnais, brother-in-law of the Empress Josephine, who for a year had urged Napoleon to intercede in his behalf. The Emperor, however, had finally decided to the contrary. Napoleon trusted Ferdinand even less than Godoy. Moreover he feared that Ferdinand, with his popularity and coterie of prominent followers (nobles and clergymen of proven integrity and many Spanish liberals), would be more difficult to control. And if Ferdinand secured British aid, he might become a positive threat. The Bourbons must go, Napoleon had determined. Only a Bonaparte King would serve his purposes. Madrid heard of Charles IV's abdication and the approach of Murat's army almost simultaneously, however, and the people assumed that Napoleon was supporting Ferdinand.

Cheering crowds greeted the French when they entered the capital. Parading as liberators, they were led by a full division of the Imperial Guard, each regiment preceded by eagle-bearers, trumpeters, and drummers—French horsemen in blue and red, green and silver, Polish cavalry in gray and cerise, mounted on gray chargers, *gendarmes d'elite, chasseurs,* artillery, infantry, and turbaned Egyptian Mamelukes. The towering Murat outshone them all. In a green velvet uniform and red boots, white plumes waving above his shako, jewels glittering on his cap, belt, scabbard and saber hilt, he sat effortlessly astride a prancing, capering, black charger, smiling and waving a gold cane to roars of delight from the Madrileños. Unhappily, they would soon learn that the handsome Gascon, whose curly back hair was the envy of the ladies, excelled in ferocity as well as showmanship.

"Talks" at Bayonne

Ferdinand, escorted only by four *gardes-du-corps*, rode in from Aranjuez to see Murat on 27 March. He promised fidelity to Napoleon, and repeated his request for a bride from the imperial family. The old monarchs sent letters to Murat and Napoleon, pleading for support against their son and the rescue of Godoy, who, the Queen wrote earnestly, was the "innocent and affectionate friend of the Emperor, the Grand Duke [Murat], and of all the French." Napoleon responded by summoning all the Bourbons to Bayonne for "talks."

Ferdinand, who might have balked and rallied public support, received his request from the hands of General Savary, whom the Emperor ordered to bring the Prince to Bayonne by whatever means necessary—quietly if possible, if necessary under escort by gendarmes of the Imperial Guard. The general presented Ferdinand with a letter from Napoleon, stated that the Emperor was en route to Madrid, and suggested that the Prince travel north to receive him. Encouraged to believe that when they met, Napoleon would recognize him as King of Spain, he agreed, and on 10

April departed with Savary. As their ten-day journey progressed and the Emperor did not appear, Ferdinand contemplated flight. But when presented with a plan by the Duke de Mahon to escape via Bilbao, he rejected it. With French troops seemingly everywhere, he was unsure he could get away. Even if he did, Napoleon would probably either restore Charles IV, or give his crown to someone else. In either case, he could become King only by obtaining British aid and driving out the French, and, at the moment, challenging Napoleon, the master of Europe, seemed insane. Taking what he saw as his only chance to be King of Spain, he went on to Bayonne.

Charles IV and Maria Luisa set off gladly for Bayonne; clearly they had nothing to lose. Other members of the royal family were dispatched a few at a time, as was Godoy, who was hustled, bearded and haggard, directly from his prison cell to General Exelman's coach and wheeled away.

At Bayonne Napoleon easily got his way. On 4 May 1808 Charles IV surrendered his rights to the throne. On 6 May Ferdinand did the same. By a treaty of 10 May all those in line of succession renounced their claims. In return Napoleon promised to preserve the integrity of Spain, protect the Roman Catholic Church, and grant the Bourbon estates and incomes in France. Within a few days the deposed family had moved meekly to places of detention. Charles and Maria Luisa took possession of the Chateau de Chambord; Ferdinand and the others, went to Talleyrand's estate at Valençay. In Spain the throne was vacant, and the stage set for a new regime.

Dos de Mayo

Meanwhile Madrid, which had grown ever more sullen and angry since Ferdinand's departure, had suddenly turned on the French. Napoleon had expected trouble, and instructed Murat to locate cannon where they could rake the streets. On 2 May trouble had come. Early in the morning Guard cavalry escorted a carriage into the great plaza before the royal palace to take the last of the royal children, Don Francisco, to France. Like a catalyst, their appearance turned bystanders into a mob, which suddenly closed around them and attacked. Their officer was dragged from his horse and mauled, but managed to run up the palace steps to safety, while his men spurred their mounts and fought their way out. Frustrated, the people turned on the carriage and tore it apart. In every open square in the city, other mobs formed.

Murat was ready. Troops from all quarters moved toward the great hub of Madrid, the Puerta del Sol, pressing the mobs before them, clearing the plazas with cannon, fired at point-blank range, and cavalry charges. Into the central square galloped the Mameluke horsemen of General Friedrichs, scimitars slashing mercilessly. Madrid was soon quiet. Don Francisco was sent off to Bayonne.

During the evening and the next morning a tribunal under General Grouchy sat in the Hotel la Post. By noon of 3 May some two thousand Spaniards had died in the fighting or before Grouchy's firing squads. Murat boasted to Napoleon that the Mamelukes had taken one hundred heads. This was literally true. Fired on from houses, they had entered, decapitated men, women, and children, and tossed their heads into the streets.

Mamelukes! For the Spanish the word would always mean *Dos de Mayo*, blood, and horror. Napoleon had sent *Moslems* to slaughter Christians! It was forgotten that there were only *eighty-six* Egyptian warriors in Murat's army of 40,000. Napoleon had set *Moors* on Spanish women and children, the rebel propagandists would say. Could he but be the servant of the Devil?*

Napoleon did not regret the *Dos de Mayo*. Madrid had been brought to heel; the Spanish capital was his. Was Spain any different from France, where, during all the struggles of the French Revolution, possession of the capital had meant virtual control of the nation? What more was necessary to install a Bonaparte King in the great palace of Philip V?

Much more, it would prove. A pattern of resistance had been set by the Madrileños which all Spain would follow. Men had

---

* The Mamelukes were of European stock. The Egyptian ruling caste replenished itself with boy-slaves, who were reared as Moslems. So barbaric and difficult to discipline were they that the entire French army never had over 150.

fought with sticks, rocks, and knives if they had no better weapons. Snipers had fired from windows and rooftops. Women had poured filth and boiling water from balconies on formations of gaudy French cavalry. The French were slow to realize it, but the "whiff of grapeshot" would not suffice for Spain. And of the French, perhaps none was more innocent of events and their meaning than Joseph Bonaparte, who left Naples for Bayonne on 23 May to serve his brother, and, he truly hoped, the Spanish, as King of Spain.

⚜

CHAPTER VI

José Napoleón

NAPOLEON, REGENERATOR

"**I** want your children's children to preserve my memory and say: *He is the Regenerator of Our Fatherland*," ran Napoleon's proclamation to the Spanish of 25 May 1808. His mission, he said further, was to rejuvenate the monarchy, improve institutions, and give Spain the benefit of reform "without force, hurt, insult, without disorders, without convulsion." Joseph received a copy while en route to Bayonne, and was delighted. It expressed the spirit in which he had governed Naples, and hoped to govern Spain. He accepted the Emperor's profession at face value. Napoleon, though he truly meant to regenerate Spain, expected her in turn to serve the Empire, and (as he would tell Joseph repeatedly later) at the sacrifice of national interests, if necessary, "until the general peace." To Napoleon, this was a fair bargain. Joseph, already straining to see himself as a Spanish monarch, would never agree.

MURAT REWARDED

Charles IV, before leaving Madrid, made Murat provisional head of government, and at Bayonne appointed him lieutenant general of the realm. "Legally" armed with both the civil and military executive power, the marshal (on Napoleon's orders) secured as many petitions as possible for the designation of a Bonaparte King—from the national ministry, the Council of

Castile, the municipality of Madrid, and other governmental and consultative bodies, as well as from the captains-general of various provinces and their officers. He also ordered the convocation at Bayonne of a National *Junta* (Assembly) of 150 delegates, to be elected by the three estates of the realm. Principally, it was to adopt a constitution, a draft of which the Emperor sent to Madrid for circulation among Spanish officials. The preamble named Joseph "by the grace of God" King of Spain and the Indies.

While he did Napoleon's bidding, Murat made bold to suggest that calling the *Junta* would introduce delays and allow opposition to develop. A government should be quickly proclaimed— under a soldier-king. The new French ambassador, the Count de la Forest, echoed his sentiments, partly because he feared Joseph, whom he knew well, was too softheaded to govern Spain. At Bayonne, Caroline Bonaparte Murat campaigned for her husband in person. *NO*, Napoleon finally told them. Choose between Portugal and Naples. They chose Naples, and Murat, after expressing his gratitude with proper Gascon exaggeration, shortly informed the Emperor that he was ill, and asked to be replaced at Madrid. Napoleon refused until mid-June, when affairs at Bayonne were well advanced, then sent General Savary to relieve him. Joseph's throne in sunny Naples was thus filled (though Caroline and Napoleon wrangled over terms for weeks). There was no going back.

ENTER JOSEPH

With the greatest appearance of sincerity, Napoleon announced on 6 June that he would grant Spain's petitions, and proclaimed Joseph her King. The next day His Majesty Don José Napoleón arrived in Bayonne, and was greeted by leading delegates of the National *Junta*, who had been there for some days.

Emerging from his carriage in the uniform of a French colonel, Joseph Bonaparte looked every inch a King. At forty he was still slender and graceful. His blue eyes were arresting, like his brother's, but wider and without the slitted eagle-hardness. His expression was open, inquisitive, knowing but kind. He could be, some delegates surely reflected, the philosopher-king his admirers thought him. In contrast to Napoleon's spring-steel intensity, which produced a sensation close to alarm at first meeting, Joseph had a relaxed affability which made men want to know him better. His smile was bright, like the Emperor's, but warmer. The delegates were impressed with him.

In his presence the prepared speeches had a ring of real sincerity. He was "ardently desired in Spain," intoned the Duke d'Infantado, representing the grandees. The Spanish would give him "affection and fidelity," said the Inquisitor Don Raymondo Ettenhard y Salinas. The army would defend him, said the Duke del Parque. And so it went. Joseph was overwhelmed, and replied, off-the-cuff, in the same spirit.

In the ensuing weeks, as the delegates became his friends, he lost all skepticism, and became impatient to enter Spain. His optimism was increased by a flood of letters pledging fidelity from, among others, the Cardinal de Bourbon, cousin of Charles IV, and (astonishing to him if not Napoleon) Ferdinand VII, who sent affectionate regards to his "brother" and "Most Catholic Majesty," Joseph. Don Gaspar Melchor de Jovellanos, the dean of Spanish liberals, wrote of his desire to contribute "to the service of Your Majesty and the good and happiness of the Nation."

THE JUNTA OF BAYONNE

When the Junta convened it was apparent that it was an "Assembly of Notables" (as one of Napoleon's proclamations called it) rather than a representative body. Three-quarters of the members had been appointed by the Emperor or Murat. Nevertheless the membership further convinced Joseph that he would be well received in Spain. It included, in addition to those already mentioned, the Prince de Castelfranco and the Duke de Frias, two archbishops and the vicars-general of both the Franciscan and Augustinian orders, Don Pedro de Cevallos, General Gonzalo O'Farrill, and Don Sebastian Piñuela y Alonso, all former ministers, Don Miguel José de Azanza, onetime viceroy of Mexico, and Admiral José de Mazarredo y Salazar, a national hero who had been ambassador to Paris.

Present also was a heavy contingent of eminent liberals, such as Francisco Cabarrus, Mariano Luis de Urquijo, and Manuel Romero. Cabarrus, a French-born financial expert, had been made a Count by Charles IV, who had, nevertheless, allowed the Inquisition to imprison him (1790–92). Though he had since been an ambassador, he had remained suspect, and all too outspoken a progressive. (It had not helped that he was also the father of Paris's notorious Madame Tallien, twice a divorcée, famous for her bare-breasted evening gowns and her unfeminine political activism.) Urquijo had also been imprisoned by the Inquisition, and Romero, probably the most brilliant public servant of the era, had been relegated to obscure positions by Godoy. Joseph saw these men as fellow-spirits, and spent hours in conversation with them.

THE CONSTITUTION OF BAYONNE

The Junta approved a constitution which denied freedom of conscience, as a concession to deep-set Spanish feeling, recognizing the "Catholic, Apostolic, Roman religion" and stating flatly "no other is permitted." Otherwise it was, for the time, an extremely liberal document. Individuals were guaranteed freedom from arrest without warrant or imprisonment without court order; torture was forbidden (though, as in the French codes, there were loopholes). Taxes and obligations were to apply equally to all classes. Titles of nobility were recognized, but the principle of "careers open to talent," regardless of social status, was forcefully stated. Feudal rights were abolished.

A one-chamber Cortes was specified, with the majority of deputies elected (indirectly) by universal male suffrage, though seats were allocated for nobles, clergy, intellectuals, and businessmen, whom the King appointed from lists prepared by the groups concerned. Elected deputies had to be landed proprietors; thus commoners chosen would be mostly middle class, but they would have to be attentive to voters of all classes.

THE CABINET: JOVELLANOS DEMURS

Joseph assembled a royal household which included Infantado, del Parque, and Castelfranco, and appointed as ministers Cevallos, O'Farrill, Urquijo, Piñuela, Mazarredo, Cabarrus, Azanza, and Romero. By letter, Joseph offered the ministry of the interior to Jovellanos, but he declined, pleading ill health.

Jovellanos' refusal was more significant than it seemed at the moment. Though he, like most Spanish liberals, cherished French thought, he feared that his people were violently anti-French and traditionalist. Even if, as was probable, a Napoleonic government would be an improvement over the old, he doubted that Spain would submit to it. In letters to Azanza and O'Farrill, who asked him to "campaign" for Joseph in his native Asturias, he wrote that "words" would have little effect on his people. Essentially, he felt that Spanish liberals, if they expected to gain any sizable following, would have to be "patriots," that is francophobe, also. Despite the optimism among the French and their Spanish adherents (*afrancesados*) at Bayonne, time would prove him right.*

ON TO MADRID

On 7 July the Junta, before dissolving, received Napoleon and Joseph. Before the Archbishop of Burgos, Manuel Cid Monroy, the King swore fidelity to the constitution and the delegates loyalty to the King. Such was Joseph's "coronation." It was hardly regular, but the renowned Archbishop gave it distinction, and Spanish protocol style. Moreover, until the ceremony proper was over, it seemed that Napoleon would not mar the occasion with a dramatic gesture. Then suddenly he was on his feet, hurling threats, standing silent for awful minutes between outbursts. When he sat down, after an hour, he had really said only one thing: *Those who oppose me will be destroyed.*

Why? He had greeted the delegates with smiles and promises; he wanted to leave them with a taste of fear. Joseph would never show strength; he would. Then too, he was angered by news of scattered revolts in Spain. Far from being grateful that the Spanish, so far, had made his task easy, he had developed a great disdain for them. His opinion that they were spineless and be-

---

* Jovellanos was destined to die in 1811, under suspicion as a moderate by the rebel government he had helped to launch.

nighted had been confirmed. If, he said in so many words, they were so stupid as to reject the benefits he offered, he could whip them into line—and easily.

On 9 July Joseph departed for Madrid under escort by imperial cavalry and Royal Guards (who, significantly, were mostly Frenchmen). He was accompanied by his ministers, all of them Spanish. He knew that Spain was no longer altogether quiet, but if Napoleon was unworried, why should he be? For his part, he had gotten on well with the Spanish leaders at Bayonne; with their help, he was sure he could win over the people. Actually Napoleon underestimated the Spanish, and Joseph was totally unprepared for the reception they would give him.

⚜

CHAPTER VII

Not Peace But a Sword

RECEPTION COMMITTEE

WHILE the drama at Bayonne proceeded, rebel armies had formed in Spain. On the morning of 14 July 1808, one stood by its guns before Medina de Rioseco. Commanding was Gregorio de la Cuesta, Captain-General of Old Castile, sixty-eight and ill, but the personification of grandee and soldier. His tight-lashed corsets holding him boldly erect, the defiant old eagle sat on his charger and watched the approach of a French army. If he could stop it he would block the route to Madrid, and King Joseph, then at Miranda, would be able to go no farther.

Cuesta had 22,000 men; the French, under Marshal Bessières, only 14,000. Most of the Spanish, however, were Galician recruits. Their commander, the Viking-tall, half-Irish Don Joaquín Blake had recommended a defensive stand in the mountains, but Cuesta had haughtily refused. Blake's men occupied a low hill, set to engage the French first; Cuesta's Castillians were to his left rear, ready to take advantage of developments. Almost a mile separated them.

Bessières, moving forward, noticed the gap between the Spanish forces. Sending off a screen of cavalry to hold Cuesta's attention, he turned on Blake. Artillery raked the Galicians; infantry attacked frontally; then the *chasseurs* of the madcap General Lasalle, who had galloped lazily into the gap, wheeled and charged, shouting and cutting, into their unprotected flank. Blake's lines collapsed, and his recruits flooded back toward Medina. Cuesta, too proud to retreat, ordered his Castillians to charge, and they did, but only to break themselves against the oncoming French.

Bessières, however, found pursuit impossible. The Spanish army scattered and melted into the hills. Happy with his easy victory (and on Bastille Day), he thought little of it. But this scattering was part of a pattern with which the French would soon become painfully familiar. Spanish armies generally fought poorly in conventional engagements, but when dispersed they simply reassembled out of reach, and had to be fought again and again.

For the moment, however, the French had triumphed; Joseph could go on his way to Madrid.

Dust and Silence

Two days before Bessières' victory, Joseph had sent a delegation to Cuesta, hoping to win his allegiance and avoid bloodshed. Napoleon, almost simultaneously, wrote Joseph, urging that he join Bessières at Medina de Rioseco (naming the place) and "preside at the victory, announcing your arrival to Spain with a striking event, making afterward . . . gestures of peace and conciliation." The letter came too late for Joseph to comply, and its wording angered him. "Preside" at the battle, the Emperor said; the King was supposed to *command* French forces in Spain. Yet, he reflected, "preside" was all he was prepared to do, for he had been kept all but ignorant of military developments while at Bayonne. In fact, Napoleon had told him that organized opposition was negligible, and public opinion in his favor. Neither was true, but surely his brother would not have deceived him! With understandable exaggeration, he had already tried to tell Napoleon how things really were.

"Until now no one has told Your Majesty the truth," he wrote on his third day in Spain. "The fact is not a single Spaniard will stand up for me, except the few people . . . who travel with me." Joseph considered that he would not have taken the crown if he had known the people did not want him. Had Napoleon known? No matter. He was King; he would do his best. More troops were needed, he wrote, or "the whole country I am crossing will revolt."

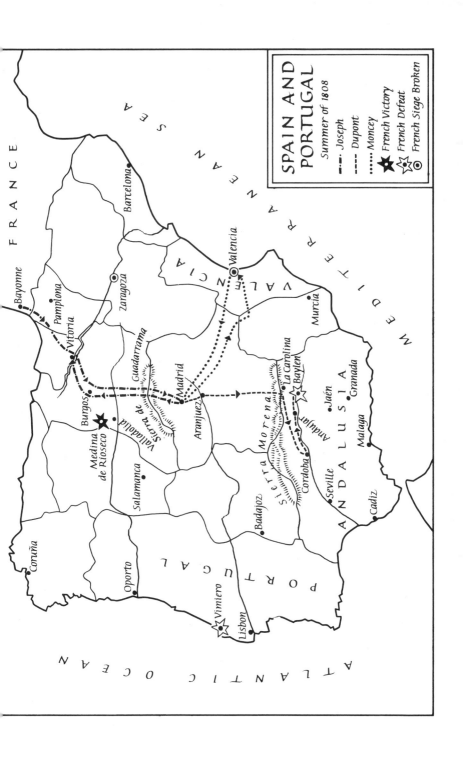

SPAIN AND PORTUGAL

Summer of 1808

Joseph —·—·—
Dupont —–—–—
Moncey ··········

★ French Victory
☆ French Defeat
⊙ French Siege Broken

FRANCE

MEDITERRANEAN SEA

Bayonne
Pamplona
Vitoria
Barcelona
Zaragoza
Valencia
VALENCIA
Murcia
Guadarrama
Madrid
La Carolina
Baylen
Burgos
Aranjuez
Jaén
Granada
Medina de Rioseco
Valladolid
Sierra de
Sierra Morena
Andujar
Malaga
Salamanca
Cordoba
Seville
Cadiz
Badajoz
ANDALUSIA
Coruña
PORTUGAL
Oporto
Vimiero
Lisbon

ATLANTIC OCEAN

Moreover, a single command was needed; it was dangerous to have orders coming from Bayonne, Madrid, and himself (at least Napoleon had said he was commander). "I ought to have your absolutely complete and entire confidence." He, the King, ought to command.

It was a strange request for Joseph, but he had been driven to it. With every day his sense of danger had increased. The people did not fawn, as had the nobles at Bayonne. They did not cheer as he passed. In fact in village after village no one appeared at all. The King looked out at deserted streets, shuttered windows, barred doors. His kingdom, hot, dusty, silent, seemed to be populated by occasional stray animals, bony dogs dozing in the shade, distant shapes of people darting for cover like frightened deer.

Menace charged the air. Even his troops marched silently, the footsteps of the infantry muffled in dust, the cavalry mounts plodding, heads down. During the first days Joseph had concerned himself with civil matters, inviting to his carriage most frequently Cabarrus, minister of finance, and Piñuela, minister of interior. Gradually, however, military affairs become his consuming interest, and O'Farrill, minister of war, rode with him constantly.

Where were the armies? What were they doing? "Be happy and content," wrote Napoleon. "You have many partisans in Spain . . . all the better men." "Don't be disturbed, nothing will stop you." "The position of the French armies in Spain is excellent." Joseph's impatience grew. Was he some sort of royal child? Dispatch riders passed him en route to Madrid and returning, but usually had nothing for him, he complained. Napoleon advised he write Bessières and Savary, and finally, nine days after Joseph had left Bayonne, sent him a listing of French forces. The King issued orders; Savary wrote that they contradicted those of Berthier (Napoleon's chief-of-staff).

Joseph was exasperated. "Is it I or he [Savary] who has the right to command? That right cannot be shared." Napoleon had been temporizing. Fearful that Joseph would make a botch of things, he had tried to command for him, through Berthier, until Marshal Jourdan arrived to serve as the King's chief-of-staff. Faced with Joseph's blunt question, however, the Emperor answered positively: "My brother, you are in command. I told you that; I make it an order." The letter arrived after Joseph reached Madrid, but his authority was finally clear. Moreover, he was allowed to exercise it. Unfortunately, major decisions were almost immediately required which he was ill-prepared to make, for, through no fault of his, French armies had overextended themselves, and the rebels had taken advantage of it.

THE REBELS

Since the *Dos de Mayo*, the spirit of resistance had flamed in all parts of the Peninsula. The Count de Toreño, dispatched to London by a rebel *junta*, found the British happy to give aid. At Cadiz, Spanish shore batteries and a British warship captured a French fleet. In May and June revolutionary *juntas* seized the governments of every Spanish province not heavily occupied by the French. At Seville a self-styled National Junta declared war on "His Majesty Napoleon, Emperor of the French," in the name of Ferdinand VII. Urged on by a priesthood which saw Napoleon as the enemy of religion, the people were in an ugly mood. Corunna, Seville, Badajoz, Ciudad Rodrigo, Jaen, and Malaga, finding their Spanish governors urged moderation, put them to death. At Cadiz, mobs stormed and murdered until Francophobe leaders took over.

Recruits for rebel armies appeared in droves, though they were, and would remain, resentful of discipline and prone to desertion. Arms, equipment, even clothing were scarce, and there was little time for training. Armies were organized, however, usually around loyal regiments of the old royal army—in the north by Cuesta and Blake, in Andalusia by Castaños, in Valencia by Llamas and Cervellon, in Murcia by Montijo and O'Neill. Many foreigners became rebel generals, among others Theador Reding, a Swiss mercenary, the Marquis de Coupigny, a French *émigré*, and Felix Jones, an Irish soldier of fortune.

By the time of Joseph's "coronation," Spanish resistance was beginning to tell (*ergo*, Napoleon's irate speech). At Zaragoza, Don José Palafox, another Spaniard of Irish descent, had since mid-June withstood a siege by 15,000 French under Lefebvre-

Desnouettes, and showed no sign of giving in. "War to the knife!" he shouted at a French officer bearing a surrender demand. In Catalonia the provincial army (*Miquelets*) and home guard (*Sometenes*) had joined detachments of the old royal army to seal the French into Figueras and Barcelona. Valencia, in June, had withstood a siege by Marshal Moncey, who, threatened from the rear by Cervellon, had withdrawn to Madrid.

In the summer of 1808, however, the rebels scored only one spectacular victory, which occurred just as Joseph arrived at Madrid. It was won in the south, in Andalusia. There the bull-fight had survived in purest form since Roman times, its rituals, music, and costumes, developed during a Moorish occupation of seven hundred years, lending beauty and drama to a savage gladiatorial contest between man and beast. There, where the Moors had kept a foothold centuries longer than elsewhere in Spain, were bred the bravest bulls, the finest horses, and the most violent and passionate people, disciplined only by a fanatical Christianity, the faith bought by the bloodshed of many generations.

BAYLEN

In June General Dupont, with 20,000 troops, had scattered peasant armies in the Sierra Morena and marched into Andalusia. When he appeared before Córdoba the city officials offered to surrender, but while terms were being discussed a few shots were fired at the French from housetops. Dupont demolished the city gates with cannon fire and his troops sacked the city. Much of the treasure of the centuries-old cathedral went into the general's own baggage wagons.

Enraged peasants closed in on his rear. Hardly a courier or a straggler escaped them. French soldiers were stoned to death—blinded with pikes, crippled, and left to perish in the withering sun—castrated and allowed to bleed to death. The most hardened of Dupont's soldiers had never seen such a war; their memoirs and letters ring with anger, shock, and outrage. Wrote the Swiss mercenary, Captain Gaspard Schumacher: "At La Carolina we established a hospital and left 167 of our sick and wounded men. That hospital was set afire . . . all were burned alive or horribly massacred. The barbarians believed they had done a glorious thing for God and religion!" General René, captured en route to join Dupont, was lowered inch by inch, toes first, into a cauldron of boiling water. The peasants were entertained by his screams for a whole afternoon before he died.

Dupont's communications with Madrid were almost cut. Large rebel armies were reported to the south, officered by men he had been told were pro-French, like the Swiss general Reding. Suddenly cautious, he retreated to Andújar, behind the Guadalquivir River, and called for reenforcements. There he remained for a month, though his supplies dwindled, his sick multiplied, and few new troops arrived.

On 11 July, he was suddenly faced by a Spanish army of 30,000 under Castaños. The Guadalquivir River was between them, however, and Dupont was dug in on the north bank, so he simply waited. Handed the initiative, Castaños sent the corps of Reding east along the river with orders to cross and block Dupont's line of retreat. The French noted their movement, but soon lost touch with them and decided they had marched for La Carolina to block the passes to Madrid. Actually the Spanish force had blundered about, crossing and recrossing the river several times, and finally deployed west of Baylen, in Dupont's rear.

Dupont, fearful of losing the passes, marched for La Carolina during the night of 18–19 July. When day dawned he found Reding before him and Castaños coming up behind. To cut his way out, Dupont would have had to abandon his trains, leaving his sick and wounded to their fate (and losing his loot). Dashing tactics seemed impossible anyway, since his troops were sluggish from weeks of idleness, tired from a night march, and by the time the scorching summer sun had reached its peak, entirely without water. Instead of making a maximum effort, however, Dupont pushed small attack after small attack up the road toward Baylen until he found himself hard pressed front and rear, with his demoralized troops giving on all sides. Wounded himself, he called for a truce, and the next day surrendered, giving over

18,000 men to the tender mercies of the Spanish. (Many were massacred in the next few days; most of the rest died in prison.*)

Dupont's capitulation freed Andalusia and enabled the Seville Junta to take the lead in organizing a national rebel government. The blow to French prestige was devastating; the effect on the morale of the ragged Spanish armies immense. But to the north were more French armies, the closest at Madrid. In the immediate future, the reputation of French arms was in the hands of their commander, Joseph Bonaparte.

Fight or Retreat?

Joseph entered Madrid on 20 July. The Madrileños, generally, watched sullenly as he passed, without great fanfare, to the royal palace. There were occasionally cheers, not unlike those given a monster bull at the arena. This "Don José" was a brave one to come at all, they told each other.

Joseph was deeply depressed; hostility was everywhere. If they could but know his heart! Savary, with his narrow shoulders and hooded eyes, angered him immediately. Had His Majesty seen the rags hung from some windows? He had ordered bunting. The people would be punished. NO! Murat and his Mamelukes have done enough already! Joseph pored over the military dispatches. Dupont . . . he has been reenforced? A division? But you have recalled Gobert's division to Madrid? Order him back! But Sire, Marshal Berthier commanded me to cover Madrid! Order him back! It was too late. News of the death of Gobert arrived on 23 July—the first hint of the disaster at Baylen.

Fifty thousand additional troops were needed in Spain, Joseph wrote Napoleon. With increasing urgency, he repeated the message on five successive days. "You have a third more forces than you need," replied the Emperor laconically, "if they are directed with proper precision. . . . I will find in Spain the Pillars of Hercules, but not the limits of my power."

Madrid knew of Baylen on 23 July, but no one told the French.

---

* Dupont himself was returned to France, where Napoleon destituted him. He was retored to service by Louis XVIII, and was later minister of war under Louis Philippe.

The city, however, became more silent, the atmosphere more ominous. A veritable exodus of the common people seemed in progress. Even palace servants made bold to announce they were joining the rebels. Some of Joseph's more timid Spanish followers simply disappeared. Grandees haughtily made excuses for not attending him. Wrote Joseph to Napoleon, "Honest men are no more for me than the worthless. No, Sire, You are in error; your glory will be wrecked in Spain. My tomb will be a monument!" But, significantly, the grandees did not leave Madrid. They were waiting and watching. What would Joseph do?

On 28 July a courier brought Joseph word of Baylen; the next day an officer appeared with a copy of the capitulation.

Fight or retreat? New French troops had continued to enter Spain. Some 20,000 were pinned down in Catalonia, 15,000 were besieging Zaragoza, but fully 75,000 were available to Joseph. At Madrid he had Moncey's corps, his guard, and other units, altogether around 30,000 (though 3000 were in hospital). Bessières could have appeared within a few days with some 20,000. Even if key garrisons, for example at Burgos, had been left in place, Joseph surely could have fielded an army of 50,000. (Joseph himself estimated 40,000.) Opposing him? Moncey volunteered that there was an army of perhaps 20,000 in Valencia. And Castaños? No one knew. Getting what information he could, Joseph estimated that Castaños had, or would soon have, at least 100,000. After all, to *capture* Dupont! If he called Bessières to Madrid, what of communications with France? The troops at Zaragoza could take Bessières place on the routes, perhaps. But then Zaragoza would become a rallying point. What did his generals think? Savary? Retreat, Sire, to Burgos at least. What will the Emperor think? "His Majesty will scream but that will not kill him!" Marshal Moncey? the situation is dangerous, Sire. We know so little of the enemy. Your Majesty must decide.

Retreat! Joseph gave the order on the day he heard of Baylen (28 July) to send off the hospitals. He would retire to the Duero, he wrote Napoleon. The Emperor must understand his position! "I repeat to you that we do not have here a single partisan, and that the entire nation is exasperated . . . !" The Dukes del Parque and d'Infantado, Pedro de Cevallos, and Piñuela y Alonso announced they would remain in Madrid. Why? By Your Majesty's leave. . . . Our profoundest respect and good wishes. . . . Piñuela? I shall retire to a monastery, Sire. At my age. . . . Lesser men left also. "All my Spanish officers have abandoned me except five or six," Joseph wrote Napoleon. By the early hours of 31 July— eleven days after Joseph had entered Madrid—all the French were on the march.

NAPOLEON REACTS

Initially, the Emperor did not condemn Joseph for abandoning Madrid. To his brother's call for 200,000 troops and assertion that too many of his men were young draftees, he announced, "The Grande Armée is on the march [from Germany]." He even gave Joseph sympathy: "You can hardly realize, *mon ami*, what pain it gives me to see you grappling with events outside your experience, foreign to your natural character." And he paid him a rare compliment: "I learn with pleasure that you have displayed character and [military] talents." All would be well, Napoleon assured him. "You will have to conquer your subjects before you can be their father. Good kings have passed through that school. . . . Overall health, gaiety . . . spirit."

Napoleon commanded Joseph, however, *not to retreat beyond the line of the Duero*. Joseph went farther—*across the Ebro*— and, to consolidate his forces, ordered the siege of Zaragoza lifted, giving the Spanish another victory. Palafox, who had rallied the whole population behind his soldiers—women, children, old men, priests and monks—became a greater hero than Castaños.

It was too much for Napoleon. "To cross the Duero and the Ebro is to evacuate Spain," he shouted at General Mathieu Dumas, who was leaving Paris to join Joseph. "This coat must be washed in blood!" he roared, grabbing Dumas's lapels. Then turning away, he added, "I can see very well I must return and set the machine in motion again."

Angry with Joseph, the Emperor could not damn him enough. He even decided Madrid could have been held—after hearing that Castaños had not entered until three weeks after his brother departed, something no one could have predicted.

Joseph, beset with conflicting advice and insubordination among his generals, especially Bessières, had taken the safest course. His forces behind the Ebro, their lines tightened, he established headquarters at Vitoria, where he could communicate easily with his commanders and with Paris. He sent off Azanza and Savary to confer with Napoleon, asking that the Emperor *believe* what they told him about the situation in Spain, and waited for orders.

For himself, Joseph wrote, in effect, that he was not the king for Spain. Could he not retake Madrid, for honor's sake, and then return to Naples? The suggestion only made Napoleon angrier. Naples? Joseph must be mad! He did not even answer.

The Emperor heard bad news from Portugal also. In August, Sir Arthur Wellesley landed with a British army and defeated Junot at Vimiero. On condition that his army be returned (by sea) to France, Junot surrendered the whole country to the enemy. Napoleon was appalled. Did he have to wet-nurse all his commanders? No matter.

Portugal could wait. In Spain, *national* armies, not a small legion of British "saviors," defied his power. He turned furiously to building up the army behind the Ebro. Spain would pay for her insolence! He, Napoleon, would make the Spanish *beg* to have Joseph as their King. If they did not, he would rule them himself! *He* would teach them how to obey!

THE RECORD

Joseph had not done badly as a commander. Napoleon had plunged him into a situation which would have challenged any of the marshals, and if he had not won glory, he had not suffered the fate of Dupont or Junot either. But Napoleon could not, would not, admit that *he* had misjudged the capacity of the Spanish to resist. That Joseph had given him good advice—that the whole nation was "exasperated," that more troops were needed —advice that he had refused to take, only made him more determined to deny responsibility for the fiasco. He made Joseph a scapegoat. Taking their cue from the Emperor, the generals nodded sagely and said yes, of course, Joseph had no talent for war. Commanding had been difficult for Joseph in 1808; it would be more difficult later.

To the Spanish, the matter was simple. *Napoleon's brother* had come to Madrid, stayed a week, and fled without fighting. Rebel propagandists, from this time forward, while they pictured Napoleon as an agent of the Devil, made fun of Joseph. He became "Pepe Botellas," "Protector de los Jugadores," "Pepe Coxo"—a squint-eyed, vice-ridden incompetent. Joseph, in person, gave them the lie; but most of his "subjects" would never see him, much less understand his great desire to do good.

⚜

CHAPTER VIII

The Emperor!

"ALL THAT EVIL . . ."

WITH every dispatch from Spain, Napoleon's ire increased. His letters to Joseph became bitter and derisive. "The Army, it would appear, is commanded not by generals who make war, but by inspectors of posts. . . . In all that has been done there is not the first sign of aptitude for war. I hope Marshal Bessières has advised you not to evacuate the whole country without seeing the enemy."

Joseph was hurt. He felt his brother did not understand the situation. But if errors had been made, he would take the responsibility. "I alone made the decision to evacuate Madrid . . . I decided to abandon the line of the Duero. . . . I have no apologies to make to anyone." The army was not demoralized, he said, but if Napoleon continued denouncing him, it would be.

The Emperor's condemnation continued, however, in the galling form of minute supervision (insofar as it was possible from Paris). It became evident, further, that Napoleon meant to conquer Spain, and to make her pay the cost—with her northern provinces, if necessary. Joseph was shocked. Violate the integrity of Spain, guaranteed in the Constitution of Bayonne? Who would believe the rest of it? No matter, *the people did not want him*; he did not want to rule Spain.

Even if "France would gratuitously squander her blood and money to place me on the throne of Spain," Joseph told Napoleon, he wanted no part of it. "Becoming the conqueror amid all the horrors of a war against *all the Spanish* [soldiers and civilians], I would become an object of terror and execration. *I am too old to live long enough to atone for all that evil."*

Napoleon had a few problems himself. Would his enemies in northern Europe strike while the Grande Armée was in Spain? Not, he hoped, if Russia remained his ally. Carefully, so as not to show weakness, he was arranging a conference with the Czar. Damn Joseph! The prestige of the Empire is at stake, and he babbles about a few miserable Spaniards not wanting him! Six pages to say *that*. He ignored the letter, let Berthier send instructions, and favored Joseph only with snarling notes: "Herewith [confiscated] letters for your instruction. People are too circumspect around you. Attack the enemy; don't let him attack you. N."

Joseph tried again: "I repeat only one thing . . ." And he summarized it all, adding a few touches. "Not a Spaniard will be for me if there is a conquest . . . in the army . . . or the ministries. . . . Two thousand civil servants quit me at one time, in spite of the heavy salaries I gave them: we can't find a guide or a spy. Four hours after the battle of Rio-Seco [sic] Marshal Bessières could not find the enemy. Anyone who writes or says differently has no eyes." Replied Napoleon: "I received your letter . . . and the duplicate." That was all. Joseph, he was sure, was exaggerating things—a green soldier, after all, saw the enemy double. Joseph was equally sure Napoleon could not face facts. Both were partly right. So it would always be.

ADVICE FROM PARIS

Napoleon's appearance was expected, though *when* remained uncertain. As French forces poured into Spain, Marshal Berthier, in the Emperor's name, pressed Joseph and his chief-of-staff, Marshal Jourdan (who arrived in mid-August) with ever more detailed orders. Worse, the imperial chief-of-staff corresponded with the King's subordinates, weakening his control over marshals and generals, who, in any case, would have been difficult to control.

At his headquarters in Vitoria, Joseph did his best to comply with Napoleon's wishes. But the Emperor and Berthier often seemed out of touch. Wrote Berthier to Jourdan, "It is preferable that [the army] maintain its position and await reenforcements." Wrote Napoleon to Joseph, "The insurgents act with vigor, and the French army indulges them to the point of feebleness." The marshals had their own ideas. Bessières: "Vitoria is in the air [unprotected]; the King is practically alone. . . . I am going . . . to Vitoria, unless otherwise ordered."

Throughout, Napoleon's impersonal tone hurt Joseph deeply. "Your Majesty does not write me [as a brother] any more. . . . I don't know what I have done; but his silence afflicts me; it is not natural." He was angered and saddened that the official *Moniteur* seemed to treat the abandonment of Madrid as inept and cowardly. This attitude was reflected by Berthier also: "His Majesty [Napoleon] would have preferred that Madrid not be evacuated . . . but in the actual state of things . . ."

In mid-September, considering that reenforcements had secured his position and communications, Joseph again advanced his plan to retake Madrid. After that, as he had already said, he could honorably retire. He wanted no part in a total conquest. Ney and Jourdan, he wrote Napoleon, agreed that he could retake Madrid with 50,000 men and force the rebel government, which had installed itself there, to flee. No, came Napoleon's reply: Not according to the "rules of war."

Joseph's discouragement deepened. "I pray that Your Majesty give orders only to me, and I will have them executed." But nothing changed. Frustrated and sick at heart, the King let matters drift, and spent much time in seclusion at a villa near Vitoria. There, unexpectedly, he found a love which would outlast the Spanish adventure. The lady was his hostess, Donna Maria Amalia Zuargo, Marquise de Montehermoso.

THE MARQUISE DE MONTEHERMOSO

No longer a girl, the Marquise de Montehermoso was more—a beautiful woman, and a sophisticated one. The Marquis, liberal and anti-clerical, had been among the first to welcome the French. Donna Amalia had shared his enthusiasm—for reasons of her own. Her husband was tall, elegant, educated, and traveled, but he was aging, and provincial society drove her to tears. She had given a ball for Junot's officers in 1807, leaving the startled commanding general standing awkwardly while she led the first dance with the dashing Baron Thiébault (Junot got the second). Later in the evening she returned to Thiébault: "Are you enjoying the ball?" Replied he, "I'm sharing all the fun to be found." "In that case you aren't sharing much," she said suggestively. "It all bores me; if you like we can leave." He turned her down, says Thiébault (who, by the time he wrote his memoirs, had a very jealous wife), but there were those who did not.

At Bayonne, Joseph had made the Marquis his chamberlain, and en route to Madrid had stopped at the Villa Montehermoso. The Marquise, dark, lithe, wearing high fashion with the disdain of a perfect female animal, had not escaped his attention, nor he hers. When he returned to Vitoria with his army, Amalia had not rested until he was installed in the villa. Disconcertingly, however, Joseph treated her with detached formality, and confined his indoor sport to the pursuit of an overblown chambermaid of eighteen. With feline ferocity, the Marquise assailed Joseph's equerry, General Girardin: Shocking conduct for a King! Must he consort with servants? Laughing, Girardin went to admonish His Majesty, who soon mended his ways.

Amalia conquered, but found herself entrapped. Joseph's reputation with women was well deserved, she knew, but, she found, he was not merely a man. The world swarmed with men who wanted her as a woman. So did Joseph, but he also needed her comforting, and he listened to her opinions; he was not like all the animal-lovers. He was a little boy—*and a great man!* She had sneered at his ideals, his goodness—an act! But *no.* He was really concerned over the people he had been sent to rule. She had not cared about the people—were they not born to serve? —but now she did, because Joseph did. Napoleon had fascinated her, frightened her. If he had come first . . . but now she hated him. Why did he make his brother suffer so? Could he not see that Joseph was a great man? The coquette began to change, turn domestic, protecting.

She entertained for the King, with the dignity of a royal consort, but it was their quiet evenings she loved. They talked. If only the people—all of them—could know him as she did! She played the harp and mandolin and sang for him. He learned a Spanish song. Had she learned music, unknowing, just for him? Villa Montehermoso would soon be behind him. Would they stay together? Yes. But was he determined to leave Spain? Yes . . .

The idyll was short. Napoleon was soon at Vitoria.

THE ARMIES FACE OFF

By the end of October Joseph found himself in command of 286,000 troops. With them had come French commanders whose names conjured up memories of already legendary Napoleonic victories: the lean and towering Marshal Ney, Duke d'Elchingen; Marshal Lannes, Duke de Montebello; the small, tough, remorseless Marshal Soult, hero of Austerlitz; Victor; Mortier; and Lefebvre. There too was Junot, spoiling to repair the reputation sullied in Portugal.

Rebel forces were pitiful by comparison, altogether less than 90,000 men, deployed in small armies along a 150-mile front. Blake's army of Galicia, on the Spanish left, was in the mountains near Bilbao; Palafox's army of Aragon was anchored on Zaragoza. Between them, in a line stretching south to Burgos and east along the Ebro, were the armies of Extremadura, Castile, Leon, and Andalusia. There was no overall commander. A central staff, hastily organized in Madrid, sought to promote cooperation among the generals, but they paid it little heed. Every commander's first loyalty was to his province. Through the struggle, the bane of rebel strength was *provincialism*. In 1808, Blake, above all, meant to defend the mountain passes leading into Galicia; Palafox's chief interest was holding Zaragoza, and thereby Aragon. Catalonia had refused to send any men to the national army; they would fight the French at home!

THE EMPEROR!

Napoleon met Czar Alexander at Erfurt in October 1808 and bought his neutrality with promises (which he would never keep) of lands on the lower Danube. The meeting over, he made for Vitoria, with stopovers at Paris and Bayonne. "The war must be finished by a single *coup par manoeuvre*," he wrote Joseph, "for that my presence will be necessary." His appetite for information grew apace. Has a reconnaissance of the Ebro been made? How are the roads to Logrono? What is the condition of the fort at Burgos? Have French and Spanish officers who know the terrain meet me at Bayonne. Does Marshal Jourdan not know how to write a report? "Tell me about every skirmish—how many are killed and wounded, everything, to the last detail." On 5 November he arrived at Vitoria, incognito.

On the morning of 6 November the measured reports of a sixty-gun salute echoed through the misty air over Vitoria. The Emperor had officially arrived. Cheers went up from the encampments, spread out for miles on the plain. *Vive l'Empereur!* On to Madrid! In fact, advance elements of the army were already in motion; Napoleon had ordered Bessières's corps to march on Burgos two days before. By 10 November the whole Grande Armée was surging forward. The main force had already swept over Burgos, and Napoleon, trailed by a cavalry reserve almost as large as the enemy armies before him, was galloping to join it.

AGAINST INEVITABLE EVILS

A few days before Napoleon's arrival, Joseph issued instructions to the royal commissioners he had appointed to accompany the army. "The King," it began, ". . . desires to protect his people against the inevitable evils of war, and all the calamities which accompany . . . occupation by armies." Pairs of officials (a layman and a priest) were to enter the assigned areas with the French, enlist the help of local officials in maintaining order, halting irregular resistance (sure to bring reprisals), and securing essential food, supplies, and labor for the army. ("The war must feed the war," was Napoleon's rule.) Pillaging and lawlessness of troops were to be reported to commanders, and if not stopped, to the King. Churches, convents, and monasteries, (even if empty) were to be protected, and their treasures safeguarded. The privacy of families was not to be disturbed. Prisoners of the Inquisition were to be freed.

This fat circular of twenty-six articles testifies to Joseph's humanity, but also indicates a change of heart. He had decided to remain King—at least for a time—and to devote himself to mitigating the horrors of conquest. How he reached this resolution is uncertain, though perhaps it was in his nature that he should. Certainly, he was guilt ridden—for bringing suffering to "his people," for being helpless to end it, *and for failing Napoleon.* Privately, reasoning soberly, he blamed Napoleon for everything, and felt he had done his duty—but Napoleon's anger made him doubt himself. His conscience would not let him simply leave Spain—not yet—and so he placed himself—bravely, nobly, *foolishly*—between people and conquerors. To serve both he would have had to accomplish miracles.

Excellent! ruled Napoleon. He gave Joseph no command position whatever. If Joseph wished to play the saint, the Emperor would play the Devil. The Spanish would scream to have Joseph back on his throne. "I am here with the soldiers who conquered at Austerlitz, at Jena, at Eylau," the Emperor told an audience at Vitoria. "Who can beat them? Not your miserable Spanish soldiers who do not know how to fight!" For a group of monks, he had a more personal message: *Monsieurs les moines,* if you are determined to meddle in military affairs, I will cut off your ears, I promise you!" Letters to Spanish officials, prepared for the Emperor by Joseph's advisers, took a hard line. "The time for illusions is past . . . !" The Grande Armée is in Spain. Choose between war or peace, conquest or constitution, "a King full of sagacity and enlightenment, just and good, OR . . ."

But the Emperor had come to Spain to act, not to talk. He intended not merely to defeat the rebels but to annihilate them. His forces were massive, overwhelming—and that was the way he wanted it. War was no sport, but a deadly business. The greater the odds in his favor the better he liked it. The more crushing the victory the more telling the effect. *He would teach them!*

THE EAGLES ADVANCE

The right wing of the Grande Armée, under Victor, smashed Blake's army of Galicia; the left wing, under Lannes, Moncey, and Ney, put Castaños to flight and drove Palafox into Zaragoza and besieged the city. In Catalonia, Gouvion Saint-Cyr, relieving Duhesme, went on the offensive with 50,000 men. Napoleon, with Soult (replacing Bessières with the advance corps), Junot, Mortier, Lefebvre, and shortly Victor also crashed through the Spanish center and rolled almost unimpeded to Guadarrama range. Beyond lay the plain of New Castile, and Madrid.

On 30 November, however, the Grande Armée stalled in the pass of the Somo Sierra. Blocking it were 9000 men under Benito San Juan, their cannon trained on the single road to the summit, a narrow track carved into precipitous slopes which dropped into the raging torrent of the Duraton River, and on which only a few men could move abreast. Infantry had led the way, but the advance files had been pinned down by murderous cannon fire. Behind them, stretching for miles in winding column, the glittering regiments of the world's finest army came to a halt.

Napoleon angrily rode forward with his escort of the day, the Polish Lancers of the Imperial Guard, seven officers and eighty men, young noblemen all. Spanish *canaille!* He turned to Colonel Korjietulski. Charge the guns!

The Poles obeyed, but the cannon felled a third of them before they had covered a hundred yards, and they took cover in a shallow depression. General Walther, commanding the Guard, approached the Emperor. Sire, we could bring up more cavalry. *NO.* "My Guard must not be stopped by peasants!" Count Philippe de Ségur galloped forward with the order: Charge! With Colonel Korjietulski in the lead, and Ségur at his side, the Poles rode full-tilt into the blazing muzzles of the Spanish cannon. Forty-four were killed (including Korjietulski), sixteen were wounded (including Ségur). But the Spanish had time for but one volley. Their infantry deserted the cannoneers before they could reload, and what remained of the brave band of Poles rode down the gunners and pursued the infantry across the pass.

When its guns were overrun the Spanish force lost all cohesion. Panic seized the troops, who made off in whatever direction seemed to promise escape. San Juan rode frantically about, brandishing his pistol and shouting threats, but he could not re-

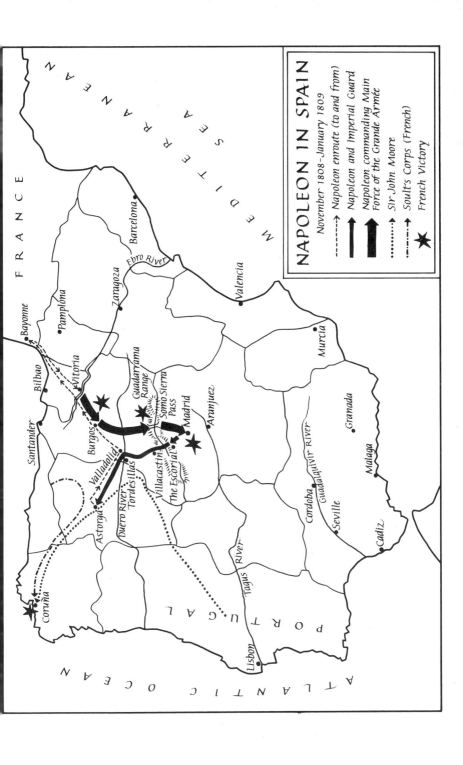

NAPOLEON IN SPAIN

November 1808 – January 1809

- - - → Napoleon enroute (to and from)
━━━▶ Napoleon and Imperial Guard
━━▶ Napoleon commanding Main Force of the Grande Armée
········ Sir John Moore
—·—·— Soult's Corps (French)
★ French Victory

FRANCE

MEDITERRANEAN SEA

ATLANTIC OCEAN

PORTUGAL

Bayonne
Pamplona
Vitoria
Bilbao
Santander
Burgos
Zaragoza
Ebro River
Barcelona
Valencia
Murcia
Guadarrama Range
Somo Sierra Pass
Madrid
Aranjuez
Villacastín
The Escorial
Valladolid
Tordesillas
Duero River
Astorga
Coruña
Córdoba
Guadalquivir River
Seville
Granada
Málaga
Cádiz
Tagus River
Lisbon

cover control. (Some days later, when he tried to reorganize the remnants of his force, he was shot by his own men.) His army disintegrated.

Napoleon, who had seldom seen such gallantry as his Poles displayed, was moved to tears by the sight of their dead and wounded. He wordlessly gestured for the survivors to assemble before him, and decorated them on the spot with the cross of the Legion of Honor.

On 2 December 1808 (the anniversary of Napoleon's coronation and of Austerlitz), the Grande Armée was before Madrid. The city had been abandoned by the rebel government and armies, save a small garrison, but the Madrileños refused to surrender. On the next day, however, negotiators were brought forth by a light bombardment and the quick capture of the Retiro, the high fortress commanding the city's main gate. Speaking for the proud delegation, General Tomas Morla harangued Napoleon on the errors of French policy in Spain. The Emperor listened quietly, then gave the city three hours to capitulate. On 4 December he entered Madrid.

THE ROYAL SPECTATOR

Initially, Joseph was in no hurry to leave Vitoria, since the role assigned him (and which he had chosen), required that he organize territory as it was conquered. Within a day after Napoleon's departure, however, he had changed his mind. He felt like a shirker:

I find myself much displaced at Vitoria . . . an invincible spirit, stronger than all human considerations, tells me that I ought not to be in the rear of the Army. Spain and France, and myself, all want to see me in a post of honor; where there is danger I ought to be . . . I saw on the faces of my own ministers this morning their astonishment to find me in Vitoria, when Your Majesty was in the advance posts.

He departed to join Napoleon, but was met with orders to follow the army by stages. He complied, traveling slowly; his progress became a nightmare. At Burgos he and Miot de Melito walked sadly through the Convent of Las Huelgas, which had been converted into stables. The tombs of the church and cloister had been opened and stripped of valuables; corpses and bones littered the courtyard. Napoleon, who had stayed at the Episcopal Palace, had warmed himself before a fire of broken furniture. The city stood in ruins, its streets full of rubble, its buildings shattered and burned. In many peasant villages beyond, no life stirred; in others pitiful delegations, usually led by priests, appeared to beg Joseph's aid. The soldiers were taking their food, their livestock, their valuables; there had been murders; their daughters were not safe.

Joseph sent orders to the generals. They were ignored. Why, he wrote Napoleon, had the chief-of-staff not ordered officers to obey him? "Does my character merit that I should be the laughing stock of the army in a nation where I am King?" The Emperor gave him no answer. He implied one, a stock military one, which meant nothing to Joseph: *Make* them obey you. The King could not; he was helpless. Ever more depressed, he avoided contact with his commissioners and the heartbreaking local petitioners. It was no good. He must abdicate.

Joseph approached Madrid on 2 December, and took up residence at the Pardo, a royal hunting lodge some miles from the city. The Marquise de Montehermoso joined him there, but found him inconsolable. His frustration was deepened, after his efforts to protect his people, by rebel propaganda sheets, which the French found everywhere. "José the intruder," lecherous, cross-eyed and bloated, was shown in cartoons stumbling after women or asleep among bottles, a crucifix always under his feet.

Napoleon, who had deliberately let his troops run wild to terrorize the population, tightened discipline, and even had two of his guardsmen shot, but he gave Joseph no authority over the military. Moreover, the Emperor began to govern Spain himself, and announced that the Spanish must petition to have Joseph restored. "The King's authority is sort of suspended," reported La Forest, with vast understatement. In Madrid, Napoleon's minions seized property of rebels, and of some grandees who had done nothing worse than refuse to take sides, and to raise cash went to the length of holding furniture sales in the streets. Military tribunals sent men before firing squads daily, and though

Napoleon intervened to grant reprieves occasionally, Joseph was appalled. Would the horror never end? On 8 December he asked Napoleon to let him abdicate.

Shame covers my face before my pretended subjects. I supplicate your Majesty to receive my renunciation of all rights which he has given me to the throne of Spain. I prefer honor and probity to power bought so dearly. In spite of these events, I shall always remain your most affectionate brother, your most tender friend. I become again your subject and await your orders to do with me as it pleases Your Majesty . . .

Joseph, Joseph. Could he never be positive? "Affectionate brother," "tender friend," and "subject." Napoleon ordered up his carriage and sped to the Pardo. Joseph, for whom the writing of the letter had required supreme effort, had relaxed. It was finished. So it was, said his brother sympathetically; Naples could not be recovered, but perhaps the throne of Italy . . . Yet it would be a blow to family prestige if he left, but no matter, he, Napoleon, would manage. A viceroy for Spain would be better, perhaps. Another like Murat—that "beast," that "hero"—someone to follow orders.

Joseph felt shame. Suddenly, leaving seemed to mean further degradation. Will the Spanish petition for me? No doubt; the *corregidor*, the *alcades*, the clergy, the councillors of Madrid have already decided. Perhaps then, I should wait. . . . Joseph was conquered. "Perhaps" meant *yes* to Napoleon. Joseph would stay. A few days later the Emperor persuaded him to visit Madrid for a few hours and tour the royal palace. Like a happy child, Napoleon banged his fists on the heads of the marble lions of Castile, guarding the immense central staircase. Laughing, he took Joseph by the arm. "You are better lodged than I am!" A sumptuous prison it would be, indeed.

NAPOLEON RULES

Placarded all over the capital was Napoleon's proclamation to the Spanish:

You have been led astray by treacherous men. . . . The defeat of your armies was an affair of a few marches. . . . I have destroyed everything which challenges your prosperity and grandeur. A liberal constitution gives you, in place of an absolute monarchy, a limited and constitutional monarchy. If all my efforts are in vain, if you do not respond . . . I must treat your provinces as conquered. I will put the crown of Spain on my own head, and I know how to make it respected, for God has given me the power and will to overcome all obstacles.

With alacrity the municipal authorities, guild-masters, clergy, and other notables framed a petition for the restoration of Joseph, ". . . that Spain . . . may enjoy the tranquillity and benefits which attach to the gentleness of character of His Majesty." It was "laid at the feet of His Majesty Imperial and Royal" by the *Corregidor* of Madrid. Napoleon replied with a long speech, terminated by a pledge to restore Joseph—if the population signed an oath of allegiance which he ordered placed on the altars of all churches. The population, asked to choose between Joseph and Napoleon, appeared by thousands to sign.

The Emperor declined to step down, however. He intended to strike at those who had opposed him—including the most offending clergy, despite the guarantees given the Church in the Bayonne Constitution. By imperial decree he abolished the Inquisition, ordered most convents and monasteries suppressed, proclaimed the immediate end of feudal rights and privileges, eliminated seignorial courts, and confiscated the property of all rebels. (He expected the Spanish masses to be grateful. They were not—even for the end of the Inquisition. For centuries their churchmen, in church and in school, had taught them that these courts protected them against subversives—Moors, Jews, heretics, masquerading as Christians—at once the enemies of Church and crown.)

Funds to defray the cost of war were raised in every possible manner. The treasury of the Inquisition was seized. Wool, valued at 20,000,000 francs was seized at Burgos and elsewhere. Soult was ordered to ship some 3,000,000 francs worth of quinquina, found at Santander, to France.* The cash assets of the Bank of Saint Charles were confiscated. Certain of the more valuable rebel estates were declared imperial property and held for liquidation (or distribution by Napoleon as rewards). And in Madrid, rebel

---

* Franc = 3.75 reals = about $0.20 U.S. (1808 purchasing power).

property, whether officially royal (Joseph's) or imperial, was
disposed of wholesale. The Spanish looked on, numb. Napoleon
showed no sign of relinquishing power. Then suddenly he was
gone—in pursuit of (it seemed impossible) the English!

LES ANGLAIS!

Unaware of the extent of French victories, Sir John Moore,
with an army of 30,000, had marched from Portugal to reenforce
the Spanish rebels. On 19 December Napoleon received word
from General Mathieu Dumas, at Burgos, of Moore's approach.
At about the same time, Moore realized he was striking into the
rear of an army ten times larger than his own, and retreated on
Astorga, making for Coruña, where a British fleet was anchored.

Soult, whom Napoleon had earlier sent north, reported Moore's
movement, and got orders to pursue the British, while Ney was
told to block their route to Coruña. The Emperor, eager to be
in on the kill, marched for Astorga with his guard on 22 December.
To fight the British! And with such odds! "It is a gift of
Providence. . . ."

A somewhat bewildered Joseph was left in command of forces
south of the Guadarrama. "The mission of the King is to protect
Madrid. All else is of little importance," ran Napoleon's hastily
dictated instructions. Pages and pages followed, however. Joseph
was to resume his civil functions (except that the French ambassador, La Forest, was charged with managing confiscations),
implement the Emperor's decrees, continue collecting signatures
on the loyalty oaths, strengthen the Madrid police, dispose of
Spanish prisoners, and more.

Joseph moved from the Pardo to Aranjuez, to be nearer the
corps of Victor, guarding Madrid from the south. He was haunted
by the fear of losing his capital again, but for a time there was
no challenge, and at Christmas and New Year's Amalia arranged
entertainments at the Villa Florida, former home of the scan-
dalous Duchess of Alva, Goya's *amie délicieuse*.

Relaxed and less apprehensive, Joseph returned to the Pardo,
where he was informed that an army under the Duke d'Infantado
had appeared to the south. Victor, however, surprised the Span-

ish at Ucles on 16 January, killed a thousand and took 6000 prisoners. Joseph regretted not having been present, and clashed (in his mild way) with Victor over his treatment of the prisoners, many of whom died en route to prison. But his capital now seemed safe. He exultantly announced the victory to Napoleon, and prepared to make his official entry into Madrid.

EXIT NAPOLEON

Dispatches had arrived almost daily from the Emperor. He had crossed the Guadarrama under "disagreeable conditions" (actually on foot, leading his guard through a snowstorm with winds that blew men and horses off cliffs); he was at Villacastin . . . Tordesillas . . . Valladolid . . . Astorga. Moore was in full flight, Ney had failed to block him, Soult was in pursuit. Napoleon was returning to Valladolid. Soult would deal with *les Anglais*. (On 16 January Soult and Moore fought at Coruña, and Moore was killed, but his army escaped aboard British battleships.)

On 15 January, Napoleon, laconically, revealed why he had turned back to Valladolid. "The circumstances existing in Europe oblige me to spend twenty days in Paris," he wrote Joseph. "If nothing prevents it I shall return toward the end of February. . . . The court of Vienna is behaving badly. They shall live to regret it. Don't worry about anything." Austria was mobilizing, and trying to organize a crusade of all the Germans against France. Moreover (and this Napoleon did not say) Fouché and Talleyrand, encouraged by Caroline Bonaparte Murat, were intriguing to have Murat named successor to the Emperor in the event of his death in Spain. The plot infuriated Napoleon as much as the Austrian menace alarmed him.

Attached to the Emperor's letter were orders making Joseph commander of the entire army of Spain (what had been, with Napoleon present, the Grande Armée, reduced only by the Imperial Guard). He was again King and commander, and, for a while, the Emperor would be able to give him little supervision.

Napoleon, on horseback, left for France on 16 January. Thiébault saw him near Burgos, galloping hell-for-leather, whacking

Savary's horse, ahead of him, with his crop, far ahead of his guards, aides, and Mameluke attendant. He would never return to Spain. Perhaps, if he had remained, the conquest would have been completed; but as it transpired, it would never be.

The Emperor's voice echoed in Joseph's mind as he read the letters that came back. Watch the Madrileños! Strength! ". . . arrest a hundred scum . . . shoot twelve or fifteen . . . send the rest to France to the galleys!" "Sire . . . I shall carry out the instructions of Your Majesty," wrote Joseph. But he could not.

❧

CHAPTER IX

Dreams of Progress

KING BY . . . LOVE

O N 22 January 1809, a cold but sunny day, Joseph made his official entry into Madrid. Not by accident, the King, a fine rider and acute judge of horseflesh, rode a plump and pleasant dapple-gray mare. He was in uniform, but his manner was casual, studiedly unmilitary. Bemedaled French generals, on their fiery steeds, displayed an embarrassed lack of flamboyance. The King was escorted by the Royal Guard, resplendent in newly designed lavender and white uniforms, and followed by a modest parade led by his "Spanish" troops—the Royal Foreign Regiment, the Irish Brigade, and two half-filled regiments of Spaniards. Beside the King rode Marshal Jourdan—wearing the red Cockade of the Royal Foreign!

The procession halted at the church of San Isidoro, and Joseph made a speech from the steps. "I pledge to sacrifice my own interests, for I believe that you need me to promote yours. [I shall protect] . . . the Holy Religion, the independence of the monarchy, the integrity of its territory, and the liberty of its inhabitants." To the music of the *Te Deum*, the King and his party entered the church. When they emerged Joseph's carriage was waiting, and as he proceeded to the royal palace, newly minted coins, bearing his profile, were flung to the crowds. (Napoleon had sent the gold from France.) After he had passed, stalls opened to distribute food and wine, and musicians, jugglers, and acrobats entertained in the streets.

Sounds of celebration reached Joseph as he watched the shadows lengthen in the lion-yellow canyon of the Manzanares, far beneath his windows. Madrid had received him well; there had been cheers. A general had muttered that the dogs sat because they had been whipped . . . but he had pretended not to hear. He was content. A good beginning. "I am not only King of Spain by force of arms," he wrote Napoleon later, "I can be [King] by the love of the Spanish; but for that I must govern in my own fashion. . . . Each animal has its instincts, each must follow his own."

For the next week he spent much time visiting hospitals, French and Spanish, civilian and military, paying special attention to wounded rebels, praising their valor, gently suggesting that they had been misled. Their startled expressions delighted him. "This is squint-eye? This is Pepe Botellas?" they seemed to say. Occasionally French officers stalked off in disgust. Requests came for transfer to corps in combat, or to France. "If His Majesty had seen *French blood* spilled . . . Ah!" Joseph knew their feelings, but, he tried to explain, if he could not be a *Spanish* King more blood would flow. The King also visited prisoner-of-war compounds, offering to enlist in his Spanish army all who would take an oath to him. Hundreds responded, but many, as veteran officers predicted, deserted at the first opportunity, taking their arms and clothing with them. "*El Capitán Vestuario* is what they call Your Majesty," blurted a brash aide. It was true, Joseph knew. But he was determined to show faith in "his people."

Napoleon had ordered his decrees implemented—especially those against the monks and rebel nobles. For the monasteries, Joseph decided, summer would be soon enough. After all where would the brothers go? He decreed that monks could become ordinary priests or revert to civilian life—with pensions. He gave over the Escorial, the mammoth palace of the monkish Philip II, as a refuge for the elderly of one order. As to the nobles—why sell their property immediately? Fall would be soon enough. Perhaps some of them would come over to his side.

For those loyal to him he created the Royal and Military Order of Spain and retained the traditional Golden Fleece of the former Kings. French and Spanish alike referred to the new red-ribboned medal as "the egg plant," but they took it and wore it—French generals, Spanish ministers, bishops, playwrights, artists—even Goya. Goya! First Painter to His Majesty Don José. The testy old introvert's reasoning was simple. He wanted to be left alone, to paint. A royal pension gave him freedom; besides he liked Joseph. The violence of 1808 had made him cautious, however. In secret he sketched scenes of French brutality—the "Disasters of War"—which saved his neck when Ferdinand VII returned.

To the astonishment of the Madrileños, and the livid anger of his military protectors, Joseph appeared in the palace gardens unescorted, and shook hands amiably with all who appeared. His Spanish was bad, but he managed some conversation, gesturing and laughing. He even ventured into the streets a few times, but finally agreed with his anxious generals that rebel assassins might join the crowds that always collected. He settled for a "democratic" court—almost anyone could gain audience, if audience it was. Joseph shunned throne-sitting, and circulated about the enormous Bourbon *salle*, shaking hands and talking. In the evenings his guest list was as likely to include an unwashed village mayor as the Russian ambassador.

Ministers and generals and their wives mingled with bankers and businessmen, bullfighters and actors, artists and writers. Gesticulating and translating for the King might be found Leandro Fernández Moratín, without question Spain's leading playwright. Frequently present was the tall, blond, still youthful Juan Meléndez Valdéz, poet, humanist, liberal, lawyer, and until recently the idol of the rebels' first poet, Quintana. A clutch of burbling ladies often signaled the presence of the grotesque Marchena y Ruiz de Cueto, a needle-nosed dwarf who edited the *Gaceta de Madrid*, translated French plays, and played the jester mercilessly. (Who could challenge the dwarf to a duel?) And always there were beautiful women—daughters of the nobility, opera singers, actresses—to make the company sparkle. Over all reigned the incomparable Marquise de Montehermoso, now installed in apartments near the King's.

Napoleon's chief informant, the Count de la Forest, grudgingly reported that Joseph was doing well—at least with the public.

Madrid was quieter than it had been in a year. The Emperor was unimpressed. "Joseph is . . . nothing but a *king*," he told Roederer. You have my brother's confidence; go to him. "I have conquered that country. Spain must be French. The government must be French." Joseph does not work enough. Report to me about "that marshal who wears the red cockade." Roederer went to Madrid. The Emperor, he told Joseph, considers that the Spanish have *no rights*. They rebelled. They are conquered people. No treaties, no agreements, not even the Constitution of Bayonne are binding on France. Complete the conquest. Govern. Make Spain pay. The King sent Roederer away laden with gifts (paintings, bottles of wine; he had no money to give), but he remained determined to rule as he saw fit.

He gave his thoughts to Napoleon:

I am convinced that what is best for Spain and France is their close union, their intimate alliance, but not the subjection of one to the other . . . the Spanish would all be at my feet if they knew what was in my heart; all would be the very best of friends of France if they knew that, while I am a French prince, I want to be what I must be, and I must be . . . governor of a free and independent nation. . . .

Constitution and Government

Joseph ordered the Constitution of Bayonne printed in the *Gaceta de Madrid*, despite Napoleon's admonitions, and over the advice of some of his ministers, who feared its liberalism might alarm the public. For the King, it was a pledge to the Spanish people, which, if kept would make his monarchy "legitimate."

Napoleon was more interested in the war, which (impatient with Joseph, as usual) he allowed Berthier to direct from Paris. Soult was to take Portugal, then Victor Andalusia. Until Zaragoza fell, in late February, Lefebvre's siege got his closest attention. Joseph's constitutional fixation appalled him. "Tell me," he wrote bitterly, "if the constitution prohibits the King of Spain from commanding 300,000 French . . . if the constitution says that in Saragossa [Zaragoza] we can jump over the houses one after another."

The King was hurt, but adamant. He would be guided by the

constitution, insofar as conditions allowed. All executive appointments he could control went to Spanish citizens. (Napoleon reacted with "pain" when Joseph fired his French police commissioner in Madrid in favor of a Spaniard—but the Spaniard remained.) The King applied the principle of "careers open to talent," with a vengeance. (General Morla had shown spirit when he surrendered Madrid; Joseph made him a councillor of state.) Though the constitution did not require that a *Cortes* meet until 1820, he intended to call one as soon as the fighting stopped. Meanwhile, he organized his government as the document specified.

Joseph appointed as ministers progressive Spaniards of national reputation (and therefore, inevitably, aging—the average age was sixty). To compensate for their lack of vitality, he assembled a council of state of younger men whose job it was to turn the minister's concepts into detailed legislation.

Of the ministers appointed in 1808, two were with the rebels and one in retirement. The vacancies were filled, all who had remained loyal were reappointed, and thereafter none were removed except by death, though some changed positions.* The key figures were Francisco (François) Cabarrus, in Finance, and

---

* MINISTRY 1808–13

MINISTER SECRETARY OF STATE	Mariano Luis de Urquijo	1808–13
FINANCE	Francisco (François) de Cabarrus (Died April 1810)	1808–10
	Francisco Angulo	1810–13
INTERIOR	Gaspar Melchor de Jovellanos (Named 1808; refused appointment and joined the rebels)	
	Don Manuel Romero (and Justice)	1809–
	Almenara (José Martinez Hervas)	1809–13
JUSTICE	Sebastian Piñuela y Alonso (Retired to monastery November 1808)	1808–
	Don Manuel Romero (Died 1812)	1809–12
	Almenara (and Interior)	1812–13
FOREIGN AFFAIRS	Pedro de Cevallos (Deserted to rebels July 1808)	1808–
	Campo-Alange (Manuel José de Negrette)	1809–11
	Miguel José de Azanza (Made Duke de Santa Fé, 1810)	1811–13

(Cont. p. 138)

Manuel Romero, in Justice and Interior. Neither had the strength to be a hard-driving executive, and Cabarrus tended to overfortify himself with drink (once, touring a distillery with Joseph, he sampled the wares too enthusiastically, and fell on his face). Both however, were men of genius and superb planners.

The council of state included both Spaniards and Frenchmen (since the members were advisers, not executives). Among the former were Juan Antonio Llorente, a former Inquisitor, who later authored a scathing indictment of the Inquisition, and the Count de Montarco, a liberal noble whose career had been frustrated by Godoy. Outstanding among the latter were two who had served Joseph in Naples—Miot de Melito and Ferri-Pisani. Miot seconded Romero, and Ferri-Pisani helped ease Cabarrus's burdens in finance, among other things. The working membership was augmented by luminaries such as Meléndez Valdéz and Marchena y Ruiz. One could hardly have assembled in Spain a more talented and energetic group.

PLANS AND PROJECTS

Reform! Sacrifice was required. The King should set an example. Joseph ordered vast stretches of the royal lands placed under long-term lease, rents to be counted toward purchase by the tenants. In Madrid was a beautiful but unneeded palace, the Prado. He ordered it converted into a museum, to house, initially, the artworks of confiscated monasteries, and the royal library, the expansion of which was placed in the hands of Moratín. Other crown properties and confiscated buildings were set aside for schools, hospitals, asylums, orphanages, and homes for the aged.

Spain needed roads, bridges, and canals. Plans were ordered.

WAR	Gonzalo O'Farrill	1808–13
POLICE	Pablo de Arribas (*de facto* minister)	1808–13
MARINE	José Mazarredo y Salazar (Died 1812)	1808–12
	O'Farrill (and War)	1812–13
INDIES	Azanza (Santa Fé)	1808–13
ECCLESIASTICAL AFFAIRS	Piñuela (and Justice)	1808–
	(Retired to monastery November 1808)	

(After Piñuela's retirement under various ministries, usually Interior)

Madrid needed air, light, a simplified street system, new sewage and water systems. Whole blocks of buildings were earmarked for demolition; Spanish and French army engineers, hydraulics experts, architects and landscapists, were put to work on plans for broader, straighter avenues, plazas, parks, and fountains, and beneath them, great ducts to supply water and carry away waste. On the side, a royal botanical garden was envisioned. Sculptors were called in to design fountains. Many statues and busts were commissioned—not of Joseph but of Spanish heroes and men of culture—Lope de Vega, Pedro de Calderón, Agustín Moreto.

Epidemics were common, usually sweeping inland from the ports. The King appointed a National Junta to devise means of stopping them or attenuating their effects. French army medical personnel were enjoined to help the Spanish. Vaccination for smallpox was made compulsory and the assistance of the clergy asked in overcoming the fears of the superstitious.

Romero and a dozen councillors were put to work on plans for schools. A National Junta would advise the King. Public primary schools, later others at a higher level, would be established. (*Any* public schools seemed radical in Spain, where the Church still had a monopoly in education.) Joseph was in his element. His students would take the laurels of Europe! Begin them at seven with Latin, Spanish, and French—history—literature—philosophy—mathematics—science, and give them discipline and strength—some military exercises, games, fencing—and a sense of beauty and grace—drawing, dancing. By the time they are ready we shall have secondary schools! Meanwhile science and technology must be fostered. In Madrid we shall have a conservatory for machines, models, and instruments, with a library and laboratories; another conservatory for geometry and design; a school for artists in the Prado. Agriculture must not be neglected: The King shall stand as sponsor to the "Society of Friends of the Country."

New systems for the administration and judiciary were a crying need. Romero, Miot, Almenara, councillors and aides were asked for plans for reorganization. Be guided by the constitution, Joseph instructed. The provinces must be broken into prefectures. Appointed prefects? Yes, but elected councils to advise. The courts? All the old ones must go—of viceroys and captains-general, royal prerogative, the feudal lords, the Church. Uniformity! Use the French model—justices of the peace, criminal and civil courts, appeals courts, a supreme court of cassation.

Plans and more plans were produced; the work would continue throughout the reign. But *money* was required. Where would it come from?

FINANCES

The Bourbon revenue system had produced 40,000,000 reals per month; Joseph's revenues in 1809 were about 10,000,000 a month, and never got much higher.* Napoleon supplied him an additional 10,000,000 (and paid the French army 30,000,000 to 40,000,000 per month). Still, by mid-1809, Joseph already had a deficit of 40,000,000 reals. He pinned his hopes for financial salvation on two things: the sale of the "National Properties" (confiscated from the Church and rebels) and the establishment of a free-enterprise economy. (Liberals of the period were in reaction against mercantilism. Laissez-faire economics was the philosophy of progressives, including Joseph.)

According to Cabarrus's calculations the National Properties were worth over 9,600,000,000 reals. It was decided to liquidate the properties by issuing *cédulas hipotecarias* (mortgage certificates) to the government's creditors, who would then buy properties with them. *Cédulas* for some 7,000,000,000 reals were allocated to cover the Bourbon debt. (The constitution required it be paid, and doing so would serve to "buy" the loyalty of creditors for Joseph's government.) Properties valued at 2,600,000,000 would remain for financing Joseph's progressive projects and general expenses. As side benefits it was hoped to strengthen Spain's small middle class, and increase the number of landowning peasants.

---

* The vellon real (15.06 reals to the peso) equaled .266 francs (3.75 reals = 1 franc). The vellon peso was not the same as the silver peso (piece of eight) containing 8 silver reals and minted only in the American colonies. The U.S. silver dollar was made the same weight, fineness, and shape. We shall deal herein only with the vellon real, which was the basic money of exchange.

Freeing the economy was less involved—seemingly. Joseph issued decrees abolishing the guilds, the Mesta (the sheepman's organization which had been the scourge of farmers), and (by steps) internal tariffs. He abandoned the royal monopolies on the sale and manufacture of playing cards, brandy, liquors, sealing wax, crystal, certain types of cloth, and tobacco products. Government textile mills were ordered sold, as were the royal crystal works at San Ildefonso and the royal china plant in the Retiro. Even government licensing of gambling houses was terminated. Heavy private investment in all these enterprises, and efficient capitalist management, was expected to make the economy boom, and thereby increase ordinary tax revenues.

POVERTY, PROGRESS, AND WAR

Disposal of the National Properties did not ease Joseph's fiscal problems. *Cédulas*, from the beginning, circulated as paper money. Many holders had to spend them for necessities; others doubted the validity of titles to properties. (What if Joseph were deposed, or compromised with the Church and returned all or part of its property? The King's predisposition to pardon rebels and restore property was well known.) Speculators bought the paper at bargain rates, depressing its value. Inflation was further promoted when the government, desperate for cash, began selling better properties for specie or using them for collateral for loans, and simultaneously, issued more and more *cédulas*. Paper was used to meet current expenses, and by the King to reward service or as largesse. By the end of 1809 *cédulas* were going at 20 percent of face value, and, with slight fluctuations, the trend was downward thereafter. The government's credit was so damaged that soon Joseph could not even secure loans on unsold properties.

The laissez-faire program also produced disastrous results. Investors would have been difficult to find, considering the British blockade and other disruptions in Spain's foreign markets, even if a civil war had not been in progress. As it was, Joseph found no buyers for many of the royal factories, and those he did sell, mostly on credit, did not prosper. Workers employed in cloth mills at Guadalajara and Brihuega rapidly dropped from 20,000 to 2000. Joseph ultimately repossessed these plants, but lacked the resources either to revive them or buy back others. The unemployed, perforce, tended to turn to the rebels. The abolition of the royal monopolies and internal tariffs lost the government income not recoverable from other sources. Joseph was forced to reinstate both.

From the beginning, Joseph's government was in thinly disguised bankruptcy. The imperial treasury, during his five-year reign, lent him some 600,000,000 reals, and sent almost 3,000,000,-000 in specie to support the French army. Despite the fact that many bills were paid in *cédulas*, he still ran up a huge debt. Funds were lacking for the most ordinary expenses. Civil servants were usually paid (if at all) with a little gold and many *cédulas*. (But for the graft and polite venality traditional in Spain, most would have had to resign.)

Under such conditions, most of Joseph's progressive projects had to be shelved, though he did not give up hope. He did manage to keep institutions of charity operating, began the beautification of Madrid, and, on token budgets, opened conservatories, a few public schools, and pushed the conversion of the Prado into a museum.

Without *peace*, no fiscal program could produce adequate funds; without funds, Joseph could not build and enlighten. The war had to be won. The King, hoping against hope that the marshals would do the job, stayed at Madrid and satisfied himself, in effect, with keeping informed on their progress. He preferred to dwell on what would be done after Spain was subdued.

His enemies, however, gave major attention to the war.

"ATTACK AND DESPOIL"

When Joseph evacuated Madrid, a new National Junta had been organized there under the presidency of the Count Floridablanca. On Napoleon's approach the Junta had fled to Seville, proclaiming as it went all-out guerrilla warfare against the French (sanctioning what was already in progress), proffering commissions as generals and colonels to chiefs of bands (in return for a share of their loot), and calling on the clergy to support the war for the Holy Religion and Ferdinand VII.

All the inhabitants of provinces occupied by French troops . . . are authorized to arm . . . to attack and despoil . . . French soldiers, alone or in groups, to seize food and material destined for them; in a word, to do them all possible hurt and cause all possible damage.

All who served Joseph were declared outlaws and could be shot on sight; his ministers and other prominent *afrancesados* were listed and described as if criminals. "They have kidnapped our well-loved King . . ." read one appeal. "How can religion survive under the rule of an atheist? . . . they have destroyed our laws, our rights, our customs; they have sacked cities and villages, burned houses, devastated fields, raped women, and sacrificed . . . little children with incredible cruelty."

Who would not fight the barbarians, the servants of the monster Napoleon and his imbecile brother at Madrid? The Junta had proclaimed every Spaniard—man, woman, and child—a soldier (entitled to protection, if captured, under the customs of war) and legalized the murder of Frenchmen. Though the Church, officially, took no position, some clergymen organized guerrilla bands, and hundreds preached the holy war. "Are we at liberty to kill the French?" read a widely used catechism. "Not only may we, but it is our duty to do so." Irregular bands proliferated. Wrote Miot:

An invisible army spread itself over . . . Spain, like a net from whose meshes there was no escape for a French soldier who for a moment left his column or his garrison. . . . Frequently troops sent out to do battle with the guerrillas passed through them without seeing them.

In Old Castile the priest turned predator, Jéronimo Merino, sat in treetops with spyglass and rifle spotting the French for his band, galloping with them for the kill. In New Castile the bands of the dashing Don Juan Martín Diez, "El Empecinado," dominated the mountains of Guadalajara and ranged to the very gates of Madrid. The *partidas* of the elegant Marquis de Villacampa roamed the highlands of Aragon. In Catalonia it was Mílans del Bosch, in Leon "Capucino," in Asturias, Juan Porlier. Navarre boasted the pink-cheeked Xavier Mina, "the Student," whose daring led him into a French trap and brought forth a more vicious fighter, his uncle, Don Francisco Espoz y Mina, the "King of Navarre."

Striking from ambush, with odds of five or fifty to one over small French units, the larger bands seized convoys and killed indiscriminately, capturing men only to torture them or hold them for ransom. "Land buccaneers" they were called, with justice. Though the majority were patriots, many fought solely for profit, and refused to share loot with the central Junta. Exceptional leaders, like Villacampa, enforced military discipline, but most did not. The smaller bands often included men with a blood-lust, who silently moved among the French at night, strangling guards and slitting men's throats as they slept.

The armies which Napoleon had scattered were being re-formed. British ships unloaded arms at Cadiz and elsewhere. The Junta had established liaison with Wellesley (soon Lord Wellington), who had returned to Portugal with more British troops. But whatever the fate of the Allied armies, the work of the *partidas* went on incessantly. Joseph's aide, General Bigarré, estimated they were killing one hundred Frenchmen a day (and later that the toll had continued for over four years). Terror was the rebel order of the day.

"IF THEY KNEW . . ."

"[The Spanish] would all be at my feet," Joseph had said "if they knew what was in my heart." But the King could not reach "his people," and if he had, his progressive ideas would have shocked them. They had been schooled to believe that liberalism was the work of the devil, and were, in the mass, uneducated peasants (8,000,000 in a population of 10,500,000) loyal to their traditional leaders, almost 1,000,000 nobles, hidalgos, and clergy.

The nationalism which moved them was anachronistic, almost medieval, the nationalism of Church and crown. Their nation had been born in a crusade against the Moslem Moors. Fidelity to the "Hero Kings" and the Church had for centuries been linked. ("Heretic" and "subversive" were synonymous terms.) The "War of Independence" against the French was, to most

Spaniards, a crusade to restore their "rightful" King, Ferdinand VII, and to expel the enemies of Catholic christianity. (Charles IV was so linked with the hated Godoy that almost no one questioned the legality of his abdication.) As Richard Herr has put it, the Spanish were for "Good" (Ferdinand) and against "Evil" (Napoleon and Godoy, whom they considered he had rescued).

Nevertheless, among the most vocal rebel leaders were liberals, predisposed to agree with the principles enunciated by Napoleon at Bayonne. From the beginning, however, many had wanted no part of Napoleonic authoritarianism, no matter what its slogans. Others, perhaps the majority, had been convinced by the popular uprising that nothing could succeed in Spain under French sponsorship, and opted for the patriotic cause, hoping to harness the power of the insurrection for progressive ends. They hoped to call a Cortes and induce it to adopt a liberal constitution, to which, hopefully, Ferdinand VII would be committed. They realized, of course, that ultimate success depended on Ferdinand, for there was little support for liberalism in Spain. Most literate persons were nobles and clergy; the majority followed their interests, which lay in restoring the old order, and they had the support of the masses. (The middle class was very small, and many of the more influential members were French or "naturalized" Spaniards, like Cabarrus, or had French connections. None were very popular with the workers, plagued as they were by unemployment, and they had no influence with the peasants.) The liberals knew that they owed their positions in rebel circles to their usefulness and influence with the British.

Joseph, wrote the rebel diplomat Toreño, "would have captivated the Spanish if they had not already been so gravely wounded as to honor and pride." Perhaps. Surely he would have captivated the liberals, for his principles were theirs. Ferdinand's were not clearly known, and if he rejected their constitution they were lost. They preferred to gamble, however, on Ferdinand rather than Joseph. In later years they would bitterly regret the decision. For now Toreño, Martín de Garay, Arguelles, Quintana, Antonio Capmany, La Huerta, and others trumpeted rebel nationalist sentiments, interspersed with liberal slogans, to the world.

THE ROAD AHEAD

The Spanish nation, *en masse*, was set on expelling the French. The British, most dogged of Napoleon's enemies, were determined to take maximum advantage of the Spanish uprising to get a foothold on the Continent. Nationalists in all parts of Europe were inspired by Spanish resistance, and prepared to take advantage of Napoleon's involvement on the Peninsula—Austria first, and prematurely, in 1809.

It was to be a war to the death, and Joseph, despite his golden dreams, would have to be a soldier-king, or no King at all.

⚜

CHAPTER X

Soldier-King

Two Points of View

To Napoleon it seemed that Joseph could do nothing but complain and offer his abdication. Spanish independence, the damned constitution, his precious people—over and over—or he will go home to Mortefontaine among his children, dogs, and books (paid for with my money) ". . . to live without humiliation, and die with an easy conscience." His crown is at my disposition. "God took away that of Naples; you may take back that of Spain." Now there is a stupid line!

In 1809, the Emperor had to build a new army to replace the one left under Joseph, keep his German allies in line, fight a war with Austria (touch-and-go until his victory at Wagram in July), contend with the defiant Pope (who would excommunicate Napoleon in May, and be imprisoned for his trouble), and more. He wrote Joseph infrequently, then usually to express indignation. Your *Courrier d'Espagne*, written in French and sent throughout Europe, carries ". . . a eulogy to the defenders of [Zaragoza] . . . without doubt to encourage [the rebels] . . ." and another to Jovellanos ". . . who is your mad, uncompromising enemy." Suppress that paper! "The affairs of Spain go badly. How can you sit so long without news [from your marshals] . . . ?" He sent most of Joseph's instructions through subordinates—Berthier, Clarke (minister of war), Champagny (foreign minister, vice Talleyrand), or Fouché (minister of police).

To Joseph, it seemed that Napoleon was bent on making his

task impossible. "I pray you to believe that I have more pains and embarrassment than I deserve, and that I should receive from you fraternal consolation and advice." Fouché, he wrote, was presuming to give him orders, and interfering in Spanish internal affairs. Berthier was not only transmitting orders to the Lieutenant of the Emperor [Joseph's military title], which was proper, but trying to instruct the *King of Spain*. "The chief-of-staff should . . . have nothing to say to the King of Spain." When French money arrived, Joseph and Cabarrus had to fight the army paymaster and Dennié, Napoleon's intendant general, to get any for the government. Champagny sent instructions through La Forest, who seemed omnipresent. The ambassador had spies everywhere, and supervised Fréville, who managed the imperial (confiscated) properties. Fréville's minions vied with the Kings's agents over possession of property, and even got into fist-fights with them. "M. de Fréville is sick, without doubt; he does not recognize my authority . . ." Joseph wrote Napoleon, "I beg Your Majesty to recall [him]." The Emperor did not respond, nor did he answer Joseph's repeated requests for *total* authority.

Most especially, Napoleon seemed ambivalent over Joseph's military role. Officially, the King was commander, but Berthier (and occasionally Napoleon himself) sent orders to armies and corps, and Joseph and Jourdan got copies late or not at all. The marshals reported sporadically, and disputed or ignored the King's orders. Ney, in Galicia, sent no word for weeks at a time; Soult, in Portugal, was totally out of touch with Madrid from mid-April until mid-June 1809. Napoleon seemed indifferent to all this, and yet, periodically, directed Clarke or Berthier to berate Jourdan (and Joseph, indirectly) for lack of energy and decision. The King was not greatly concerned over the war, which, despite increasing guerrilla activity, seemed to be going well. Yet, he asked himself, if an emergency arose, and he *did* have to command, would he be obeyed? In mid-April 1809, he voiced his frustration:

Sire . . . the minister of war complains that there is no instantaneous central impulsion which directs the movements of the armies. He ought to know that such *instantaneous and central impulsion* cannot exist . . . when every day various generals receive . . . orders which I cannot change without running the risk of seeing my orders disobeyed because they contradict those which come from Paris. . . . If . . . the minister . . . will correspond only with Marshal Jourdan . . . if Your Majesty would give me his advice . . . it would be possible to have central and instantaneous impulsion. . . .

As if to further weaken Joseph's control of the military, Marshal Jourdan's name was left off the *tableau des maréchaux* for 1809. It was no oversight; there were only nineteen marshals. Napoleon was punishing the old "republican" for wearing a Spanish cockade. But after such a slight how could the marshal who issued the King's orders make himself obeyed? Joseph begged Napoleon to restore Jourdan's name to the list and bolster his prestige by making him a duke. (Marshals Ney, Victor, Mortier, and Soult, and even *General* Junot—all in Spain—were dukes.) The Emperor refused. Jourdan, bent on retiring, began preparing to leave, but after some weeks decided to remain for Joseph's sake. He would do his duty, he informed Clarke, but how effectively, he could not say: "A commander should have under him *militaires* of inferior grade, who obey, not comrades who believe themselves more distinguished than he."

Napoleon, at death grips with the Austrians, had no sympathy for Jourdan or Joseph. Jourdan! Bah! Joseph! He has orders to command. Why does he not command? Why does he not join one of the corps instead of puttering around Madrid! *Mon Dieu!* When I was twenty-seven, in Italy, I took those veterans by the nape of the neck and *made them obey!*

He would neither trust Joseph completely nor strengthen Jourdan's position. Meanwhile the military situation had worsened, and, in the summer of 1809, the Emperor would expect the whole army of Spain to be maneuvered by the King he had accused of fleeing Madrid "without seeing the enemy," and the marshal he had defamed.

CALL TO ARMS

During the first months of 1809 the war seemed to be going in favor of the French. Surely Joseph had no reason to think differently. Zaragoza fell in February, and the valiant Palafox, delirious with fever, was taken captive. South of Madrid, the corps of Victor and Sébastiani easily parried weak rebel thrusts. The capital, garrisoned by some 15,000 reserves, Royal Guards, and "Spanish" troops, was quiet. With the protection of 15,000 Imperial Guards, under Bessières, couriers and convoys traveled the main route to France with little mishap. Ney was subduing Galicia, while Suchet (vice Junot) in Aragon and Gouvion Saint-Cyr in Catalonia were making headway against rebel forces. Soult, presumably, was meeting little resistance in Portugal, and a corps under Mortier stood ready to reenforce him from Valladolid if trouble developed. (See map, p. 151.)

Then, suddenly, on 10 June, a dispatch from Paris drove all but war from Joseph's mind. He *had* to command, like it or not. Soult, he was told, had been defeated at Oporto by Sir Arthur Wellesley on 12 May—a month before!—and had retreated into Galicia to join forces with Ney. Soult had reported *to Paris, not Madrid*. Napoleon, in Vienna, had the news two days after Joseph did. Both had known that Wellesley had landed in Lisbon with 16,000 British in mid-April, and probably joined with a small (British-commanded) Portuguese army already there. But where was he now?

Interestingly, the brothers reacted with almost the same orders. Joseph directed Ney and Mortier to give Soult maximum support if the British threatened. Napoleon was more specific: "The corps of the Duke d'Elchingen [Ney] the Duke de Trevise [Mortier] and the Duke de Dalmatie [Soult] form one army . . . under the command of the Duke de Dalmatie." Soult!

Marshal Nicolas Soult had not only let himself be surprised by Wellesley, lost hundreds of men and most of his artillery, and failed to report to Joseph, but earlier, he had held up his march on Lisbon to comport himself as "King" of Portugal. "Nicolas I," the Paris wags called him. Napoleon, says Thiébault, could either laugh or have Soult shot. Napoleon laughed. A canny, aggressive fighter, the leathery, diminutive marshal was (under the Emperor's command) one of the best soldiers alive. If he showed the characteristics of a *condottiere*—well, Napoleon might

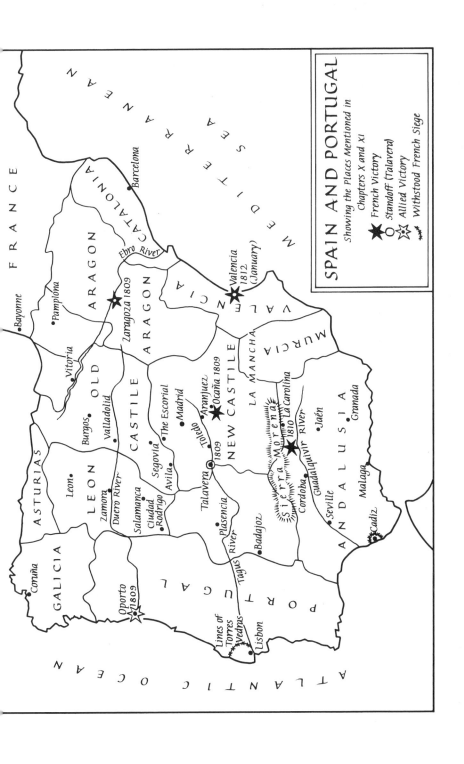

SPAIN AND PORTUGAL

Showing the Places Mentioned in
Chapters X and XI

★ French Victory
○ Standoff (Talavera)
☆ Allied Victory
〰 Withstood French Siege

have reflected, so had he himself. The Emperor had need of Soult; he forgave him.

Joseph, who received news of Soult's appointment on 1 July, manfully tried to make the new organization work, though he felt compelled within two weeks to recommend the recall of both Soult and Ney (Napoleon refused). Neither reported to him, and Ney responded to Soult's orders with arrogant inertia. The King did his best, nevertheless. "The defeat of the English army is the important thing; the rest . . . can be arranged after the army is beaten."

The King was dead right. The British army was small, but its success had rallied Spanish armies, and a major offensive force was in the making. In May, Wellesley had quickly broken off pursuit of Soult, and hurried to Abrantès, where he met with Cuesta and Venegas, who commanded rebel armies cantoned in southern Spain. They agreed to attack Madrid—Venegas from the south with an army of 26,000—Cuesta (36,000) and Wellesley (30,000), combined, from the west. Venegas would strike from the Sierra Morena, into which he could retreat if necessary; the larger army would follow the Tagus River route. (See map, p. 151.)

In June, Joseph was alerted to the presence of Venegas and Cuesta to the south. He personally went after Venegas, with Sébastiani's corps, and sent Victor to meet Cuesta. Venegas, however, fled into the Sierra Morena, and Cuesta retreated southwest, devastating the country as he went and even herding the peasant population along with him. In mid-July, Joseph was back in Madrid, and since he assumed Wellesley would attack in the north, left Soult's army there to check him. Meanwhile, informed of French dispositions by guerrilla chiefs, Wellesley prepared to bring 100,000 men against the 50,000 Joseph had under his personal command.

WELLESLEY

The street performers in London had a song about Wellesley, who had defeated Junot at Vimiero in 1808, and his two superiors, who had agreed to evacuate the French army to France:

Sir Arthur was a fighting cock,
But of the other two
Sing doodle doodle doodle
doodle· doodle-doo.

A fighter he was. Though of a politically prominent Anglo-Irish family (his brother Richard became foreign secretary in 1809), he had earned his knighthood on battlefields in India. Lanky, square-jawed, taciturn, and more than a little haughty, Wellesley disdained the common man, even his fine British regulars. "They are the scum of the earth," he once said, ". . . fellows who have enlisted for drink." Fear of flogging, he believed, was the only thing that could move them. His men did not love him; they feared, respected, and trusted him. He demanded absolute obedience, and got it. But Wellesley was no spit-and-polish soldier. In the field he habitually wore a dark blue jacket, often without insignia, a short cloak, and a plain cocked hat. He was a fighting general of a fighting army. He judged his men, as they did him, by performance in battle; they leaped to his command because he *won*. At Oporto he had sent them across the wide Duero in broad daylight—and they had almost captured Soult himself, sitting at breakfast. "Old Duoro," they had called him since.

Careful, professional, impassive, Sir Arthur was a believer in long-term decisions in war. Always alert to the exact capabilities and limitations of his forces, he avoided battle unless the odds were clearly in his favor. He was an infuriating opponent for French generals, who were prone to impetuous dash and felt a frantic compulsion to make quick reputations. Though he could sense the right time for attack (as at Oporto), his forte was the defense of carefully chosen ground. Depending on the staying power of his regulars, he had stood at Vimiero and let Junot dash himself to pieces. It would be his standard tactic on the Peninsula until he judged the allied forces fully ready to go over to the offensive. His was the "Cautious System."

The fates, it would prove, had made Wellesley the Nemesis of the French on the Peninsula. He would leave covered with British and Spanish honors, of which the proudest was the title Duke of

Wellington. Among the troops, "Old Duoro" became alternately "The Peer."

TALAVERA

On 18 July, while the drums for the dead of Wagram still sounded in Vienna, Napoleon wrote Clarke:

Recommend to the King of Spain that if the English should invade Spain he should not give battle until all his forces are united. He has the 1st and 4th Corps [Victor, Sébastiani] with the garrison of Madrid, which makes more than 50,000 men. The 2nd, 5th and 6th Corps [Soult, Montier, Ney] form about 60,000 men.

Before these instructions reached Madrid, however, Joseph had met the Allied challenge in his own way.

At 9 P.M. on 22 July one of Victor's aides galloped into Madrid to notify Joseph that an Anglo-Spanish army of almost 70,000 men was marching up the Tagus toward Madrid. Wellesley and Cuesta! The King was up all night. He ordered Victor to withdraw before the allied forces and report hourly. Officers with orders for Soult were sent flying north (by different routes, carrying duplicates, to ensure a copy reached him): Assemble your three corps on Salamanca; march south to Plasencia; take the enemy in the flank or rear; keep the King informed.

On the 23rd, leaving 7000 men to garrison Madrid, Joseph joined his guard with Sébastiani's corps, and on the 24th reenforced Victor west of Talavera. He had 45,000 men facing the enemy, under his command. If Soult got his orders on the 24th (he did), Joseph could reasonably expect to have 60,000 men in Wellesley's rear by 30 July. (See map, p. 155.) The plan was brilliant—Napoleonic—if it succeeded Wellesley would be outnumbered and beset from the east and west. Victor had earlier destroyed the Tagus bridges, so that escape to the south would be difficult; to the north lay mountain passes fit only for goats or guerrillas. Success, however, depended on Soult—and on Joseph's battlefield decisions—and on the movement of Venegas, as yet not accounted for, but to whom Madrid was open from the south.

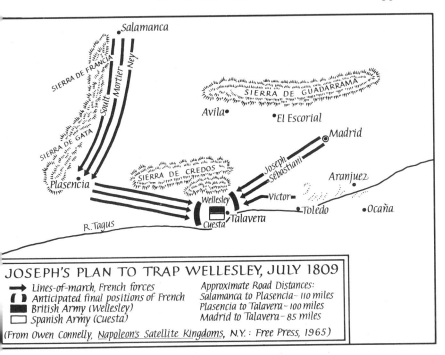

Cuesta, contemptuous of Wellesley's deliberate movement, pushed ahead of him, through Talavera. On 26 July his advance units blundered into French cavalry, which charged and sent them flying; their retreat panicked the whole Spanish army, which flooded back into Talavera, where it was reorganized behind a British line. Outraged and humiliated, Cuesta ordered up firing squads and decimated regiments like a Roman consul.

Wellesley was appalled rather than reassured by Cuesta's actions. Whatever faith he had in the Spanish and their commander evaporated. Though his army outnumbered Joseph's he decided to take a defensive position. On the morning of 27 July he stood behind the shallow Portiña, which flows into the Tagus at Talavera. On his right, in Talavera and behind orchard walls to the north, were the Spanish; on his left, on higher ground, their flank on the precipitous Cerro de Medelin, were the British and

Portuguese. During the afternoon, amid haphazard engagements, the French took up opposing positions.

Victor, on the French right, moved haltingly during the afternoon. Pressed with orders to advance, he stormed into Joseph's headquarters, shouting and banging tables with the flat of his saber. *Marshal Jourdan would give him satisfaction!* Neither the time nor place, said Jourdan. Joseph ordered Victor to move up, and he galloped away, livid with anger. Later, without reporting to the King, he threw his corps into a night attack—uphill against Wellesley's left flank—the enemy's strong side, on the highest ground, with the steadiest troops.

Victor's men struggled through the ravine of the Portiña, up the rocky side of the Cerro, and reached the British squares half exhausted and thoroughly disorganized. The defenders had every advantage—fixed position, better communication, greater firepower. And piercing the darkness suddenly, as the first shots were exchanged, was a sound in itself enough to unnerve many a French recruit—the unearthly squall of the bagpipes of the Scots regiments. Amid furious, often hand-to-hand, combat, the attackers were hurled back.

In the early morning hours Victor again appeared at headquarters. He had failed but in daylight things would be different! Joseph, jaded from lack of sleep, faced with a hero of fifty battles, who charged in from the night, smelling of gunpowder, looked numbly at Jourdan. A reconnaissance in the morning? Victor shouted that "His Majesty, Your Brother, The Emperor," would not hesitate. Very well, attack, said Joseph.

On the morning of 28 July Victor attacked, and again was thrown back. Joseph and Jourdan made a reconnaissance, and called a council of war. Meanwhile word arrived that *Soult had not yet left Salamanca!* He could not be at Plascencia until 2 August, perhaps 5 August! And Venegas's Spanish army of 30,000 was approaching Aranjuez—only thirty miles from Madrid. The capital was reported in an uproar; the garrison was trying to cram the *afrancesado* and French families into the Retiro, and making plans to evacuate them to San Ildefonso.

Joseph asked Jourdan's advice. Sweeping his hands over the maps, the old marshal held forth at length, suggesting and then rejecting various plans, while Victor made disrespectful noises. Finally? *Hold this position*, Sire, until Marshal Soult appears. Victor had fewer words. "Your Majesty's Brother, the Emperor!" *Attack,* Sire, with both corps. "It will succeed, *or we should give up war altogether!*" Joseph got his meaning; Victor would tell Napoleon an opportunity to crush *Les Anglais* had been missed. Jourdan was recommending they stick to the original plan—but if they delayed for long *Madrid would be lost.* How could he face Napoleon if he lost Madrid again? If he could win a quick victory, perhaps there would be time to save his capital also. Very well. Marshal Victor's plan. *Attack! Both corps.*

The battle began in mid-afternoon and raged into the night, with neither side gaining the advantage. At about 10 P.M. officers began arriving at the King's headquarters with verbal reports from Victor. His flank had been turned said some; others that he was turning the British flank. Unable to get a clear picture, Joseph sent off a written note to him, but got no answer. Nevertheless, he ordered the reserves up to support Victor, but as he did, the sounds of battle faded, and he recalled them. The next morning, the French line was about the same as before the battle. Victor remained silent, but he would later accuse Joseph of losing the battle by failing to commit the reserves.

On the morning of 29 July, Joseph ordered Victor to stay in place and observe Wellesley, retreating or advancing as necessary, until Soult was heard from. He then marched to engage Venegas with Sébastiani's corps and the Royal Guard. *Madrid would not be lost again.* Napoleon would not slander him as he had in 1808. Before he left he dictated a report for Napoleon. He regretted not capturing "the whole English army," but *Les Anglais* had been fought to a standstill, and the battlefield was "covered with their dead." One enemy thrust at Madrid had been stopped; he was marching to parry another.

"*Le Maréchal* Victor," he said generously, ". . . charged with the attack on the English left, pressed it with the force of a great soldier." "Marshal Jourdan gave me the benefit of great experience, which I lack." Two days later, hearing that Wellesley had not tried to advance, he was sure he had won a victory at Talavera. Moreover, he was between Madrid and Venegas. How could Napoleon ask more? "For a month, Sire, I have maneuvered with 40,000 men against 100,000 enemies, and I have embarrassed them in the worst way."

On 11 August, Joseph and Sébastiani defeated Venegas at Almoncid, and the Spanish army withdrew in disorder into the Sierra Morena. Four days later the King was back in Madrid. Wellesley, meanwhile, undeterred by Victor, marched west, and got past Plasencia before Soult (with Ney and Mortier) reached his blocking position, and shortly made for Lisbon. Cuesta followed, crossed the Tagus, and fled south. Soult began a pursuit of Wellesley, but Joseph called him back (8 August). The King considered the campaign over. The enemy had fled. Moreover, as Napoleon himself had observed, August and September were the worst months for campaigning. The heat had felled hundreds. Joseph reported 8000 in hospital at Madrid alone; most were sick rather than wounded. (Typically, he had also made room for 6000 enemy casualties.) Enough of war for a while! Madrid was safe.

The King was surprised to find the ladies of his court somewhat cool toward the gallant knight who had defended them. His civilian followers had been evacuated to San Ildefonso when Venegas approached, then returned within a few days. The heat, Sire! *Mon petit Jean* was ill; he cried all the way. Mama fainted three times. Oh, the dirt, Your Majesty! My carriage broke down. The filthy servants deserted us! It had taken Miot three days to organize the convoy of carriages, wagons, carts, and pack animals, loaded with baggage. The chief-of-household was as exhausted as the King. Joseph agreed that Miot had "been on campaign too."

Joseph was pleased with himself. Madrid had been in greater peril than in 1808, but this time he had fought. What was more, because of Soult's foot-dragging, he had, in truth, put to flight "100,000 enemies" with half their numbers—alone. Napoleon, however, did not see it that way.

"MY ARMY WAS BEATEN"

The Emperor, still at Vienna, envisioned Joseph smashing his enemies with an army of 100,000, united. "It will be a fine chance to *give the English a lesson and finish the war*," he wrote before hearing of Talavera. If the British could be crushed, once and for all, he thought (probably rightly) that Spanish resistance would collapse. To Napoleon, the object of the campaign was to *crush Wellesley*. On receiving Joseph's first reports he wrote hotly to Clarke:

I do not understand the affair in Spain. . . . Where was the French army on the 29th and 30th [of July]? Where was the English army at that time? The King tells me that he has maneuvered for a month with 40 thousand men against 100 thousand men: write him that [if he has] it is his own fault. . . .

After the reports of Jourdan, Victor, and Soult arrived, he was furious. "My army of Spain has been defied by 30,000 *Anglais!*" Jourdan lied to me! He sent an order to Clarke:

Make [Jourdan] understand that untruthfulness . . . is *un véritable crime* . . . that after having been told that the English were beaten . . . I find out that *my army was beaten*, that is to say that it took neither Talavera nor the plateau [on which the English stood].

Wellesley had escaped. Napoleon could see nothing else. He scorned the Spanish armies involved. He condemned Joseph's strategy: What if Wellesley had defeated Joseph and then turned on Soult? Why was Soult not ordered to Madrid instead of Plasencia? Since he was not, *Les Anglais* should not have been engaged at Talavera until Soult arrived. But since they were, why were they not crushed? Why had Joseph not committed the reserve? (Victor knows he could have won the battle!) "[In battle] . . . the outcome is always doubtful, but once engaged, it is win or die, and the Eagles of France should not retreat until every man is thrown at the enemy."

"Notify the King of my discontent with *general* Jourdan." Napoleon chose to ignore Soult's faulty execution of Joseph's plan, and that *Victor*, not Jourdan, had advised Joseph to attack at Talavera. Jourdan was the scapegoat—for Joseph—because to the Emperor's military mind the *commander* was responsible for his decisions, no matter whose advice he had taken. Nothing Jourdan wrote was acceptable: "He sends me *carmagnoles* and schoolboy amplifications." English newspaper reports of the battle, he believed, were more accurate than Jourdan's. The marshal sent in his resignation, and was recalled to France.

Joseph asked that Victor and Soult be recalled. Napoleon left them both in Spain, and named Soult to be the King's chief-of-staff. Joseph received the news wearily; a statement of his feelings had already gone off to his imperial master:

When a marshal does not obey me, and when Your Majesty knows about it and allows him to continue to command his corps there is nothing left for me to do but to march on him with troops who are loyal to me or to suffer the ignomy and disorganization of the army; or to supplicate Your Majesty to give command of his troops to someone other than myself; and as *the whole royalty of Spain is in the commanding of the French Army, I supplicate Your Majesty to accept my formal renunciation of the throne of Spain.*

KING WITHAL

Napoleon did not answer, but announced unofficially that he would soon return to Spain and personally carry the war to Wellesley (now Lord Wellington of *Talavera*). He ordered Clarke to expand French forces on the Peninsula to 355,000 by January 1810. From this mass the Emperor intended to take an "Army of Portugal" of at least 100,000. (Actually Napoleon would not come; but he meant to, and Joseph expected him imminently.)

Joseph brooded. Napoleon could at least answer his letters. He had *tried* to be a soldier. Perhaps he had not done well. . . . But had he done as badly as Napoleon said? Even if he had failed, was he not still the Emperor's *brother*? He wrote Julie:

The Emperor . . . doesn't write me anymore. If his conduct has been for the purpose of disgusting me with Spain, his object is accomplished. Any other political destination would suit me better. If he would agree to let me retire to the depths of a province, far from the frequented roads, with my family and a small number of persons of little significance, I would promise him to live as if I had never known another kind of life. I would never appear in Paris: the books, the trees, would distract me and my children would amuse me.

Napoleon. And the *people*. What did they want of him? While he was away fighting, Madrid had become dangerous for anyone connected with him. In the city and countryside monks and priests had preached the rebel cause. He knew some of them. He had talked to them, made presents to their churches. How could they? Some of his officials had gone over to the rebels; several hundred of his Spanish troops had deserted. In anger he ordered rebel properties sold more quickly, and all remaining monasteries dissolved forthwith; he allowed police and soldiers to comb the city for subversives—entering homes without warrants—going everywhere. But he had relented, softened his policies. Thank God he had the power to pardon. No one denied that—yet.

Should he just leave without Napoleon's permission? He would have to face him. Napoleon would shame him. And what of the family? Madame Mère—his brothers—his uncle Cardinal Fesch —Julie. Would they understand if he fled like a criminal? Lucien would, perhaps. That rebel, that troublemaker; how the English loved him for defying Napoleon. He could not be like Lucien. And—one must be practical—what of his property? What of Mortefontaine? What of Julie and the girls if Napoleon ruined him? His brother could be vengeful. Had he not threatened to destitute, even imprison Jérôme if he did not divorce the beautiful American girl—when even the Holy Father in Rome refused to say the marriage was illegal? Could he, Joseph, live if his brother denied him, refused to see him, recognize him—if only that? No, he could not. Napoleon must give him permission, or he could not leave.

Of course it was not bad to be a King—to live in the palace Philip V had designed—to have around him the paintings of the great masters of Europe. And his Marquise was with him. Amalia had become a little arrogant—now demanded that the Royal Guard escort her everywhere. Ministers bowed to her as if she were the Queen. And what a temper! When she had heard he had visited the singer Fineschi! How she and the Countess de Jaruco hated each other! But she got more beautiful every day. And how angelic she was at mass. The little page, Hugo's son— not Victor, yes Abel—how he worshiped her.

TO PROVE HIMSELF

In November Joseph was again in the field. He and Soult, with 30,000 men, marched to attack the Army of Arizaga, who had united what remained of Venegas's and Cuesta's armies. They found the Spanish at Ocaña—45,000 or more—routed them and took no less than 26,000 prisoners, including three generals. Joseph reported to Napoleon, adding a personal note:

It has been a long time, Sire, since I have heard from Your Majesty. . . . If I have lost your love, find it in your heart to let me retire to some obscure retreat, if you cannot, then I will find a glorious death . . . where the name I carry and the troops I command have yet found only victory.

Reflecting on his letter after his return to Madrid, Joseph had to admit he had been melodramatic. The battle and its aftermath had sickened him—the dead, the wounded, the terrified prisoners. Soult had sickened him. Did the man thrive on carnage? Joseph wondered how long he could carry the sword without becoming brutalized. It was not really a "glorious death" in battle he expected, he had to admit, but death of the soul.

But if he must stay. . . . Why not fight? Why not get the conquest over? Napoleon reserved Portugal for himself. Why should the King not take Andalusia? No French had ventured into that land of horrors since it had consumed Dupont's army. The rebel Junta was at Seville. If he could destroy it perhaps the war would end. If not then at least the revenues of Andalusia would make him more independent of France. Perhaps he could rule as he chose while Napoleon marched against Wellington. Andalusia. What better place to prove himself?

Joseph ordered Soult to have an army of invasion ready by New Year's 1810.

EFFICACY OF POWER

As 1810 began, Napoleon's star shone more brightly than ever. The Austrian Emperor had promised him a daughter in marriage; the Czar was his ally, as was every ruler still on a throne in Europe; five kingdoms and some lesser states were ruled by his relatives; he was himself King of Italy and Protector of the Confederation of the Rhine; the Pope was his prisoner and Rome was part of France. He was actively opposed on the Continent only by the British and the Spanish rebels, the former represented by perhaps 40,000 Anglo-Portuguese troops, the latter by five widely separated armies totaling altogether some 120,000 men, aided very indirectly by the uncoordinated efforts of guerrillas.

The French army on the Peninsula, at the same time, was twice as large as all the enemy forces together (including guerrillas). Spanish armies were hard pressed, save that in Andalusia, which had not yet recovered from its total rout at Ocaña; the bulk of Anglo-Portuguese forces were entrenched at Lisbon. Even guerrilla activity had slackened; renowned chiefs, such as Mina, were in hiding.

None of this was lost on the Spanish. Joseph and La Forest (for once in full agreement) reported that "public spirit" in French-controlled areas had improved markedly. From the rebel side came deserters, civilian and military, to offer their services to the Bonaparte King. They told of violent dissention among the leaders of the Seville Junta, disorders in rebel cities, and a general deterioration of faith in the future of the insurrection. Lord Byron, in Seville, versified of inevitable French victory, and deplored (and enjoyed) the degeneracy of society:

> Nor bleed these patriots with their country's wounds:
> Nor here War's clarion, but Love's rebeck sounds;
> Here folly still his votaries inthralls;
> And young-eyed Lewdness walks her midnight rounds.

From Ferdinand VII, shining knight of the rebels, came a letter asking Joseph to "use his influence with His Majesty the Emperor, his august brother, for the realization of a wish dear to my heart" —marriage to a Bonaparte bride.

In Andalusia, especially, disaffection seemed rife. Joseph was encouraged to hasten preparations for an invasion. Wrote Soult to Berthier:

After all the reports he has received, His Majesty is persuaded that the greatest anarchy reigns in Andalusia, and that the inhabitants of that unfortunate province are only waiting for a plausible excuse to declare in his favor.

Joseph knew the reasons behind the rapid change of attitude among "his people," but he did not believe in the long-run efficacy of power. However, he was convinced that if conquest brought peace, he could win the affection of the Spanish, and make true supporters out of those who declared for him out of fear. In this spirit he pressed Napoleon for permission to invade the south, and when the Emperor did not reply, he marched anyway. The reason for his brother's silence would be apparent later.

ANDALUSIA

On 8 January 1810, Joseph and Soult marched for Andalusia with the corps of Victor and Sébastiani, the Royal Guard, and reserves—in all 60,000 men. His troops easily forced the passes of the Sierra Morena, driving before them the army of Arizaga (25,000 survivors of Ocaña), which literally dissolved. The only other rebel army at hand, 10,000 under the Duke of Albuquerque, made for Cadiz, the rebel National Junta in tow. On 20 January the King was at La Carolina, where Dupont's wounded had been massacred in 1808.

A delegation of officials and clergy waited on "His Catholic Majesty" outside the gates, and wildly cheering crowds greeted him in the streets. In the villages beyond it was the same. His march became a triumphal procession. On 25 January Córdoba opened her gates without a fight, and he was received with frantic enthusiasm. While bands played and girls threw flowers in his path, the King proceeded slowly to the cathedral of Córdoba, the magnificent Mesquita, with its hundreds of marble and jasper pillars, its domes and towers, eternally more Moorish than Christian.

There the *Te Deum* was sung, and afterward the Bishop of Córdoba presented Joseph with Dupont's standards, lost at Baylen. He was deeply moved, and got on a chair to voice his happiness and hopes: "Spaniards unite. . . . On this day begins a new era of glory and well-being for the nation." With variations, he repeated the line many times in the ensuing weeks. After all his months in the north, in an atmosphere of hostility and war, Joseph was all but overwhelmed. On he went to another gigantic reception in Seville, the former rebel capital, happily reporting to Napoleon en route:

Sire, Andalusia will shortly be pacified. All the cities are sending me deputies; Seville is following that example. The Junta has retired to the Isle de Leon [Cadiz]. I am preparing to enter Cadiz without a blow being struck.

The spirit of the people is wonderful. I hope that after a little, Your Majesty will be charmed by the progress we are making here, since the triumphs of our enemies are founded on the most absurd and black lies, which are being dissipated.

He was giving the lie to rebel propaganda. The people could see he was no monster! It was a beginning . . . and when they had the benefits of his government. . . ! After all this time, what a beginning! And so it was. Wrote the amazed Bigarré: "Posterity will refuse to believe that the brother of Napoleon was in 1810 the idol . . . of Andalusia." And he gave some evidence:

The nobles . . . sent him . . . magnificent bulls . . . horses, perfectly harnessed, and several put at the disposition of His Majesty their wives, their daughters, and their homes.

One of the most beautiful women [of Malaga] . . . belonging to one of the best families of the kingdom . . . asked him, in writing, to accord her the signal favor of visiting her in her bedchamber.

Cortes at Cadiz

While Joseph's triumphal procession continued, Victor pursued the rebels to their last point of resistance, Cadiz. Albuquerque's army brought the garrison, which included Anglo-Portuguese infantry, to 30,000 and British warships rode in the harbor. "Cadiz is loyal to His Majesty Ferdinand VII," was the terse reply to Victor's summons to surrender. He began a siege, but as it proved, the city would never be taken.

The rebel government had a permanent refuge. Further, its liberal element found allies in the radical mobs of Cadiz. The calling of a Cortes, on which all their hopes depended, was accelerated. Within a few months it was both governing Spain and producing a constitution—one more liberal than Napoleon's Constitution of Bayonne—which would become famous as the "Constitution of 1812."

JOSEPH THE GOOD

Joseph, happy as he had not been since leaving Naples, concentrated on reassuring and conciliating his people. He explained the constitution and its benefits, spoke of his plans for education and public works, promised to be a *Spanish* King, and guard the integrity and honor of the kingdom. "France is my family, but Spain is my religion!" He promised amnesty for all if they would take an oath to him within twenty days. Even those whose property had been declared forfeit were eligible; their estates would be restored! (Details he left to his harried finance minister, Cabarrus, who was called south in March; he died within a month.) Professional soldiers were offered service in his army, or they could retire on pension. Civil servants were guaranteed their jobs if they would swear loyalty.

He endowed schools, ordered the Alcazar Palace of Seville converted into a museum and gallery, decreed that the Alhambra of Granada would be restored, and asked that plans be drawn to finish the palace begun by the Holy Roman Emperor Charles V. He visited factories and summarily ordered pay raises for the workers. He directed a Spanish regiment to escort the Madrid Opera Company to Granada for performances. Returning to earlier plans, he decreed an administrative organization of all of Spain—thirty-two prefectures to replace the old provinces. By mid-March most of his ministers and half his council of state were traveling with him. La Forest, at Madrid, turned from complaining that Joseph paid too little attention to the war and wrote bitterly that he was neglecting affairs at his capital.

Joseph allowed himself to hope that *now* he could be an enlightened monarch. Spain was all but conquered. If Andalusians accepted him—if the people who had butchered Dupont's men were at his feet—how could he fail to win over *all* the Spanish? Surely his days as soldier-king were numbered.

Actually, at the moment of Joseph's triumph, both his military and civil power had been virtually destroyed by imperial decree. He soon found that he was hardly a King at all—and that all his promises to the Spanish had been turned into lies.

✣

CHAPTER XI

King without Kingdom

THE IMPERIAL AXE

IN Napoleon's eyes, Joseph had served him badly. There were reasons for his failures, but the Emperor was not interested in excuses—only *results*. As a soldier Joseph had let Wellington escape from Talavera and lost a prime opportunity to end the Peninsular War. As a governor—primarily he had not made Spain *pay*, either for his government or the war. During 1808–09 the imperial treasury had expended in Spain 1,125,000,000 reals (300,000,000 francs) in specie. (In addition, the costs in blood and material were gigantic.) As for the war, Napoleon planned to win it himself—or, as he soon decided, direct it from Paris. For the rest, military governors would be installed where necessary.

"Let the King know that my finances are deranged," Napoleon wrote Berthier, ". . . I cannot afford the enormous sums Spain is costing me." On 8 February 1808 he decreed Catalonia, Aragon, Biscay, and Navarre to be "military governments," under generals responsible only to Paris; they were empowered not only to administer finances, but to *govern*, and were troop commanders as well. Joseph was King no more in the provinces adjacent to France. (See map, p. 169.)

The King was stunned by the news, which reached him in Andalusia on 27 February. Part of Spain was being *governed from Paris*—in effect had been *annexed to France*. How could he continue proudly to tout the Constitution of Bayonne, which

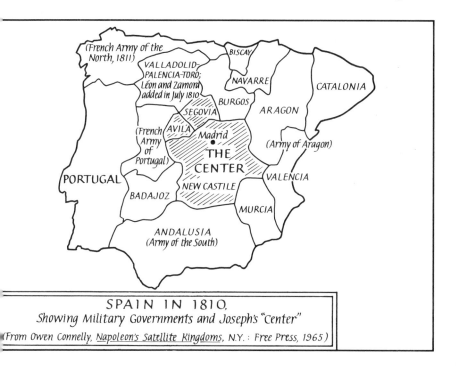

SPAIN IN 1810,
Showing Military Governments and Joseph's "Center"
(From Owen Connelly, Napoleon's Satellite Kingdoms, N.Y.: Free Press, 1965)

guaranteed the integrity of Spain? Miot de Melito advised that he abandon his throne, immediately: ". . . before the eyes of Europe, separate your cause [from Napoleon's]." Joseph refused: ". . . surely [the Emperor] does not wish his brother to be humiliated . . . [to] make me look ridiculous before my new subjects." Besides, no Spanish territory had *formally* been annexed to France. If any were, he *would* abdicate. Even the *afrancesados* would abandon him if that happened. What had been done might well ruin his chances of truly becoming King.

How could he best present his views to Napoleon? Letters would go through the ministers, perhaps be misinterpreted to the Emperor. How could he even be sure they would reach his brother? An emissary would be better—his first minister, Azanza. He could go, officially, to congratulate the Emperor on his marriage, so as not to further alarm the Spanish, among whom rumors were flying that Spain would either be annexed to France or that Napoleon would take the crown. He dispatched Azanza, after dubbing him Duke de Santa Fé to enhance his prestige.

While he awaited his minister's return, Joseph went about his work of conciliation, but soon found his task impossible. The public quickly learned of Napoleon's move. The King was charming, but powerless. Who could depend on his promises? At Easter, Joseph personally participated in the traditional celebrations at Seville—a gesture unheard of for a Spanish monarch. But, Miot reported: "That condescension earned him not the slightest acclaim." With a sweep of his pen, Napoleon had destroyed his brother's popularity. Ill with frustration, Joseph gave up his "campaign," and returned to Madrid, arriving on 13 May in the dead of night, escorted only by twenty cavalrymen. Arches of triumph which the city had begun building for his reentry had to be pulled down. He could not bear passing under them.

From Paris came word that Azanza could not get an audience with the Emperor. "Do you really have much to say to His Majesty?" the foreign minister had asked skeptically. Queen Julie wrote that the family treated her coldly. (Earlier she had feared Napoleon would deny her a proper place at his wedding.) Joseph asked her to talk to Napoleon. "What does the Emperor want of me and of Spain? If he would tell me . . . I would not be hanging between what I must pretend to be and what I really am." If she could not make his brother "see the truth," he would have to "retire."

When Azanza finally saw Napoleon, after three months in Paris, he got nothing but a torrent of abuse for his trouble. The Emperor was gentle with Julie, but she got nowhere either. Joseph, meanwhile, read versions of his speeches to the Andalusians in the *Moniteur*; Napoleon's censors had deleted all references to the "regeneration of Spain" and altered the text to emphasize right of conquest. Worse discouragements were in the offing.

In May two more military governments were created—Burgos and Valladolid-Palencia-Toro. In July Leon and Zamora were added to the latter.* (See map, p. 169.) Another decree extended the authority of the French minister of public treasury to the military governments (exactly as if they were part of France). It specified that in the rest of Spain, "receipts destined for the armies," were to be paid directly to the paymasters of army corps. Between April and August, a series of decrees divided the army of Spain into five separate commands—the army of Portugal (Marshal Masséna), of Catalonia (Macdonald), of Aragon (Suchet), of the South (Soult), and of the Center (Joseph). Soult's orders advised him to give due respect to the King, but "adopt the most effective measures to supply and pay your army." He was, in reality, governor of Andalusia. Finally, Joseph's income from the imperial treasury was cut off (it had been about 3,750,000 reals a month); Napoleon promised 7,500,000 a month for his troops, but it was to go directly to the army, not through the King's government.

Joseph was reduced to governor of "the Center"—New Castile plus Avila and Segovia in Old Castile. (See map, p. 169.) His Army of the Center—15,000 men—was the smallest in Spain.† He had no more authority than the military governors, a less productive area than most of them, and greater expenses. Napoleon, apparently, expected him to live in a style befitting a King, keep a court, and maintain, for ultimate use, a government

---

* Military governments and governors were as follows:

1.	Catalonia	Augereau (Macdonald in June 1810)
2.	Aragon	Suchet
3.	Navarre	Dufour (shortly Reille)
4.	Biscay	Thouvenot
5.	Burgos	Dorsenne
6.	Valladolid-Palencia-Toro-Leon-Zamora	Thiébault (Kellermann substituted for a few months during 1810)

† The armies and other troop dispositions were as follows:

ARMY	COMMANDER	STRENGTH	MISSION
Army of the Center	Joseph	15,000	Occupation
Army of Portugal	Marshal Masséna	128,000	Take Portugal
Army of the South	Marshal Soult	70,000	Occupation, take Cadiz, assist other armies
Army of Catalonia	Marshal Macdonald	50,000	Subdue Catalonia
Army of Aragon	General Suchet	30,000	Subdue Aragon, then take Valencia

(Cont. p. 172)

and bureaucracy manned to govern all Spain. His position seemed impossible.

WHY?

Did Napoleon want him to abdicate? In July news arrived that his brother Louis had done so, and fled Holland. Louis had been in no worse position than he. In early 1810 part of Holland had been annexed, the rest occupied; imperial officials had moved in everywhere; when Marshal Oudinot demanded entry into Amsterdam, Louis had fled. In Westphalia and Naples, also, French commanders were flouting the authority of Kings Jérôme Bonaparte and Joachim Murat. In Italy, Eugène had been informed that he would give way in twenty years to Napoleon's (yet unborn) son. Were all the kingdoms to be part of France? Surely the cases of Spain and Holland were *very* similar.

But if Napoleon wanted him to abdicate, why didn't he say so? The *senatus consultum*, annexing Holland to France, gave him the answer. Louis had fled; all treaties with Holland were with the *crown*; they were legally cancelled. It was a fiction, but a useful one. The governments of Europe, helpless anyway, could conveniently accept that since Louis had abandoned his throne, Napoleon had a right to make other arrangements. The Dutch, who had supported Louis with amazing unanimity, could comfortably believe that they *were not pawns*; the Emperor was merely giving them another government; they could save their pride. (Earlier they had accepted that their leaders freely chose to request Louis.) Their leaders, who had taken oaths to the King, could consider them fulfilled, and honorably give their allegiance to the Emperor. Historians would see that Louis had been *driven* from the throne, but with Europe's press almost totally under Napoleon's control, that fact would be slow in

Military Government Troops	Military governors	45,000	Occupy military governments except Catalonia, Aragon, and Burgos
Imperial Guard	Dorsenne	17,000	Occupy Burgos, police routes to France
	TOTAL	355,000	

reaching the public—especially when it was soothing to believe the official fictions. *Marriage of King to country had been relatively simple; divorce was very complicated—unless the husband fled.*

In Spain, Joseph saw, his followers perforce considered him their *legal* King, by the *legal* Constitution of Bayonne (not publicly repudiated by Napoleon). If he fled his followers would be free to take service with Napoleon *or* (a choice not available in Holland) join the rebels and fight for Ferdinand VII. *What a choice! Only he, Joseph, by standing firm, could keep them from having to make it.* If Napoleon refused to restore his power, a good part of the *afrancesados* would probably defect, *in time.* But, if Napoleon *took* his crown, Joseph reflected, he would be taking Azanza's dukedom, O'Farrill's ministry, and in fact every honor and title he, Joseph, had bestowed, down to that of the simplest mayor. The Emperor would lose *all* his Spanish supporters, *immediately.* That was the price his brother would pay for deposing him.

Good and Evil

Joseph saw his choice as between good and evil. To abdicate of his own volition would be evil; he would abandon his followers, betray the Spanish people, and fail in his duty to Napoleon. To remain, no matter how attenuated his power, would be good. No. He would not abdicate. Napoleon, he felt, could choose a greater good; the Emperor could restore his power and let him regenerate Spain, which only he could do. *Or,* Napoleon could do greater evil; he could take his crown (or give him permission to retire, which, since the imperial wish was a command, would be deposing him). In that case Spain would either be dismembered and plundered by Napoleon's minions, or lapse into medievalism under Ferdinand VII, depending on the fortunes of war. Joseph could see but one course for himself—to remain in Madrid, no matter what, unless his brother deposed him. As in 1808, he placed himself between the Emperor and the Spanish people.

His own choice made, Joseph undertook to force a decision from Napoleon. With the skill (and exaggeration) of an advocate, he presented a case for the restoration of his power, asking permission to retire if it were not convincing. If his power were not restored, he wrote on 7 August 1810, what would he be? "The *concierge* of the hospitals at Madrid, the depots of the army, the prisoner-of-war compounds?" Impossible! Any day he would find himself abandoned by his "Guard . . . service . . . all that constitutes a government." "Sire, I am your *brother*."

If the French army is put under my orders . . . if I have the right to dismiss officers who conduct themselves badly . . . if I am authorized to reassure the nation [that Spain will not be dismembered] . . . if Your Majesty will demonstrate due confidence in me by letting me speak and write to the Spanish what I believe . . . without being subjected to poisonous interpretations . . . I promise that the French army will not cost France a sou . . . that Spain will soon be pacified . . . [and] as useful to France as she is now destructive. If, on the contrary, I am forced to retire . . . I fear that Your Majesty will never see the end of this horrible convulsion.

To elaborate on his "brief," if necessary, Joseph sent Almenara (minister of finance, vice Cabarrus) to Paris. Azanza, meanwhile, had succeeded only in getting another imperial tongue-lashing. Joseph expected Almenara to do little better, but his conscience demanded that he do his best to recover his power. Failing that, his real hope, he wrote Julie, was that the Emperor would soon "fix the date of my departure." Then he would be free. The blood would be on Napoleon's hands.

NAPOLEON TIGHTENS THE SCREWS

Joseph tried to put up a brave front. He assumed an air of bluff optimism, entertained beyond his means, attended the theaters and opera, and held reviews of his troops. He even showed himself at the bullfights and valiantly pretended to enjoy what he privately considered to be an orchestrated bloodletting. (Charles IV had banned the *corridas de Toros*; Joseph restored them, and for once got universal applause from the masses. He had decided to be Spanish first and worry about the bulls later.) He tried to carry on normal governmental business, meeting his ministers and council of state, mulling over new tax plans, supervising off-again-on-again building in Madrid, appointing prefects (according to his proposed national system) for areas near Madrid.

It was evident, however, reported the cold-blooded La Forest, that everything was "suspended" pending the arrival of Napoleon's answer to Joseph's pleas. It came in mid-September. Azanza and Almenara had been informed that the Emperor would soon annex northern Spain to France. Otherwise there was no reply —neither permission to retire nor hint of restoration. Obviously if Joseph wanted out, he would have to abandon his throne. Surely that was what Napoleon wanted. Would he? *No.* The King was strapped to the rack of Spain by his conscience. Napoleon, irritated by his opposition to imperial policy, tightened the screws.

THE RACK

The King's self-control had begun to deteriorate before the summer was over. During the celebration of the Emperor's feast day (15 August), he lost his temper, damned Napoleon for treating him like a prefect, and threatened to abdicate. As the fall progressed and the Emperor ignored his plight, he became more edgy and sensitive, berated his astonished ministers and councillors, and got into arguments with his best friend, Miot. The Marquise had to endure his flights into the arms of others, and his returns, little-boy guilty and irresistible. Sometimes he seemed to have lost his reason: Let Napoleon take his damned troops and butchers away, he told Bigarré, La Forest, and others. My Spanish troops will protect me! My people will rally to me.

His dual allegiance plagued him: "France is my family; Spain is my religion." "My primary duty is to Spain." "I have duties of the heart to France. . . . I have duties of conscience to Spain. I will never betray either." But how could he remain a King without a kingdom? "Soon the pity and ridicule which assails me will turn to justified contempt . . ." he wrote Julie.

His government was in unadmitted bankruptcy. The Center was poor and the military, with or without authorization, took the lion's share of meager revenues. As Soult fixed his control over what his proclamations called his "Nation of Andalusia" (again, as in Portugal, he was playing the King), receipts from that area dwindled. Angulo, who took over the ministry of finance when Almenara went to Paris, personally collected some 3,000,000 reals in August, and sent it to Madrid. But by the time he got there, it had been spent, and little more came. Soult had instructions to contribute to Joseph's treasury—after the expenses of the army were paid—but he did not. With Napoleon's tacit consent, he used any surplus to support his Andalusian government.

Joseph's income fell to 4,000,000 reals a month; his expenses were 12,000,000 reals—only 2,000,000 lower than when he had been King-in-fact. How could he dismiss his civil servants? His government had to be prepared to resume national functions. Yet he could offer them only occasional pay in hard money, and his paper (after a temporary climb to an unbelievable 32 percent of par during the Andalusian campaign) was so worthless that many of them declined to accept it, preferring simply to be "creditors" of the government. In an intensely personal way, Joseph felt responsibility for this, and frustration at not being able to decrease unemployment by reviving government industries, letting building contracts, and the like.

Especially, was the King's pride rubbed blood raw because he could not protect "his people" from Napoleon's bullies in the military governments. The more successful governors, like Suchet, in Aragon, showed remarkable restraint, but the mass of Joseph's reports concerned those who ruled by terror. In Burgos, Dorsenne perpetually kept three bodies hanging on gibbets as a warning to guerrillas and their sympathizers. When a family claimed one for burial, another prisoner was dragged from jail and hanged. Since this slight and foppish tyrant was also commander of the Imperial Guard in Spain, charged with protecting the routes to France, he had subordinate emulators in garrisons from Madrid to Bayonne. In Valladolid, the bull-necked General Kellermann vied for honors in brutality, tempering his policy occasionally (it was said) to sell captured guerrillas to their chiefs. Even for the most judicious governors, the first rule was to *pay and feed the troops.* None ever quite succeeded except Suchet, and most, whether with vengeance or reluctance, resorted to confiscations, special levies collected by troops, the burning of recalcitrant villages—whatever seemed necessary.

Joseph protested to Berthier, Champagny, and Napoleon. Again and again he called in La Forest for talks, hoping to gain

*Joseph Bonaparte in exile. Painted at Philadelphia about 1820
by Charles Willson Peale, famous for his portraits of
George Washington.*

Julie Clary Bonaparte and daughter Zénaïde, by Lefevre.
COURTESY MUSÉE NATIONAL DE VERSAILLES. CLICHÉ DU SERVICE DE DOCUMENTATION
PHOTOGRAPHIQUE DES MUSÉES NATIONAUX

Joseph Bonaparte, King of Spain, by Wicar.
COURTESY MUSÉE NATIONAL DE VERSAILLES. CLICHÉ DU SERVICE DE DOCUMENTATION
PHOTOGRAPHIQUE DES MUSÉES NATIONAUX

The Marquise de Montehermoso as a young girl,
by Goya.
COURTESY BIBLIOTHÈQUE NATIONALE, PARIS

Caroline Charlotte Bonaparte Benton, daughter of
Joseph Bonaparte and Annette Savage. The photograph was
taken some years after her marriage, in 1839, to Colonel Zebulon
Howell Benton of Oxbow, New York.
COURTESY THE JEFFERSON COUNTY (NEW YORK) HISTORICAL SOCIETY

his support. The generals were driving the people to desperation —robbing, killing. Was there law only for Frenchmen? "I am surrounded by the wreck of a great nation," he wrote Napoleon, and to Julie: "The whole face of the nation has changed . . . opinion is entirely against us. The evil could still be repaired if the Emperor did what I asked." Napoleon replied not a word, but his attitude was clear. "Express by satisfaction to General Dorsenne . . ." began a letter to Berthier.

Deeply troubled, Joseph poured out his heart to Julie, both for comfort and in the hope that she could sway the Emperor. He saw no solution but "the most absolute retirement," but "duty and honor demand that I play this part to the last extremity." To go home would be heaven! "I embrace you with my children." "Hug Charlotte and Zénaïde for me." He wondered if his sacrifice, the insults he endured, were really worthwhile. What was he proving? In letter after letter he announced he would leave Spain, then qualified his stand. "*Chère amie*, I hope to return to you in a few weeks . . . if the Emperor approves and retains a little affection for me." Yet by November his tone had hardened, and it seemed that any day he would take the final step and flee his throne.

Abased, plagued, Joseph also had to face physical danger. "At any instant of day or night," he told Julie, "I may have to take to horse and defend my life against . . . insurgents, who are all around the city." The guerrillas, quiescent in early 1810, were back in force, and their confederates were inside Madrid. On separate days, Bigarré's house was sacked, a servant killed, and a French soldier shot down before his door. Joseph, with some justice, blamed the new violence on the cruelties of the military governors, Napoleon, and, typically, on himself. Had he done everything possible to retrieve his power? A major factor, however, was the dispersion of French forces, and the departure of the Army of Portugal from northern Spain.

THE WAR AND NAPOLEON

In 1810 many matters required Napoleon's presence in Paris, among them integrating Holland, the Hanse cities, and most of Hanover into the Empire. But he might have gone to Spain had he not married the Archduchess Marie Louise of Austria. Hoping merely to produce an heir and cement his alliance with the ancient Hapsburg dynasty, he found his whole life changed. "Marry a German girl," he said after their wedding night, "they are the best wives in the world—sweet, good, simple, and as fresh as a rose." His opinion did not change. The genius was paralyzed by happiness, something he could ill afford. The battlefield held no charm; he became a homebody. When, in April 1810, the Army of Portugal was ready to march, he gave command to Marshal Masséna, Prince of Essling. Wellington has 20,000 *Anglais*, perhaps 30,000 other rabble, he told the marshal; you have 100,000! Chase him into the sea!

In the field, unhappily, Masséna's advantage quickly evaporated. When he marched (June 1810), he was forced to leave 15,000 men behind to protect his rear from guerrillas. For corps commanders he had Ney, *prima donna* of French commanders, Junot, offended at not being allowed to command the second invasion of Portugal himself, and Reynier, but for whose arrogance Napoleon would have given higher command. Masséna could never be sure his orders would be obeyed. Ciudad Rodrigo, the border fortress, had to be taken and garrisoned, reducing his numbers further. As he moved into Portugal, the Allies exacted a heavy toll for his passage, guerrillas interdicted his communications with Spain, and before him the peasants withdrew, scorching the earth as they went. In October, his effective strength reduced by one-half, he was stopped cold at the lines of Torres Vedras, which ringed Lisbon. Wellington had devoted a year to preparing these fortifications, which stretched for fifty miles, included 150 forts, and delivered fire from 600 cannon. For a month the French hurled themselves against them, but could not break through. In November Masséna went into winter quarters, dispersing his troops as much as he dared for foraging. The campaign was over for the year; he had failed.

Napoleon was baffled and angry. How could Lisbon be held by 24,000 *Anglais*? (The figure was from the London *Times*; Napoleon always disdained mentioning Wellington's non-British troops.) Soult, meanwhile, ordered to assist Masséna, had sent a force belatedly, then withdrawn it. The Emperor's wrath fell on him too, doubly, since he had also failed to take Cadiz from "10 thousand miserable Spaniards." Napoleon again made plans to take command himself, but he could not tear himself away from Paris.

NAPOLEON RELENTS

The Emperor's relations with the Czar had meanwhile deteriorated badly; Russia was expected soon to throw down the gauntlet to France (and did). That, and the impending birth of his child (already titled the *King* of Rome), kept Napoleon in Paris. The Russian challenge also caused him to stay his assault on his satellite Kings. If he had intended to force their abdication and establish a centralized empire, which seems probable, he decided to postpone the program. In the short run, Westphalia, Naples, and Italy could furnish more troops and money if not disrupted.

Spain, in any case, would furnish little, cost much. But the expense would be less if Joseph were *not* restored, Napoleon believed, and chances better of winning the war there before the Russian campaign began. For the moment, keeping costs down seemed more important than pleasing the Spanish. (Napoleon admitted, at least to himself, that restoring Joseph would have *some* calming effect.) In 1812, if Spain were not yet subdued, restoring Joseph, if expensive, might ease problems there until he could deal with Russia. Then too, though he could direct the Spanish war from Paris, he could not do so from Russia. He hesitated to trust a marshal with overall command. Joseph, if not a good soldier, was trustworthy—and surely he could hold Spain during a (hopefully) short Russian campaign.

The Emperor decided to encourage Joseph just enough to keep him in Madrid. In 1812, depending on the situation, he would restore him, depose him, or let him be.

In November Azanza and Almenara, thoroughly discouraged, waited on Napoleon for permission to return to Spain, and were stunned to find the Emperor all sympathy. Their patriotism was worthy, he told them; he did not wish to fragment Spain, but the rebels had forced his hand. There was still a chance to save their country. If the rebel Cortes would recognize Joseph and accept the Constitution of Bayonne, then Joseph could recognize the Cortes as the national parliament; he, the Emperor, in turn, would guarantee the integrity of Spain.

Ready to grasp at straws after months of browbeating, the ambassadors informed Joseph of the proposition, and in early December appeared in Madrid to confirm it, adding that Napoleon gave permission to delay negotiations until after Portugal was conquered. Joseph was elated, then depressed. What chance was there? True, the Cadiz Cortes was under liberal control; its leaders well knew that he sympathized with their principles. Perhaps after Portugal was conquered, and Wellington expelled, they would compromise. But when would that be? Still, he would have to try. His conscience would not allow him to pass up any chance to save Spain.

Again the Rack

He had O'Farrill, Almenara, and others send messages to former friends in the rebel Cortes (all unofficial), and induced friends in the clergy to enter Cadiz to feel out opinion. The results were not encouraging. Joseph's mood blackened. Napoleon knew him all too well! He had tied him to the Spanish rack even tighter. Now it was even more his duty to endure and hope that after the conquest of Portugal the scheme would work. Meanwhile nothing had changed. Nothing!

Napoleon had members of the family, including Cardinal Fesch, their uncle, write Joseph, urging that he stay at Madrid for the good of the dynasty. No, the King replied. He wanted to retire in France or return to Naples. But he always added that Napoleon must give permission. He wrote Julie asking that she purchase property more remote from Paris than Mortefontaine. Napoleon forbade it.

As 1811 began Joseph's moods veered from morose depression to anger to indifference. La Forest respectfully requested a budget for Napoleon's information. A budget! Ha! There is not even money for the hospitals and orphanages! What does the Emperor want me to do? That is the question! Reign? Return to

France? Get myself killed in battle! All right! Whatever he says. Why does he not treat me as a brother? Why does he not write? Even with Julie he uses the *formes diplomatiques!*

For days at a time, Joseph hid himself at Casa del Campo, brooding, walking in the gardens, often drinking too much. Always there was the temptation to run—anywhere. Lucien was the smart one. He was out of it all. To sail for America! Well, yes, the British had captured him, but he was living in England like a hero! "The novel is drawing to a close," Joseph told Bigarré in February, "I say officially I will retire!" But he did not leave. His mental anguish was accompanied by frequent bouts of physical illness, which kept him longer in seclusion. When occasionally his old spirit revived, it was quickly crushed. In February 1811, he authorized masked balls at carnival time (a brave gesture; they had been banned for fifty years). Arriving happily at the largest of them, at the Opera, Joseph heard his beloved Amalia insulted by masked revelers; she fled in tears, and the King followed; he did not appear again.

All his troubles intensified, beginning with poverty. He suggested a cash payment to civil servants in honor of his feast day (15 March), but Angulo could raise only one-third of a month's pay. Joseph was ashamed to offer it; he made a donation to charity, and let his name day pass uncelebrated. Guerrilla depredations alarmed even Napoleon, who created a new Army of the North, under Bessières, to police the most dangerous areas and a *gendarmarie* of old soldiers to assist the Imperial Guard on the main highways. The generals continued to use the noose and firing squad—"perpetuating the war by exasperating the people."

Why did Joseph stay . . . *really*? Even so close a friend as Miot wondered. Was "the title of king . . . still a powerful seduction from which Joseph had not escaped"? Perhaps. But the King saw himself always as defending his people, though sometimes he weakened. La Forest kept pressing him to "submit" to Napoleon, to give his agreement to any settlement Napoleon wanted to make—including annexation of northern Spain to France. In March, catching Joseph sick and depressed, the ambassador got his signature on a "blank check" for Spain. Now that he had shown the "right spirit," La Forest assured him, Napoleon would remedy his situation. Joseph, however, hated himself for being so weak. Publicly, he never admitted he had signed the paper, and talked with La Forest as if he had not. Napoleon, he decided, must hear the *truth* about Spain; *he would tell it to him personally.*

"Sire, my shattered health . . . forces me to leave this country . . ." he wrote on 24 March; "My presence here is completely useless. In Paris I will conform to the wishes of Your Majesty." He made no move to depart, however; he was waiting for permission, as subsequent letters made clear. "I hope . . . my journey will not be without use to Your Majesty." And to Julie: "I hope . . . the Emperor will not disapprove of my trip." Napoleon was silent on the subject, but inadvertently gave Joseph an excuse to go to Paris, and the King did not hesitate to use it.

GODFATHER OF THE KING OF ROME

On 20 March 1811, a 101-gun salute announced the birth of the King of Rome to Paris. Madame Blanchard rose in her balloon from the Place du Carrousel to give the news to the world (only to come down with a resounding bump sixty miles away), while the whole city got drunk on the Emperor's wine. On a balcony of the Tuileries, Napoleon held his son aloft to the roar of huge crowds below. Exultant, he sent off announcements to those relatives not present.

To Joseph, momentarily only the well-beloved brother, he sent two letters. The first was formal: "Monsieur my brother, I announce to Your Majesty . . ." But the second was touchingly familiar: "Yesterday, at seven in the evening, the Empress asked me to come to her room. I found her on the chaise longue beginning to feel the first birth pains." He ended by asking Joseph to be godfather of the King of Rome. General Defrance, Napoleon's equerry, muttering bitterly that he was too old for an aide's job, was packed off to Madrid with both letters. He was to present the personal one to the King, and allow La Forest to deliver the other. Joseph's "invitation" to Paris was on the way. *Did not godfathers always attend christenings?*

Apprised of Defrance's mission before he arrived, still grumbling, on 9 April, Joseph made receipt of the letters a great event. The general was informed that he and La Forest would be granted audience the next morning at eleven. They duly appeared at the palace, uniformed and bemedaled for the occasion. An aide led them between lines of blue-coated and helmeted halberdiers to the head of the great staircase. Beneath the gigantic crystal chandelier of the mezzanine they were received by the first master of ceremonies, the Marquis de San Adrian. Around them in subdued elegance, glowed the works of Rafael, Michelangelo, Veronese, Tintoretto, Van Dyke, Valasquez, Murillo, and a host of other master painters. Up they went to the vestibule of the throne room, passing at the head of the marble stairs David's "Napoleon Crossing the Alps" (placed there by Charles IV). The Count de Campo Alange, First Minister, greeted them; halberdiers swung open the massive doors of the throne room, where, surrounded by his court, Joseph sat, robed in the scarlet and ermine of the Most Catholic Kings, bedecked with the jeweled cordons of the Order of Spain, the Golden Fleece, and the Legion of Honor.

In accordance with the punctilious protocol of the ancient Spanish court, they were presented, in turn, to the King, who received their letters, and heard their compliments. Speaking as King of Spain and Prince of the imperial family, he spoke of the joy he felt at the birth of the King of Rome, and the additional joy of being honored by the Emperor with official notification. Formal to the end, he sent after the emissaries an invitation to dinner, where he was his usual "democratic" self, though somewhat preoccupied and melancholy.

On 23 April, Joseph left for Paris, taking Miot and half his ministers with him (and most of the cash from the treasury, barely enough to get him there). During the preceding week, beginning at dawn on the 15th with a 101-gun salute, Madrid had celebrated the birth of the imperial heir with nightly balls, banquets, concerts, and fireworks displays, afternoon parades and reviews, and religious ceremonies including a *Te Deum* in the royal presence. At celebrations for the public before the Prado, Joseph, leaving his escort behind, walked through the crowd, smiling, waving, shaking hands, admiring children. At court, the King distributed decorations in honor of the occasion and appeared at a grand ball afterward. "The birth of the King of Rome," reported La Forest, "has overcome the *invincible répugnance* he has had for some months for holding court or going out in public. He appears very happy. . . ." The ambassador of the Emperor, however, could not help keeping Joseph reminded, even during the festivities, of imperial power (and affluence). Joseph held a dinner for sixty; La Forest for a hundred. The King's functions were not so lavish as the *grande assemblée* for the ladies and grand ball at the Embassy. La Forest spent thousands on fireworks displays, gigantic cascades of color surrounding a succession of glowing tableaux, imperial arms and eagles, all accompanied by music, finishing with the "Marseillaise" as fiery letters spelled out "THE EAGLET FOLLOWS THE FLIGHT OF THE EAGLE." Joseph took it all in good spirit; his mind was on his journey to Paris, and he had the satisfaction of having kept La Forest ignorant of his exact plans until he was ready to leave.

FACE-TO-FACE WITH NAPOLEON

The King moved north slowly, traveling only by day, stopping often to make speeches. "Spain is my religion." I shall return. The Emperor will hear from my lips the true plight of our country. Joseph's followers believed that whatever happened in Paris he would come back. The people, however, thought they were seeing the last of him. They could not but feel sadness. Unable to believe that, La Forest observed that Madrid had reacted strangely; all was quiet; there were no "groups" in the squares, where Madrileños were generally found—talking, arguing, and sometimes fighting—forming public opinion.

Just north of Bayonne a courier met Joseph with orders from Berthier, in the Emperor's name, not to leave Spain. Too late. The King was too proud to turn back. He went on to Paris as fast as he could, arriving on 15 May.

Napoleon was at Rambouillet with Marie Louise when the news reached him. Joseph in Paris? What is he doing here? He has deserted his post! Louis, Lucien. Now Joseph! Not *Joseph*!

See him? No. That evening he relented, however, and sent word that his *brother* could come the next day. Napoleon and Joseph talked alone; neither ever revealed what the conversation was like. They met awkwardly, both embarrassed; the Emperor was heard shouting, slamming about. Joseph emerged looking somber, buried in thought, ordered up his carriage, and returned to Paris. He had not been invited to dinner.

Until the day of the christening, on 9 June, Joseph alternated between the Luxembourg and Mortefontaine. He played with his children, spent time with Julie (but they were quickly talked out; her domesticity unnerved him), told his troubles and reminisced endlessly of Corsica with his mother. Napoleon would not see him. What did he want? He had Berthier instruct Joseph to make notes for him. The King did. The military governors were ruining Spain; the threat of partition had alienated the *afrancesados*, etc., etc. He needed money, authority, and a firm statement of policy, including a pledge that Spain would remain intact. Without these he could not return. Napoleon went off with the Empress to tour Normandy. "The King can leave whenever he thinks it *à propos*, without waiting for my return."

Joseph waited, appearing only in French uniform or civilian clothes without Spanish insignia or cockade. Some Frenchmen of his suite were not so cautious. Napoleon ordered them back to Spain: "Fortunately I haven't seen them at court, I would have thrown them out." With Joseph nearby, however, Napoleon's sympathy for him was roused. Twice he called the King to Saint-Cloud, all but secretly, but they reached no agreement. Retire; stay in France, Miot advised. Joseph waited. He did not want to stay. His duty was to Spain; he longed to see the Marquise de Montehermoso. Napoleon would do *something*.

Napoleon had, in fact, been feeling him out. He never bargained with subordinates. He decided what they would accept, and made take-it-or-leave-it offers. One came to Joseph through Berthier: A subsidy of 500,000 francs per month; authority over justice and ecclesiastical affairs in the military governments; an imperial order to the French military to "recognize" the King. It was all vague. A subsidy for how long? How could partial power be exerted? What did "recognize" mean? Well, all could wait until after the baptism.

In the gold-embroidered white uniform of a French prince, Joseph stood next to Madame Mère (the godmother), and Julie beside Marie Louise before the altar of Notre Dame Cathedral. But Joseph had been displaced as godfather; the honor went to the Austrian Emperor, who was represented at the baptismal font by the Duke von Würzburg. The King was resigned; after all he told Julie, the Emperor Francis *was* the child's grandfather. Why, though, had Napoleon asked him to be godfather at all? No matter. As the Emperor held up his son he caught his breath and cheered, as awed and happy as any of the hundreds of spectators. What a time to live in! Surely God smiled on Napoleon! Was he right in opposing him? Was anyone?

On 12 June Joseph again saw Napoleon, and emerged to announce his immediate departure for Spain. What passed between them is unknown, but Joseph's later correspondence shows he thought he had been promised (if not at this time some other) 1,000,000 francs a month (instead of 500,000), and the early restoration to command of the Army of Spain. Almost surely, Napoleon pledged to make a public statement in his behalf, which he did, before the *corps législatif*, on 16 June: "I have accorded to the King of Spain all that is necessary and proper to unite the interests and spirit of all the different peoples of his provinces." He spoke mostly, however, of the "second punic war" (Britain was Carthage), which would end when he destroyed British armies on the Peninsula—"all she has of troops of the line." What powers he had given Joseph he did not say. He was committed only to what Berthier had outlined for the King, which had not been clarified in writing.

THE CONQUERING HERO

It took Joseph a month to cover the distance between Bayonne and Madrid. Everywhere he conferred with local officials and mouthed his favorite ideas, promising a quick end to the war, economic revival, and government for the people. His step was light, his smile ready, his energy Napoleonic, and his confidence incredible. Wake up! he threatened the high clergy at Burgos, or I will replace you with poor and honest priests! Amalia joined him en route, and all seemed good and right. He would yet lead Spain into a new era!

On 15 July he reentered Madrid through arches of triumph. The *Te Deum* was sung, and the court and diplomatic corps turned out *en gala* to receive him (including the Russian ambassador, whom the King could see no reason to send away, even a year later). Joseph made his favorite speech: "I love France as I do my family; Spain as I do my religion. . . ." Entertainments began which continued for five days—balls, dinners, command performances at the theaters, opera, and bullring. The King took to touring the city after dinner—in an open carriage with small escort—and though no great crowds gathered to cheer him, the people were not unfriendly. "The aspect of Madrid," La Forest informed Paris, "has incontestably changed for the better, and at no time in three years has been more favorable to the King."

Progress, reform, and optimism became the order of the day. A Cortes must soon be called, Joseph told his flabbergasted council on 2 August; we must be prepared on the instant to bring it together. The Cortes of the Bayonne constitution will not do; members of the old aristocratic bodies and the Cadiz Cortes must be invited, and perhaps others as well. The nation must be truly represented—by "distinguished men of all opinions, even Castaños himself, if he will consent." He appointed a committee and gave it two weeks to produce a plan.

Apparently, Napoleon had convinced Joseph that Britain would soon make peace. He had proposed to restore Portugal to the Braganzas if London would recognize Joseph, and agree to a mutual withdrawal of forces after Spain accepted Joseph. Under these conditions, no doubt, the rebels would jump at participating in a new national Cortes. Even if the British declined to treat, Joseph's Cortes might attract many rebels if the French won important victories in the next few months. This was made more probable by the unpopularity of the Cadiz Cortes, which had steadily gone more radical. Some leaders were accused of wanting to renounce Ferdinand and establish a republic; in Cadiz itself

lamentaciónes wailed of their "godlessness." Faced with a debt
of four billion reals and continual deficits, the Cortes had voted
an income tax. Socialism! howled the conservatives. Even some
of the liberals thought private property was in jeopardy.

All hope soon vanished for Joseph's Cortes, however, along
with his other newfound hopes. He had enough enthusiasm for
mammoth fetes on the day of Saint Napoleon (15 August), when
he awarded sixty crosses of the Order of Spain, and gave the
Golden Fleece to Urquijo and O'Farrill, whom he dubbed
Grandees of Spain. Thereafter his optimism faded rapidly, as
did that of his supporters. "There is a rebirth of the old doubts,"
noted La Forest. There was good reason.

RETURN TO REALITY

Joseph soon realized that outside the Center he still had no
power over the military. Berthier advised the governors to give
him "due respect," nothing more. Napoleon instructed Decaen,
who replaced Macdonald in Catalonia, to carry on *no* correspondence with the King, and not to answer letters from his
ministers. As for command, Marshal Jourdan appeared, as Napoleon had promised, to be the King's chief-of-staff—for the
tiny Army of the Center only. "Without power . . . without
command," Joseph wrote Berthier testily, "I no longer want to
play this strange role." He was also without funds.

Money had begun arriving from France in June—but only
500,000 francs (1,850,000 reals) a month. Joseph's expenses were
12,000,000 reals a month, his income from Spanish sources around
4,000,000. Even with his loan, his deficit was about 6,000,000
reals a month. He was almost as poor as ever! Soon after his
return he offered National Properties for sale, hoping to net
some 60,000,000 reals. Most of them were outside the Center,
however, and substantially no buyers appeared. Guerrillas, meanwhile, disrupted tax collection, not so much by seizing revenues
as by terrorizing the peasants, who were afraid to pay anything
unless forced by columns of troops (not the customary collector
and few police), lest they be accused of collaboration. French
commanders, therefore, supervised collections, and seldom left

themselves short. In the Center, they were Joseph's subordinates, but his ambiguous position, and his government's inability to supply them, had encouraged them to fend for themselves. They deferred to the King when he was present, but he could not be everywhere. Since they intimidated the regular civilian collectors, Joseph sent out councillors, and sometimes ministers, to claim his share of revenues. The scheme failed, however, largely because the higher officials felt insulted by the assignment, and scurried back to Madrid at the first excuse. Income fell below the 1810 level. By mid-August, the King's last hope was that taxes-in-kind from the fall harvest would give him reserve food supplies for the winter.

There was to be neither money nor food, however. "The Army of Portugal is devouring all my resources," wrote Joseph plaintively on 31 August; "it has moved to the very gates of Madrid." Masséna, his troops decimated by illness, weak and starving, had been chased from Portugal in the spring; he had returned, only to be beaten back again. Napoleon replaced him with the dashing Marshal Marmont, twenty-six years his junior. Marmont, however, could not hold a square foot of Portugal either, and went early into winter quarters, with his advance post at Ciudad Rodrigo, on the frontier. Unable to feed all his men outside the Center, he occupied, with Joseph's resigned consent, Avila and La Mancha, and later part of Segovia and Toledo as well.

The King's poverty made everything else seem minor. During the fall he demanded, in no less than twenty-five letters, that Napoleon send him the extra five hundred thousand francs a month he had promised. It became a fixation. He even convinced himself that with that small sum he could balance his budget. As the year drew to a close, he was still harping on the subject, though immediately, the Center needed grain worse than gold.

Famine struck Madrid. The *guerrilleros*, keen to the situation, concentrated on making it worse, hitting grain convoys and driving off herds en route to the city. Bread prices rose to four times the 1810 level. Joseph ordered price controls and established breadlines, but nothing seemed to help. His civil servants, even councillors and ministers, were in distress. When old Admiral Mazarredo, Minister of Marine, Grandee, holder of the Golden

Fleece, appeared to beg, with great dignity, for an army ration to keep his family from starving, Joseph was reduced to tears. "I am surrounded by the most horrible misery," he wrote Napoleon, ". . . my principal officials cannot even afford fires in their homes."

"Without money, without territory, without troops [of my own], without authority, how can there be confidence in a man?" Joseph wrote Berthier, who sent an aide to Madrid to investigate. Why did he have to repeat himself? Joseph raged. What was La Forest there for? Had he not verified the facts for Napoleon? If not he was a liar! He asked Julie to go to Napoleon: "A *decisive explanation* must be gotten from the Emperor. If I am to remain the promises made me must be kept."

No explanation came. Gamely, Joseph sent wishes for the Emperor's health in the new year (1812), and for "the welfare of that vast system of which he is creator and chief." He tried to forget his troubles by furiously celebrating Christmas and New Year's, and stole many hours with a new love, Nancy Derrieux, wife of an army *commissaire*. Blonde, full-bodied, bursting with life, she was what he needed; she was happy; she did not look at him questioningly (scornfully?) as did the Marquise.

But with Madrid hungry, with the police removing frozen bodies from the streets at each dawn, he could not escape for long. Desperately, through every possible channel, he begged Napoleon to *do something*, anything, to save him.

DESCENT INTO LIMBO

As 1812 began, Suchet announced the capture of Valencia, and a new possibility of fiscal salvation appeared. Valencia was not a military government, and the province was rich. The Valencians had practiced no scorched-earth policy such as the Portuguese had used against Masséna; the population was little displaced; winter crops had been planted and a good season seemed in the offing. Joseph anticipated excellent revenues, and as soon as he heard of the fall of the capital, sent the younger Azanza hurrying to Valencia as royal commissioner.

Almost immediately, however, he learned that Suchet had been appointed governor of Valencia. To Napoleon this was just and practical. While other commanders floundered, Suchet had won victories—in Aragon, on the borders of Catalonia, and in Valencia. (He was given a marshal's baton in 1811; made Duke of Albufera in 1812.) His careful siege of the city of Valencia had cost a minimum of French lives, and he had captured Don Joaquín Blake, twenty-three other generals, 18,000 men, almost four hundred cannon, 42,000 muskets, and ninety tons of gunpowder. Moreover, as military governor of Aragon (which he was still), he had established order, squelched guerrilla activity, organized a civil administration, and managed (miracle of miracles) not only to pay his troops but send money to France. He would make Valencia pay too! Napoleon's finances were not in the best possible order. France had been in depression during 1811, and the preparations for the Russian campaign were immensely costly. It was very important that Suchet at least support his army.

The marshal was directed to send Joseph *some* money regularly. In addition civil officials were to act in the King's name. But Suchet was governor; he owed the King "respect," not obedience. Joseph was doubly striken because Suchet was a friend, whom he felt would have cooperated with him perfectly. Big, quiet, gentlemanly, and humane, he was the one military governor with whom the King had no quarrel. "With all my heart I congratulate you, and I thank you," he wrote after the victory at Valencia. He did not resent Suchet's becoming governor—but he did resent seeing *more governments* established. He halted preparations to visit Suchet, and sarcastically asked Berthier for permission to enter "French" territory. "The business of Valencia," he told Julie, "has destroyed all confidence [in me]. . . . I command nothing." He demanded a "solution" of Napoleon, "whatever it is, it will be all right with me."

No solution was offered; more bombs fell. On 24 January, an imperial decree joined part of Catalonia (the valley of the Aran) "for administration" to the French department of Haute Garonne, and divided the rest of the province into four departments under French intendants. La Forest called to assure the King blandly that the Emperor desired him to understand that no territory had been annexed to France. Indeed, *Monsieur l'Ambassadeur?* How do I explain that to the Spanish?

In Madrid, men, women, and children still died of hunger and cold, some of them in the streets. The hospitals were full to overflowing, but short of medicine, food, blankets—everything. Joseph could not bear to visit them anymore. In the countryside, the *guerrilleros* got bolder as Marmot's troops marched north to meet a drive by Wellington.* Grain convoys were looted and burned within sight of Madrid. "El Medico's" *partidas* even stormed into the city through the Atocha gate, firing wildly at all French in sight, and killing a few before they galloped away. "*El Empecinado,*" the Don Juan of the chiefs, secure in Guadalajara, menaced every part of the Center.

A Need of Dissipation

In letter after letter, Joseph begged Napoleon to let him retire. He looked out, stunned, at the world around him, hardly able to care anymore what happened. Insanity! My brother's work! Can he still be the brother I have loved? God help Spain! God help *Europe!* He was ill for weeks, and after he recovered, lapsed, as Urquijo put it "into a profound sadness, impossible to shake off." Sometimes he tried to hunt, but he had never liked the sport, and now the killing sickened him the more. For days he confined himself in the palace, or at Casa del Campo. "Veritably," noted La Forest with clinical malice, "he seems to have a need for dissipation."

Crushed in body, mind, and spirit, he waited numbly for Napoleon's next move. A death blow? A reprieve? No. In March 1812, he was handed the Imperial Eagles to defend.

---

* See below pp. 198–200.

⚜

CHAPTER XII

King Once More

COMMAND

"INFORM the King of Spain, by extraordinary courier to depart tonight, that I give him command of all my armies in Spain . . ." Napoleon ordered Berthier on 16 March 1812. The marshals were to be informed that Joseph was commander, Jourdan his chief-of-staff, and that ". . . they will conform to all the orders of the King so that all the armies will march in the same direction."

In the midst of final preparations to depart for the Russian campaign, the Emperor had made what he considered the safest possible disposition of military authority in Spain. As discussed earlier, he did not want Joseph to abdicate (for the time being). He felt he could not command the peninsular armies from eastern Europe (dispatches from Paris reached Madrid in two weeks; from, say, Vilna, the time would be a month or more). If a marshal were given overall command, Joseph, commanding the Army of the Center, would be his subordinate. If the King's army were given to someone else, the marshal still would be *de facto* ruler of Spain. Even the long-suffering Joseph would doubtless flee, rocking the already half-swamped political boat. Moreover, Soult, though trustworthy as a soldier, had demonstrated political ambitions, and he would resent serving under Marmont. Neither Soult nor Marmont would cotton to obeying Suchet, the junior marshal of the army. Joseph *had* to be given command, and surely, Napoleon reasoned, he could at least "hold the line" in Spain until Russia was taught a lesson.

WHAT DOES IT MEAN?

Berthier's officer-courier straggled into Madrid with the ordinary mail escort on 1 April. (A rider ahead of him had been
captured by guerrillas; he took no chances.) Joseph, momentarily
elated by Napoleon's order, read it over and over, became depressed, then angry. What does it mean? I am commander, but
am I King also? Are the military governors to obey only military
orders, or *all* my commands?

La Forest was summoned. What does it mean? The ambassador
did not know, but, he asked, could not total authority be assumed? After all, if Your Majesty can give orders to the marshals,
maneuver the armies. . . . Joseph cut him short. All right. Forget
the political questions. Why does he give me command *now*? The
Anglais are on the move. Marmont is engaged in the north.
Badajoz (on the Portuguese frontier in the south) is falling at
this moment; Soult could have saved the fortress. Earlier I could
have made plans; now I can only support those of Marmont and
Soult. And what forces can I safely draw from Valencia? Earlier
I could have marched with Suchet; I would know!

La Forest had no answers. He sent off inquiries daily, and
finally, after a three-hour session with Joseph on 10 April, a
thirty-page report on the King's thinking. Earlier, the ambassador
had helped make Joseph's life miserable; now the Emperor,
apparently, had reversed his role. Good subordinate that he was,
he tried to encourage His Catholic Majesty. Take control, he
told him. Don't be afraid to assert yourself. To the foreign
minister he suggested that Joseph would be all right if the
Emperor would just show him some affection.

Joseph, meanwhile, fired off his own missives. Was Spain to
remain "dismembered" while he took responsibility for the war?
If he were King also, he would take command. In that case, how
did the Emperor want the war fought? How should he approach
the marshals? How could he do anything without more funds?
Would the imperial treasury supply him? Would the military
governors? Joseph, a tortured prisoner for two years, had been
dragged into the light and dubbed grand commander. It was too

much. Was it some cruel trick? If he stood would he be struck down again, and mocked?

COMMANDER AND KING

Napoleon had anticipated Joseph's questions (though he would never understand how Joseph felt). Before the King's querulous letters reached Paris, a coded order reached Madrid conferring on him "the political and military direction of all the affairs of Spain." Another dispatch informed him that his subsidy was increased to 1,000,000 francs (3,750,000 reals) per month—retroactive to 1 January 1812; in addition he was to have one-third of the revenues of Valencia, another 2,000,000 francs (7,500,000 reals). "Act with vigor and make yourself obeyed," Napoleon scrawled on the bottom of a letter to Joseph from Maret, the foreign minister, affirming his political power. Berthier had already given him the Emperor's terse message, word for word.

Act with vigor! For Napoleon, imposing his will on others was as easy as breathing. Still hesitant to act, Joseph lectured La Forest on the errors of the military government system. But for it Spain would now be at peace! Did he, even now, *really* have total authority? If so why could he not dispose of *all* the revenues of Valencia, instead of one-third. The marshals had developed bad habits; it would be a miracle if they obeyed him. By the end of April, however, Joseph had begun to recover from the shock of restoration.

While Jourdan pressed the marshals for reports on which to base decisions, the King developed plans for subordinating the military governments to his ministry and installing his prefectural system throughout Spain. The *Gaceta de Madrid* again held forth on his intention to enforce the Constitution of Bayonne, while voicing the possibility (as in 1811) that he would call a *Cortes* representing rebels and *afrancesados* alike. Unhappily, it was all waste motion. The war would soon demand his full attention.

La Forest, as if returning to his role of persecutor, appeared with an unsigned memorandum from Napoleon, proposing that Joseph accept the Cadiz constitution (published in March 1812)

if the rebel Cortes would recognize him. What? That piece of
"*demagogie*"! Very well, he would contact Cadiz—but Napoleon
must give a positive guarantee not to dismember Spain if the
negotiations succeeded. You have nothing in writing! "You can
put nothing in writing on the subject, but you are authorized to
talk about it all the time . . . His Imperial Majesty is protected,
and he can do whatever the situation demands." I will not deceive the Spanish! History will say I would do anything just to
keep my crown! It was a small matter, seemingly, but it shook
Joseph's confidence in Napoleon's ultimate intentions. Was his
power temporary? Was Spain still doomed to partition? "Eccen-
tric courses of his imagination," ruled La Forest, but he admitted
it was unfortunate that the matter had absorbed the King's
energies when more pressing problems were at hand.

Prospect of Command

The King might well have devoted full time to the war from
April on. In June military matters occupied an ever-greater part
of his day, and he became painfully aware that he was almost
as ill informed as in April. The marshals had stubbornly resisted
giving him full and regular reports, and neglected their correspondence with Madrid. Soult, in June, deigned to answer three
letters sent him, at intervals, in May after Jourdan sent an aide
to him with duplicates. Napoleon, surely, would have descended
on Soult (and the others), breathing fire. But Joseph was not
Napoleon.

The King did not want to command; he never had. His insistence on having command stemmed from a conviction that it
was *proper* for him to have it. He wanted to curtail the marshal's
civil functions; they could do the fighting. As long as the war
went well, he asked only that they give him formal deference
and keep him informed. What he *really* wanted was for Napoleon
to come to Spain, finish the war, and hand him the kingdom to
govern. In that his attitude had been consistent since 1808. In
1812, as late as the end of May, he insisted that Napoleon would
settle affairs in "northern Europe" with "*démonstrations
d'apparat*," and then *come to Spain*. Napoleon had proclaimed

that, if the Russians were sane, they would come to terms before he flung his "European" army upon them. (It was European—two-thirds non-French, and gigantic, for the time—over 700,000 men.) The Emperor, however, was only indulging in the confident trumpetings with which he launched every campaign. His real hope was for a short war.

Joseph wanted to believe that there would be no war with Russia, and he did. When, in June, it became evident he was wrong, he pinned his hopes on an early peace with Russia, which would force Britain, left alone, to conclude a "general peace," which, in turn, would force the Spanish rebels to come to terms.

Meanwhile, Marmont's dispatches indicated that Wellington was probably initiating a major offensive in the north. Joseph might have to reenforce Marmont with his Army of the Center. The prospect of taking to the field again was not merely unpleasant; it terrified him. It was not death he feared, but failure. Rationally, he believed he had commanded well in 1809 and 1810; emotionally, he had been crushed by Napoleon's excoriations. He doubted himself. And the marshals! Napoleon had believed marshals' reports, not his. All of them knew it. In his nightmares they laughed at his orders while Napoleon nodded approval.

Joseph was no weakling, however. His letters to the generals became blunt, acid, demanding: "In a word, are you under my command or not?" Report! He spent hours in conference with Jourdan and his staff. But he would not abandon his other labors—planning for the Cortes, establishing undercover contacts with Cadiz, conferring with provincial delegations—fiscal, administrative, judicial reorganization—the eternal guerrilla problem—plans to store grain to prevent another winter of starvation.

In mid-June he collapsed under the strain, and was forced to keep to his apartments at Casa del Campo for a week. Still he worked, summoning his ministers to him, reading dispatches, dictating letters, orders, memoranda. In the quiet, however, scanning Marmont's ever more alarming reports and Jourdan's assessments, he finally faced facts. He must be a commander first, or he might never be truly King. He emerged, on 19 June, a new man, ready to meet whatever challenge appeared. "He showed

... *sang froid,* spirit, and courage," recorded La Forest. Joseph would need it all.

THE WAR

During the winter of 1811–12 Napoleon had withdrawn 90,000 troops from Spain, and recalled some commanders, generally those who would serve him well, but might give Joseph trouble —Victor, Ney, Junot, and Dorsenne, among others. But the King still had over 260,000 men and veteran generals to lead them.* Moreover, surprisingly, his armies included more Frenchmen than Napoleon's Grande Armée, which had only 200,000.† Of Joseph's six armies, only those of the Center and Portugal (together 80,000 men) were fully maneuverable, but all but that of Catalonia could furnish him half their troops without evacuating any territory, and could, in an emergency, march to his aid. Since the major threat to the French was an army of some 50,000 under Wellington, Joseph seemed safe enough.‡ The British commander, however, did not have to worry with occupying territory, could maneuver freely in Portugal and strike into Spain where he chose, with help, at some points, from other small Anglo-Portuguese and Spanish armies. Further, he had seized the initiative long before Joseph had been given command of the French.

Wellington's campaign had begun in January 1812, when he took Ciudad Rodrigo after a short siege. Marmont, who had been

---

* ARMY OF SPAIN AS OF JUNE 1812:

Army of the Center	Joseph	18,000
Army of the South	Soult	56,000
Army of Portugal	Marmont	62,000
Army of Aragon (mostly in Valencia)	Suchet	40,000
Army of the North	Caffarelli	43,000
Army of Catalonia	Decaen	36,000
Bayonne Reserve		8,000
	TOTAL	263,000

† Of the 611,000 men who actually crossed the Russian frontier 200,000 were French, 100,000 from Dutch, German, Italian, and Piedmontese departments of France. The remainder comprised 30,000 Austrians, 20,000 Prussians, 130,000 other Germans, 90,000 Poles and Lithuanians, 32,000 Italians and Illyrians, and 9,000 Swiss.

‡ Roughly 30,000 British, 18,000 Portuguese, and 3,000 Spanish.

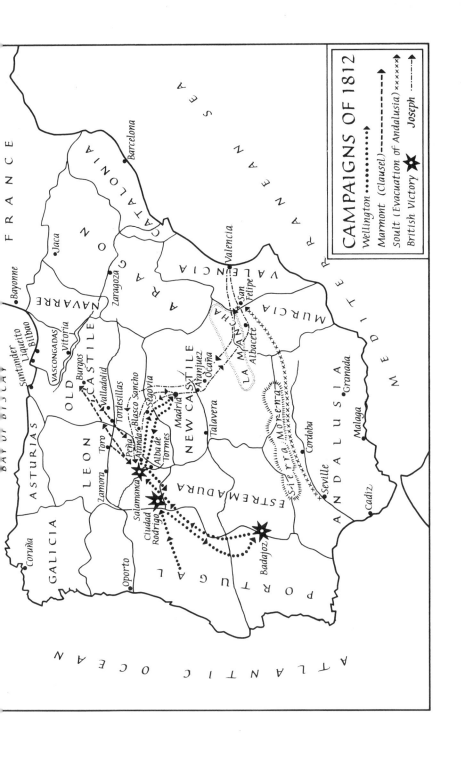

CAMPAIGNS OF 1812

Wellington ••••••••••
Marmont (Clausel) – – – – –
Soult (Evacuation of Andalusia) ×××××
Joseph – · – · – · –
British Victory ★

FRANCE

BAY OF BISCAY

Bayonne
Santander
Liqueito
Bilbao
Vitoria
(VASCONGADAS)
NAVARRE
Jaca
Zaragoza
OLD CASTILE
Burgos
Valladolid
Tordesillas
Toro
Zamora
Peña Tormes
Tirada
Blasco Sancho
Alba de
Tormes
Salamanca
Ciudad Rodrigo
LEON
ASTURIAS
GALICIA
Coruña
Oporto
PORTUGAL
Badajoz
ESTREMADURA
Sierra Morena
NEW CASTILE
Madrid
Segovia
Talavera
Aranjuez
Ocaña
LA MANCHA
Albacette
San Felipe
Valencia
VALENCIA
MURCIA
ANDALUSIA
Cordoba
Seville
Cadiz
Malaga
Granada
ARAGON
CATALONIA
Barcelona
PYRENEES
MEDITERRANEAN SEA
ATLANTIC OCEAN

gathering up units dispersed for provisioning, had just begun the march for Ciudad Rodrigo when he got news of the British victory. Assuming he had underestimated the size of the enemy force, he retreated to Valladolid, where he called on Caffarelli (Army of the North) for reenforcements. Wellington, meanwhile, shifted the bulk of his army south and besieged Badajoz, which fell in early April. (Soult, with his Army of the South, might have saved the fortress, but did not try. He did not want to divest his "kingdom" of troops.) Wellington, in possession of both Ciudad Rodrigo and Badajoz, was ready to drive deep into Spain.

He moved part of his army north again, reenforced it at Ciudad Rodrigo, and in June marched on Salamanca with 50,000 British, Portuguese, and Spanish troops. Marmont, who had again advanced, withdrew north, called on Caffarelli for help, and alerted Jourdan, at Madrid. Wellington, meanwhile, reduced and garrisoned the forts guarding Salamanca. At the end of June, with his army deployed on heights near the city, he awaited Marmont's next move.

POPHAM

Caffarelli could give Marmont little aid, though his Army of the North fought mostly guerrillas. The *partidas* had burgeoned, and to their support had come a past-master of unorthodox warfare, Captain Sir Home Riggs Popham, Royal Navy. In 1801, riding camelback across the desert, he had induced Arab chiefs to let a British army pass from the Red Sea into Egypt, where it mopped up the army Napoleon had abandoned there. In 1804–05, when Napoleon had threatened to invade England, Popham had launched submarines, unmanned and packed with explosives, into the concentrations of ships, boats, and barges in the Channel ports. He had figured in the destruction of the Danish fleet, and the invasion of Walcheren. Wherever something bizarre was afoot, this blustering, buccaneering survival of the Elizabethan age was sure to be. He even put style into routine operations. Sent to transport Russian troops, he made a sailor of the Czar, got a medal, and came back with more men than bargained for.

In the spring of 1812 he appeared off the north coast of Spain with a fleet carrying one thousand British marines and made contact with the *guerrilleros*. In June he began attacking French coastal forts and batteries, which were generally lightly manned, and depended on "flying squadrons" of cavalry for protection. Informed by the guerrillas, Popham hit where the cavalry was not. He would bombard a fort, send his marines against it from the beach, and bring down guerrillas on it from the mountains. The French cavalry, pulled toward the fighting at a mad gallop, usually got there only to view the rubble, or see Popham sail blithely away.

Popham was hamstrung by no rules. In mid-June, he and "El Pastor" assailed the fort at Lequeitio, but their men could not breach the walls. He dismounted a huge gun on his flagship, sent it ashore, where thirty-six pairs of oxen and four hundred guerrillas dragged it onto a hilltop overlooking the fort. After a few rounds from the giant muzzle crashed into the fort, the French gave up. The more irregulars Popham could command, the bolder he got. In August, with the aid of Longa, he actually held both Santander and Bilbao for a short time. When he seemed checkmated, he sailed, as always, and the guerrillas melted into the hills.

Maddening as all this was, Caffarelli's great fear was that Popham would one day land an army, instead of a few marines, and block the routes to France. He could send Marmont few troops. Major help against Wellington would have to come from King Joseph.

Marmont Buys Time

Marmont had planned to meet Wellington in late June, but his plan was based on two expectations: (1) that the Salamanca forts would hold until 1 July, and (2) that Caffarelli would send him some infantry and a heavy contingent of cavalry and artillery. When the forts fell and Caffarelli sent little but regrets, Marmont took up positions behind the Tormes, and then by stages retreated behind the Duero, concentrating at Toro, Tordesillas, and the bridges near Valladolid.

Wellington crossed the Tormes and cautiously moved toward the Duero. For three weeks British and French contingents fenced in the rugged area between the two rivers, but the bulk of both armies was idle. Napier supplies the atmosphere:

The weather was fine, the country rich, the troops received their rations regularly, the wine was so plentiful it was hard to keep the soldiers sober; the caves of Rueda, natural or cut in rock below the surface of the earth, were so immense and held so much wine, that the drunkards of two armies failed to make any sensible diminution in the quantity, and many men perished in the labyrinth. The soldiers of each army . . . held amicable intercourse, conversing of battles yet to be fought. . . .

The unofficial truce was short-lived, however. By 15 July Marmont had drawn in all available troops, mostly from garrisons and depots of the area; his army mustered 48,000. Since no definite word had arrived from Joseph, Marmont assumed he was on his own. His army was slightly smaller than Wellington's, but more homogeneous; the odds seemed good enough. He decided to risk an engagement, though he hoped to force the enemy to retreat without one. He was familiar with Wellington's deliberate style, and his reluctance to advance unless his rear was thoroughly protected. He hoped that if he drove south of Salamanca, so as to threaten the allied supply line to Ciudad Rodrigo, Wellington would fall back toward Portugal. On 15–16 July, Marmont flung his army across the Duero, and a war of maneuver began.

To Take Arms?

At Madrid, from mid-June onward, Jourdan and most of the French staff pressed Joseph to join Marmont with the Army of the Center. O'Farrill, Miot, Merlin, commander of the Royal Guard, and others gave reasoned advice to the contrary. If the King left with the army, they argued, there would be uprisings in Madrid, and the guerrillas would close in. An Allied army might march on Madrid via Talavera, as in 1809; after all the British had Badajoz, a safe rallying point. Soult gave weight to their case by reporting that an Anglo-Portuguese army, under

Hill, "menaced" Andalusia (and Madrid) from the west (Hill had only 15,000 men).

A crowd of frightened courtiers and their ladies campaigned to keep Joseph in Madrid. He had lost the capital once, they kept him reminded. What if he lost it again? What a setback! What a blow to Your Majesty's prestige! Your Majesty's followers will be "compromised"—many more than in 1808. Think of the reaction in Vienna and Berlin! And with Your Majesty's august brother away in Russia! Joseph knew they were worried only about themselves, their families, their property. But when they talked of his 1808 retreat, they hit a raw nerve. He remembered too the cold reception he had gotten after Talavera—all because they had been forced to spend a few days at San Ildefonso. The pampered women, the soft-handed men, the self-centered and irrational, had set the tone of the court. Children—all of them! But they had made him feel guilty. Somehow they did now. Their pleas hit harder than the calm arguments of O'Farrill, Miot, and Merlin.

Dispatches from Marmont (arriving in five to ten days, on the average) indicated no immediate emergency. Joseph decided to compromise. On 4 July he ordered the Army of the Center to concentrate on Madrid, but assured everyone he would not march unless absolutely necessary. Simultaneously, he asked Soult and Suchet to send him reenforcements. Soult flatly refused, citing the menace of Hill's army in the southwest. Suchet, without much grace, gave up one division, which was near Madrid in pursuit of guerrillas. The King, meanwhile, was beset by advisers at every turn, most of them urging him not to go; even his servants gave him their opinions. He listened patiently, but said little. He could not make up his mind.

While Joseph wavered, the news got worse. Wellington had the Salamanca forts; Marmont was withdrawing north. On 14 July Jourdan insisted on a decision, and got one: The King would march—"soon." A wail of protest rose from the court. Joseph and Jourdan reported themselves ill, and fled to Casa del Campo where they could deliberate in peace. Before they returned, on 18 July, orders had gone out to the army. The King marched on 21 July with 14,000 men (4000 remained to guard Madrid).

"Now that my role is decided, I feel marvellous," said Joseph. He was proud of himself; he had defied the court, and he was sure he was right. The court, however, had delayed his departure, and the whole course of the war would be different because of it.

SALAMANCA

Between 16 and 20 July, while Joseph prepared to move, Marmont, driving his army through brilliant (and exhausting) marches and countermarches, outflanked every position Wellington took. On 21 July the British commander found his back to the Tormes, recrossed the river, and resumed the position he had held three weeks earlier—on hills south of Salamanca, in the vicinity of the village of Arapiles. Marmont, now overconfident, followed.

On the morning of 22 July the French moved rapidly around Wellington's southern flank, seized one of the two hills called "Arapiles," overlooking the allied position, and sent cavalry toward the Ciudad Rodrigo road. The maneuver, by midmorning, had stretched the French army over a distance of ten miles. (See map, p. 205.) Some of Marmont's troops were still crossing the river at Alba de Tormes and other points; there was a large concentration in the forests above the crossings, and the advance elements were strung out across the south "Arapile" and off in the direction the cavalry had taken.

Marmont expected Wellington to retreat, as he had done before when outflanked. But the extended French army was too great a temptation for even a confirmed defender like Wellington. He wheeled his army, faced it south, and attacked.

The French "Arapile" was stormed. Marmont found his center under heavy pressure, his right floundering in the forests, and his left, the cavalry on the point, cut off from the main body. The French fought furiously, but as divisions or lesser units, not as a whole. Marmont, riding between his right and center in a desperate effort to organize his army, was shot from his horse so severely wounded that his arm had to be amputated. As night fell the French army was in rout, fleeing toward Alba de Tormes and across the river. Marmont, a litter case, weak and frequently

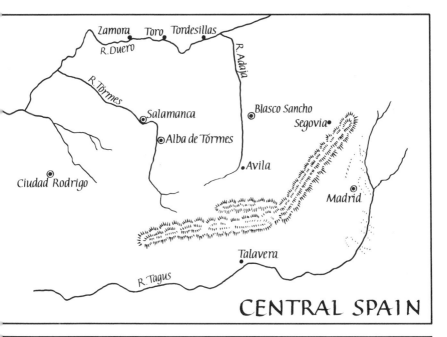

CENTRAL SPAIN

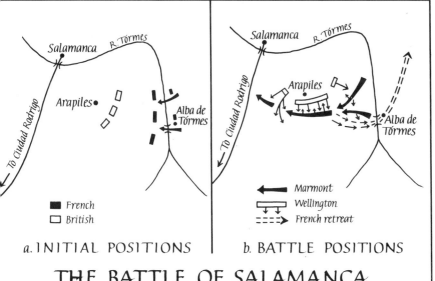

a. INITIAL POSITIONS

French
British

b. BATTLE POSITIONS

Marmont
Wellington
French retreat

THE BATTLE OF SALAMANCA,
JULY 22, 1812

(From Owen Connelly, _Napoleon's Satellite Kingdoms_, N.Y. : Free Press, 1965)

lapsing into unconsciousness, gave the command to Clausel, who directed the army toward Valladolid. Clausel hoped to make a stand behind the Duero, but under unrelenting pursuit by British cavalry and guerrillas, continued his retreat toward the Ebro.

ENTER AND EXIT JOSEPH

Totally ignorant of Marmont's defeat, Joseph appeared at Blasco-Sancho, fifty miles east of Salamanca, on 24 July—two days after the battle. His guardian angel was working overtime. Wellington had known his plans before he left Madrid, but did not know where he was. The guerrillas, who normally kept the Allied commander informed, had hovered near Salamanca to watch the clash of titans, and then, mesmerized by the stream of loot cast behind them by the retreating French, joined the pursuit. Joseph, tired but in good spirits, bivouacked his army for the night. He had laid plans to march the next morning—into the very lion's mouth—when a hussar galloped up and dumped a peasant to the ground. Sire, the man says the French are beaten! Joseph listened. The account was vague, but the man seemed honest. Stunned, only half convinced, Joseph gave the man some coins and let him go. He strengthened his outposts and waited.

The next morning, an officer brought the King letters from Marmont and Clausel. The army was disorganized still, but they hoped to hold at Valladolid, behind the Duero. Should he join them? No. Wellington might block his path. He took the road to Madrid, moving slowly, hoping for more and better news. On 27 July Marmont's aide-de-camp overtook him. If it pleased His Majesty, he could march toward Valladolid now; the enemy was breaking pursuit. No. Too dangerous. Monsieur le Maréchal may join me—at Segovia. He has the larger army; there will be less risk. At Segovia Joseph waited for four days; then on 31 July Clausel signaled that he had not been able to hold at Valladolid; he was retreating on Burgos. All hope of reaching Clausel gone, Joseph left at all speed for Madrid. Wellington, who had dropped off twelve thousand men to watch Clausel, was only a few days march behind him.

JOSEPH VERSUS SOULT

Joseph arrived in Madrid in 3 August, roundly damning Marmont. Why could he not wait! The battle could have been won! He wanted all the glory himself! Jourdan agreed; everyone agreed, for once—even La Forest. Marmont, at the same time, reported that he received no notice of Joseph's approach until 23 July (the day after the battle). That much was true. He did know, however, that Joseph meant to reenforce him, and desired that he not give battle until the Army of the Center arrived. The marshal had waited a month for reenforcements; why not a little longer? Marmont could answer that the King had temporized for a month, and that he gave him up. He could also say, with truth, that he had not planned a full-scale confrontation, but was maneuvering to force Wellington to retreat. Marmont *had* attacked first, however; the battle had begun after he seized the south Arapile. One could side either with Joseph or Marmont. Surprisingly, Napoleon took Joseph's side. "[Marmont] . . . sacrificed the glory of the Nation and the good of the service to his vanity."

Joseph ordered Soult to send 10,000 troops to Madrid immediately, and then to join him as soon as possible with the whole Army of the South (which meant abandoning Andalusia). All he got from Soult were arguments that the King should join him. Andalusia was peaceful, food was plentiful; the armies could join more safely *there* than at Madrid, and plans to stop Wellington could be laid at leisure.

Soult's main interest was holding his "kingdom," but his arguments, nevertheless, were sound. Wellington had reached Segovia on 8 August, and was closing on Madrid. From a purely military point of view, the capital was no place to consolidate forces. Joseph, however, had to consider the political effects—national and international—of losing Madrid. And what of his followers and their families? He insisted that Soult march; Soult refused. "Would Your Majesty save the capital and lose the kingdom?" Exhausting all other excuses, he said his army was spread for provisioning, and could not be assembled in time to save Madrid. Perhaps not, but Joseph had demanded only 10,000 troops be sent at once, not the whole 56,000. Perhaps 10,000 would not have saved Madrid. If Soult was right, he was still guilty of the most gross insubordination, punishable by death in any army in the world. Joseph informed Clarke, Napoleon's minister of war, of the facts, and laid his plans. He would retreat toward Andalusia, but if Soult did not reenforce him, he would march to Valencia. He trusted Suchet; Soult could be damned, and Andalusia with him.

RETREAT TO VALENCIA

Joseph evacuated Madrid on 10 August; Wellington entered two days later. At Aranjuez, Joseph waited, vainly, until 15 August for Soult's reenforcements, then marched for Valencia. "Monsieur le Maréchal," he wrote hotly to Soult; "The execution of the measures which . . . [I] specified would have saved Madrid, and perhaps Andalusia. . . . His Majesty the Emperor has conferred command on me. Whatever the superiority of your views, your duty is to . . . [obey]." Evacuate Andalusia! Bring your army to Valencia!

The King had sent his civilian supporters to Ocaña on 9 August. There were almost 15,000 of them—the families of French civilians and officers in Joseph's service, of Spanish members of the government, civil service, and military, the French and Spanish civilian functionaries themselves, and the diplomatic corps (including Baron Mohrenheim, the Russian *chargé d'affaires!*). They went in a column of over two thousand carriages, wagons, buggies, surreys, and carts, ". . . *voitures de tout gendre.*" Some rode horseback, or walked if they could do no better, carrying such possessions as they could on their backs.

On 15 August they set out across the burning plains of La Mancha, with hardly a tree to give shade, bitterly cold at night. Joseph, with the Army of the Center, rode a route parallel to the convoy, trying to give protection. Guerrillas hung on the flanks, seldom attacking, but preying on the nerves of the travelers. Large numbers of the Spanish troops, and even some of the Guard, discouraged and taunted by the *guerrilleros*, deserted. The civilians complained and heaped curses on the head of the King, when he was not in earshot, or directly on his officers and men. The French courtiers and ladies, especially, created problems. They fainted in the heat, complained of the cold at night, carped at the soldiers and their servants, went to great lengths to demonstrate their lack of familiarity with sweat, dirt, and discomfort. They were a colony apart, thinking only of themselves, acting as if the whole Spanish affair had been arranged for their aggrandisement and comfort, and was not producing as promised. *"Centaines de vampires français,"* La Forest called them. The ladies, bored, waved idiotically at the guerrillas who galloped near, especially the dashing chief, Bartholomé Muños. When Muños sent messages, in polished French, calling Joseph *Le Roi Errant*, they were transported. Droll! It became the "vampires' " favorite sobriquet.

The convoy reached the vicinity of Albacete on 22 August, and finding the fort in Spanish hands, took a long and tortuous detour around it, amid loud complaints, the breaking down of carriages, and sporadic attacks by guerrillas. This completed, however, the straggling mass found itself on the lovely plains of Valencia, and spirits began to improve. The King entered the city of Valencia on 31 August, and, since Suchet was firmly in charge, was well received.

WELLINGTON AT MADRID

Bands of guerrillas preceded Wellington's army into Madrid on 12 August 1812. Great crowds lined the route, stamping, clapping, waving, shouting. *Viva El Empecinado! Viva El Medico! Viva Fernando VII! Viva Los Ingles! Viva Weelinton!* One of Joseph's favorite hostesses, the Duchess de Frias, quickly arranged a ball for the liberators. Others followed suit. Wellington was lionized. Godlike! said the ladies.

Goya asked to paint Wellington's portrait. The Viscount of Talavera appeared, posed, grew restive; Goya snapped at him. Wellington let fly a stream of curses; the touchy artist seized an ancient pistol; the general drew his saber. But for Álava, a light-hearted Spanish liaison officer, who jumped between them, one great career or the other might have ended. The sittings were never finished; Goya painted from his sketches.

The Madrileños laughed about Goya. Ha! the old fox kill the lion? But they soon half wished he had. Wellington got fed up with his *guerrillero* friends, and their friends, who for a few days took over the city. Robbers! Scum! He put out patrols, threw disturbers into prison, shot a few. Ensconced in the royal palace, he quickly became a ruler—respected, feared, but not liked very much. *Patron*, Álava called him; it suited him. An Englishman, yes, said the Madrileños, but a Grandee.

"The Peer" did not shrink from collecting taxes (mostly in grain) in the name of the Cadiz government. The grumbling peasants did not believe he shared them with Cadiz (which he did, scrupulously). His rules (self-evidently proper to him) for classifying prizes-of-war mystified many. Joseph's private possessions were taken, but nothing else in the royal residences. The King's official correspondence was seized, but not personal letters. (Wellington personally forwarded some of Julie's letters to Joseph.) Materiel and weapons of war had to meet rigid specifications—hunting rifles did not qualify.

In Andalusia, Soult slowly drew his forces in to Seville. Joseph had left him uncovered in the north; Hill, plus Spanish armies, threatened from the southwest, and when, to concentrate all of his army, he lifted the siege of Cadiz, reenforced Anglo-Spanish forces pressed in on him from the south. He had little choice but to follow the King's orders. On 26 August he marched for Valencia.

Wellington watched the evacuation of Andalusia with mixed feelings. He was delighted and surprised with this spectacular result of his march on Madrid, which he had expected to hold only briefly, for political effect. On the other hand, Soult's march meant that Joseph would soon have over 100,000 men at Valencia. Wellington's Anglo-Portuguese forces were, as always, small compared to the French, and though the Spanish often reenforced him, he had been disappointed too often to count on it. His only chance was to defeat widely separated French armies in detail, taking advantage of his greater freedom of maneuver. Now Joseph might march on him in overwhelming strength. Wellington, moreover, in order to seize Madrid, had divided his army; he knew that Clausel would soon have the Army of the North in action again, and Clinton would be overmatched.

Clausel did reappear, in late August, sooner than expected, and quickly pushed Clinton out of Valladolid. When the news reached Wellington, he immediately evacuated Madrid and marched north. He had no desire to be caught between Joseph and Clausel. Within a few weeks, after testing Clausel's strength, he called on Hill (still in Andalusia) to join him, and asked the Spanish for reenforcements. If Joseph and Clausel combined, he wanted to be ready.

JOSEPH IN VALENCIA

Joseph found Suchet concerned over a small Anglo-Sicilian army, under Maitland, which had landed on the coast. The city of Valencia, however, was so peaceful he could ride about without guards. Suchet had money in his treasury, which he shared with the King. Food was plentiful, but 15,000 "useless mouths" (as Suchet put it), plus those of the King's troops and 7000 horses and mules, put a terrible strain on supply services. The "vampires," French and otherwise, howled indignantly over their quarters, necessarily cramped (the city's normal population was less than 50,000). Joseph relieved the situation somewhat by sending the French women and children off to France on 10 September, in convoy, via Zaragoza and Jaca. He was cold to the complaints of civilians remaining, and indifferent to the attitudes of the Valencian nobles, many of whom shunned French social functions. He was more interested in getting his sick and wounded soldiers into hospital, and seeing that the healthy were rested and well fed. Little but the army and campaign plans interested him; even his intimate dinners, where small talk had been the rule, turned into staff conferences.

Obsessed with striking back at Wellington, Joseph seemed to be turning into a real commander. His experience seemed to have toughened him. Jourdan was pleased with the way he gave orders—blunt, *"claire et laconique."* He had become realistic about "his people"—at least enough to stop recruiting Spanish troops. Of 5000 in his service, 3500 had deserted en route to Valencia. Lefebvre was right! he said disgustedly, remembering that in 1809 the crusty marshal had advised him to hire Alsatians and send ". . . *vos f—— Espagnols à tous les diables!"* He concentrated on readying the French for the coming campaign. No major decisions could be made, however, until he knew what to expect from Soult.

Where was Soult? Was he evacuating Andalusia? Joseph was sure his orders had reached Seville, but of nothing else.

SOULT CRIES TREASON

On 8 September news came in an unexpected way. A ship's captain brought a packet of letters from Soult, addressed not to Joseph, but the minister of war, at Paris. The captain, en route from Andalusia to France, had been forced to dock at Grao (the port of Valencia); he asked that the packet be forwarded. Joseph opened the letters; some were in code, but all army commanders had the key.

The King is evacuating Spain! wrote Soult. He has gone mad or *he has sold out to the rebels.* He orders me to lift the siege of Cadiz and give Andalusia to the enemy. Next he will send the armies behind the Ebro, or even into France. For that the rebels will let him keep his crown. He has often said he could rule Spain if the French armies would leave! The King's ambassador in Russia has joined the enemy! The King's brother-in-law, Marshal Bernadotte (crown prince of Sweden since 1810) has made a treaty with the English! And there was more. He would follow the King's orders, Soult said, but he did not want to be accused of treason because he did so. The letter, he hoped, would protect him. He had felt it his duty also to inform the *six principal generals in Spain of his suspicions.*

Joseph laughed. "The Duke de Dalmatie [Soult] must have been dreaming about the conspiracies . . . of the time of the Convention!" Incredible! Betray my brother, the Emperor? He became angry, serious. Not only does he accuse me, but he is trying to turn my generals against me! He breeds rebellion in the Emperor's armies. He is a destroyer, a traitor! Is it not my duty to have him put under arrest?

La Forest suggested that such a move could be "disastrous." He urged Joseph not to tell Soult he had seen the letters, to forward them to Napoleon, and keep the whole matter secret. Jourdan pointed out that Soult *was* following orders. Joseph was not sure. He called in the ship's captain. Is Andalusia being evacuated? I do not know, Sire. "The Imperial troops have evacuated all the coast of Malaga. . . . It is rumored the marshal will march . . . [toward Valencia]." It appeared that Soult was moving as directed.

Joseph decided he would have to let the Emperor judge Soult. After all, how many times had Napoleon accepted *his* opinion of marshals? He added a letter to a stack already prepared for his brother: "I demand justice of Your Majesty. Marshal Soult should be recalled, tried, and punished. I cannot put up with such a man much longer . . . send me a general to replace him as soon as possible." He locked his and Soult's letters into a pouch. During the night his aide, Colonel Després, left for Moscow to deliver them to the Emperor. Joseph felt better; the problem was out of his hands. He well knew, however, that by refusing to discipline Soult himself, he had condemned himself to work with Soult until Napoleon's judgment arrived. That would be two or three months. (Després got to Moscow on 18 October, the eve of the great retreat. Napoleon had already seen Soult's letter. A trifling matter, he said. I cannot bother with it. There are "immense things" to do.)

CONFRONTATION WITH SOULT

A direct message from Soult finally arrived on 12 September. Dated two weeks earlier, it stated he was on the march. Joseph waited. No more dispatches arrived. Impatient, he decided to meet Soult at the frontier, and departed with his guard on 21 September. At San Felipe he waited until 2 October, when he learned that Soult had come up to Fuente de Higuera, some ten miles away. On 3 October he rode to Soult's headquarters.

Joseph should have made Soult come to him. His anger had cooled, however, and he was thinking of the coming campaign.

Why not make a small conciliatory gesture? If he saved the marshal's pride, perhaps he could get his full cooperation. Moreover, he had dreaded this first meeting. He wanted to have done with it. He harbored a vague fear, also, that Soult, if ordered to his headquarters would come, storming, defiant, and make an embarrassing scene. The little marshal was a proud man—and, yes, a frightening one. Joseph could see his long, leathery face, the mouth like a knife wound, the lines like parched gullies in a desert, the eyes small, hard. Why stir him up? The calm, reasonable approach was best. (Was Joseph afraid of Soult? Some of his officers thought so.)

Soult, his staff, and a guard of honor received the King while martial music blared and cannon boomed a salute. The greetings exchanged, Joseph took Soult into private conference. Still standing, they faced each other. *Monsieur le Maréchal*, you must explain your conduct. Soult stood on his dignity (*"débuté par de grands airs,"* says La Forest). I protest my complete loyalty to Your Majesty! Joseph stared at him incredulously, thinking of the intercepted letters, of which he had resolved to say nothing. His anger rose. I have read Your Excellency's letter to the Duke de Feltre [Clarke]! You have communicated with the six generals! You revolt against the authority given me by the Emperor, my august brother! Soult was speechless. He stood rigid until Joseph ran out of invective. Sire, I have carried out your orders. My opinions do not matter; I am a soldier. Joseph looked into his face; it was a mask. Very well. We shall march together. They called in Jourdan and began discussing the campaign.

Joseph felt reassured. La Forest was skeptical of Soult's seeming change of heart. "The Duke de Dalmatie has found means of remaining the master," he reported. Others noted that Soult's headquarters remained virtually independent, and that the marshal evidently thought that he would soon succeed Joseph as commander of the armies.

COUNCIL OF WAR

Soult wanted to unite all the armies and march after Wellington, abandoning Valencia, temporarily, and ignoring Madrid.

Suchet argued that it was vital to conserve a base in Valencia, which he felt required his whole army, since he was now threatened from Andalusia, and Maitland's Anglo-Sicilian army, if it had done little more than land, had encouraged the Spanish. He suggested that the Armies of the South and Center could attack Wellington with the support of the revived Army of Portugal. (The latter now had a new chief, General Souham, who, temporarily, also commanded the Army of the North.* Jourdan agreed with Suchet, after persuading him to release a few reenforcements for the Army of the Center. To Joseph, retaking Madrid at the earliest possible moment was essential. That understood, he sided with Jourdan and Suchet. He would hold Valencia, march on Madrid, then combine with Souham to challenge Wellington. It was a good plan, but for one thing—the success of the effort depended on Soult. At the outset he commanded three times as many men as the King. Later Joseph would generously give him more.

To Madrid, and Beyond

Harassed by guerrillas, but otherwise unopposed, Joseph led the Armies of the Center and South to Madrid. His entry, on 2 November, created little stir. Melancholy, impatient, the King moved northward two days later to rendezvous with Souham and the Army of Portugal. Pending a test of strength with Wellington, he had left most of his officials, and all the "useless mouths," behind in Valencia.

The armies joined at Peña Aranda on 9 November, thanks to Souham's initiative. Joseph's order for him to push southward had not arrived until the end of October, but he had learned of the King's march weeks earlier from English newspapers. Gambling that he was expected to support the Armies of the South and Center, he had flaunted Wellington's superior numbers to make his army available. His arrival swelled Joseph's strength to 97,000.

---

* Napoleon had asked Masséna (but not ordered him) to return to the Army of Portugal, but the marshal had declined.

Wellington, aware of Joseph's march, had encountered Souham at Burgos and retreated to Salamanca, where he occupied his favorite hills, the Arapiles. On 9 November, the same day Souham reenforced Joseph, Hill joined Wellington, increasing his Anglo-Portuguese force to 52,000. Castaños had already appeared with 16,000 Spanish. The Allied army thus totaled 68,000. It was smaller and less homogeneous than Joseph's, and inferior in both artillery and cavalry. If the King could force Wellington to give battle, his chances of victory seemed good.

Joseph, before making a challenge, reorganized his army. He gave Soult the combined Armies of the South and Center (70,000), relieved Souham, and gave the Army of Portugal (27,000) to General Drouet, Count d'Erlon. Drouet was the King's great friend, and he had been serving under Soult. Joseph knew Drouet would obey him and thought he could better cooperate with Soult than Souham. But the marshal, far from being pleased, was irate. He hated Drouet, whom he regarded as a palace politician, despite his good battle record. Joseph! Jourdan! Now the *Count*! (He sedulously refused to address Drouet as "General.") Soult said little, but he resolved not to risk his neck for the glory of the "philosopher" King, the has-been marshal, and the *Count*.

FACE-OFF AT SALAMANCA

Joseph ordered his army across the Tormes on 14 November. Two days later it was arrayed opposite Wellington's force, entrenched on the Arapiles. But the King declined to attack. He had tested Wellington's defensive skill before, at Talavera; the Allied army seemed unlikely to move, and he wanted time to study the situation. Besides, both he and Jourdan were ill; they kept to their tents.

Soult, meanwhile, sent a column toward the Ciudad Rodrigo road (just as Marmont had done the previous July) to threaten the Allied line of retreat. At nightfall (16 November), Wellington saw French cavalry approaching the road. This time, however, the bulk of the French army was massed, not extended, as in

July, and numerical odds were in the French favor. He could not risk attacking; he could not let himself be outflanked. One choice was left. He began the retreat Marmont had vainly expected—on Ciudad Rodrigo.

Soult should have attacked. For a few hours, Wellington's army was as extended and vulnerable to flank assault as Marmont's had been in July. But Soult did not attack; neither did he inform Joseph of the enemy movement. Uninterested in giving the King a victory, he was content simply not to lose; he let Wellington go. The next morning the Allied army was well on its way to winter quarters on the Portuguese border.

Kingly Duties

Joseph later referred the matter of Soult's conduct to Napoleon, demanding once again that the marshal be recalled. For the moment he concentrated on pursuing Wellington. Rain had fallen on the night of the Allied escape, however, and it continued. The roads, churned up by the vehicles and wheeled guns of the retreating army, became almost impassable to the French. His columns wading in mud, his vehicles sliding, sinking, and breaking down, his men cold and sodden in body and spirit, the King soon gave it all up. On 3 December he was back in Madrid.

Meanwhile, he had reported a victory of maneuver at Salamanca. In a sense it had been. As in 1809, he had forced Wellington to retreat (though this time only to the Portuguese border, not to Lisbon). He was not dissatisfied to have the campaign over. If he had retreated to Valencia, well, Napoleon had retreated from Moscow. (Even at year's end Joseph did not know that the Emperor's retreat had turned into a disaster.)

The Army of the Center returned to Madrid with the King. Soult's Army of the South went on to Toledo and outposted the capital on the south, while the Army of Portugal, left behind at Valladolid, kept desultory watch on *les Anglais*. The King left the armies to Jourdan (or, since he was often ill, to an assistant chief-of-staff) intervening seldom except to try to protect "his people" from the generals, and limit their confiscations. Restoring Madrid to normal, preparing to receive back the refugees from Valencia, reviving his government, restoring order in his territory and confidence in himself, became his major interests.

Wellington, meanwhile, thought of little but expanding his forces and preparing for a new campaign.

🦚

CHAPTER XIII

Vitoria

EXTREMITY OF THE LINE

As Joseph resettled himself in Madrid, the snows of Russia covered the horrible debris of the Grande Armée, the winds occasionally baring the frozen, contorted bodies, the remains of horses butchered for food, the wrecked caissons and carriages, which marked the line of retreat. Murat, King of Naples, sullenly led the pitiful remnant of the army toward Germany. "It is no longer possible to serve a madman. . . !" He would soon fly to his kingdom, leaving the command to Eugène de Beauharnais, Napoleon's faithful adopted son. The Emperor's allies, Prussia in the lead, were preparing to defect.

Napoleon, back in Paris on 18 December, worked frantically to build a new army, calling in veterans from garrisons all over Europe, drafting boys of seventeen, sixteen, and finally fifteen to fill up the ranks. He ordered some 90,000 men recalled by stages from the armies in Spain, replacing about half of them with green recruits. Joseph's forces, by June 1813, mustered only 200,000 men, with 100,000 under his personal command. Many generals were also recalled; Soult, Caffarelli, and Drouet during the first three months of the year. (Gazan, Clausel, and Reille took over, respectively, the Armies of the South, North, and Portugal.)

To the Emperor, the Allied armies on the Peninsula constituted one jaw of a vise his enemies ought to close on France. Joseph, he hoped, could defend the territory he still held, but his primary mission must be to protect the southern frontier of France. Clarke so informed the King by a letter of 4 January 1813:

The Emperor thinks Your Majesty will have been informed by the 29th bulletin, of the state of affairs in the north; it is easy to comprehend that they require all our attention and effort, and that it is consequently necessary to subordinate the affairs of Spain. In these circumstances the Emperor [orders] . . . that Your Majesty move personally, with his headquarters, to Valladolid, and *occupy Madrid only as one of the extremities of the line.*

The "29th Bulletin of the Grande Armée" admitted the enormity of the catastrophe in Russia. All Paris saw it in the *Moniteur* of 16 December 1812, but *Joseph did not have it until a month later.* Moreover, the King did not receive Clarke's instructions until *16 February 1813.* He did not know until then that he was no longer to have a capital, but a *headquarters,* in the north.

PARTIDAS ON THE ROUTES

The King was late being informed because the *guerrilleros* had almost isolated him from the outside world. Some 50,000 of them were operating in the territory he had "reconquered," and his armies could not occupy it and still remain sufficiently concentrated to march if called upon. He had, in effect, sacrificed his communications to recover Madrid.

The Army of the North, by abandoning Galicia and Asturias, was still able to police the routes to France in Navarre and Biscay. Even there, however, convoys required heavy escort. Thiébault, en route to France with a Polish cavalry regiment, tells of how it was trapped in Villareal, and had to be rescued by an infantry brigade. The elder Mina managed to blockade the major fortress of Pamplona for a month. Contact with Madrid was even more difficult. It was a month after Clausel replaced Caffarelli before Joseph knew about it.

Dozens of bands interdicted communications between Clausel and Reille (Army of Portugal) at Valladolid. More stood between there and Madrid. Clausel usually sent dispatches via Aragon and Valencia, where Suchet periodically formed convoys and furnished escort to cut a path to Madrid. The Army of the South (Soult, replaced by Gazan in March), at Toledo, had continuous contact with Madrid, but not without cost. *El Empecinado* kept watch on all the roads to the capital, from whatever direction, deploying at will almost 6000 riders.

Messages from Paris reached Madrid in five to six weeks (if at all), either via Valencia or the more direct route—traveling in one week from Paris to Bayonne, and taking four to five weeks to get from Bayonne to Madrid. Since escorts of regimental size could not be spared every day, mail from Valencia and Valladolid arrived only every three weeks, on the average. As always, the irregulars killed and plundered, striking at garrisons as well as convoys, making the French pay and pay, never letting them sleep. Nothing, however, was so important as their disruption of communications. It may well have been decisive to the Allied cause in 1813.

THE ROYAL DUTY

Joseph's decision to return to Madrid had not been easy. He knew the military risks involved in separating his armies. But he also knew that if he appeared to abandon the capital permanently, his Spanish followers would lose heart, and the rebels would gain prestige by occupying it. Moreover, he would be abandoning New Castile, and since he would be too far away to support Suchet, he might lose Valencia as well. Everywhere, he had *some* adherents—peasants, craftsmen, businessmen, clergymen, all sorts of people, high and low—who could not pack up and follow him. Could he abandon them to the rebels? Sometimes the *Joséfinos* were tortured and killed, especially where guerrillas seized control; everywhere they were persecuted. Beyond that, he felt that the more of them he abandoned, the more difficult it would be for him to win over "his people," even if he won the war. Finally, he was sure that if he stayed in the north, he would be accused of sacrificing Spanish interests (and his people) to guard the French frontier. Back to Madrid he went.

Joseph, as usual, was trying to do his duty both to Napoleon and "to Spain." Surely pride and the desire to remain a King influenced him also; he was all too human. And he needed love; the army gave him little enough. His Spanish followers, for all their faults, demonstrably liked him—and among them were women who loved him—the Marquise, the Countess Jaruco, and others. He could see their faces, silently asking why he had abandoned them. In Madrid, he undertook both to prepare for the next phase of the war and reassume his kingly responsibilities. He courted disaster. Being Joseph, he could not do otherwise.

No plaudits greeted the King either from the military or "his people." The ministers, most of whom had accompanied Joseph, were tired and spiritless. The campaign had been fruitless, and bulletins from the Grande Armée, though optimistic in tone, indicated Moscow had been abandoned. Anxiety was the keynote, both among civilians and soldiers. The councillors of state, courtiers, diplomatic corps, dependents—and Amalia—were still in Valencia. Mazarredo had died during 1812, as had Romero, whose wise and gentle presence Joseph missed especially. Marshal Jourdan was too ill to perform his duties.

"Madrid was sad, the palace deserted; discouragement and disgust manifest themselves everywhere," wrote Miot, recalling the last days of 1812. The arrival of the 29th Bulletin in mid-January increased the *Joséfinos's* despair, and encouraged rebel sympathizers. Joseph had to order searches for assassins and arms in Madrid. Volleys from firing squads sent reverberations through the frozen streets, the sounds striking the King like blows to the body. The streets remained almost deserted; food was scarce, starvation common, the hospitals full. Christmas and New Year's were celebrated, wanly, as if the palaces were temporary army headquarters. Clutched in the icy, windswept wastes of the Castilian plateau, Madrid convulsed weakly in the silence, and seemed ready to die.

The ministers opened their offices, but could do little. The rebels had carried away their files, most of their employees were missing, and it was baldly evident that the King could exert his authority only through the military. The armies survived by confiscation, barely; Wellington and the *guerrilleros* had taken almost everything. The best Joseph could do was legalize their activity, attach civilian officials to foraging detachments and headquarters, and demand strict accounting. The King banked on help from Valencia and the hope that he could regularize tax collection during the spring and summer harvests. Meanwhile he tried to wring enough from military stores to ease the suffering in Madrid.

Aid from Valencia finally arrived on 14 February 1813— 6,000,000 reals in specie and dozens of wagons of grain—watched over nervously during the journey by the minister of finance, Angulo, whom Joseph had left with Suchet. In the same convoy were the refugees, joyful to be back, but exhausted from a trek of thirty days which had taken them from Valencia to Zaragoza and over the Guadarramas to Madrid. Joseph had planned for the convoy to follow a more direct route, but messages had been exchanged regarding the plan, and he sensed that the enemy might know of it. On 16 December 1812, he had sent Suchet a coded dispatch, ordering it to move via Zaragoza. As a result, it came through without serious incident. La Forest, one of the travelers, heaped praise on Joseph for his decision. The King had been right; not only had guerrilla bands been alerted to attack the convoy, but a Spanish army had shifted north to cut the route.

The treasury was no longer empty and the Marquise was back! The atmosphere of Madrid remained forbidding, but there were spots of brightness. Courtiers again thronged the palace, more motley than before, but possessed of a desperate gaiety. *"Après moi le déluge!"* said a wag, affecting Joseph's vaguely Corsican accent. He epitomized the feeling. All had seen the 29th Bulletin and listened to the tales of horror circulating in the northern cities. If their imperial world was doomed, why not enjoy the last days. They swarmed to nightly parties and balls, crowded the theaters playing French comedies, and jammed the one playing Joseph Chénier's *Fénelon et les religieuses* (a bad play with a worse cast; they could laugh). They celebrated Mardi Gras with bacchanalian gusto, troubled only by the equally frenzied participation of rebel sympathizers, who jeered at the *afrancesados* from behind masks.

Joseph indulged the court and put up a brave front before

the people, making appearances everywhere, even at the bull-fights. He encouraged preparations for unprecedented celebrations on his feast day (19 March). As his intimates soon knew, however, he was deeply worried. On 16 February, he had received Clarke's letter of 4 January together with a near duplicate dated 14 January: *Napoleon ordered him to move to Valladolid.* By the same courier La Forest got instructions from Maret to urge the King to move quickly.

JOSEPH DELAYS

"The existence of a king is incompatible with the actual state of things . . ." Joseph told La Forest heatedly. He cited all his reasons for returning to Madrid. "If Madrid and the Castiles are to be abandoned, then the best thing is to give the command of the armies . . . to a general-in-chief, who can feed them as in an enemy country." He would follow the Emperor's orders, he said, but "my heart dictates my duties." He should see the Emperor, Joseph said; a decision should be made. La Forest argued that it was hardly the time.

Joseph advised Clarke on 23 February that he was *preparing* to execute the Emperor's orders. He directed the Army of the South to Madrid. But he did not budge. The court got wind of Napoleon's orders. If the King leaves, they said sagely to each other, it is the end. It will be a *third retreat*; this time he will not return. Spain is to be sacrificed, said the Spanish; the armies will guard France. Joseph agonized; he knew what they thought. If he marched north, the *afrancesados* and French civilians would surely try to follow him. Even if the armies continued to hold Madrid, the rebels would have won a victory. He decided that if he left, he must announce he was going on campaign against the English. "To cover my retreat," he said; the courtiers' thinking was not far from his own. He considered marching toward Talavera, as if Wellington threatened from the southwest, then slipping north via Avila to Valladolid. He could not bring himself to deceive his followers, however. He sent off an officer to present his case in Paris, and waited, hoping for a change in orders.

None came. At the end of February another letter from Clarke, dated 29 January, arrived. "The Emperor . . . wills that Your Majesty occupy Valladolid and pacify the north." Communications must be restored. There has been no word from Madrid since *24 December 1812*. If the English strike in the north, Madrid will fall anyway, and the hospitals and depots with it. "It is of extreme importance . . . to profit from the inactivity of the English." Joseph ordered his armies to shift northward, by stages, but he remained in Madrid.

He had new reasons to cling to his capital. At scattered places in Andalusia, riots had greeted the news that Wellington had been reaffirmed as commander-in-chief of the Spanish armies. He had been so appointed in October 1812, but had refused to accept until given a free hand. At that time the popular General Ballesteros had protested: "A dishonor to the nation!" He had been arrested and exiled. Now it was rumored that his nephew had taken to the mountains, and was forming an army. Rebels against the Cortes! Might they not appeal to King Joseph? If he left Madrid might he not miss a golden opportunity?

There had arrived also the false news, propagated by Napoleon himself, that he had signed a new concordat with Pope Pius VII. Surely, Joseph thought, if the Holy Father has so favored the Emperor, his jailor, he will not refuse to recognize *me*, a good son of the Church, as King of Spain. If a papal nuncio came to Madrid, what a blow to the rebels! Campo-Alange was sent to La Forest with a brief which claimed that all Joseph's acts against the Church had been within the authority granted the King of Spain by previous pontiffs. Would the ambassador ask the French foreign minister to present the King's case to His Holiness?

In March there were rumors of impending peace between Russia and France. Suddenly, Joseph's *cédulas* (good for national properties) were in demand. Orders came even from *Cadiz*; quotations shot from 3 percent to 12 percent of par. Orders from Cadiz! The rumors must be true! It is not the time to abandon Madrid. The rebels are losing heart! Even though the market slumped again within days, Joseph thought he had seen proof of defection in the enemy ranks.

Convinced he should stay in Madrid, Joseph daily dredged up more reasons for doing so. Maret's letter to La Forest, he declared, gave him more freedom than Clarke's orders. He would wait for clarification. Clarke said that if Valladolid were attacked, Madrid would fall. If Madrid were attacked (as in 1809), would not Valladolid fall? Why leave Madrid when there was no enemy in sight? And what about Suchet, in Valencia? Was he to be left unsupported? Even *Marshal Soult* agrees with me! he told startled dinner guests after his old enemy departed for Paris on 2 March (Soult's orders, written in January, had been delayed). Soult? Everyone knew Joseph still thought him a traitor, and it was rumored Soult had told his officers he would be back soon to command *all* the armies.

It was as if he were trying to convince himself. Noting that despite what he said, the armies were slowly getting in motion, many of his followers began selling their property and preparing to go into exile. To reassure them Joseph announced on 10 March that his departure had been postponed indefinitely. Sorely tried, he could barely endure the courtiers. Did they think deciding was easy!

Even the Marquise irritated him with her questions. Would he stand up to Napoleon? Stand up! *Mon Dieu!* He fled from her, into the waiting arms of the blonde Nancy Derrieux. *Après moi le déluge!* So be it. Nancy had no arguments, just warmth, happy nonsense. Casa del Campo was theirs; the Marquise could keep the palace.

In Paris, Napoleon assailed Clarke. What is the King doing? Is he still in Madrid? Clarke knew nothing. How can he sit there out of contact with Paris! *Les Anglais* will strike soon! He should have been in Valladolid in December! Clarke wrote Joseph on 3 February and twice on 12 February, repeating the Emperor's orders. On 12 February he also sent Jourdan copies of his four previous letters to the King, and a brief note: "Not a moment is to be lost in transferring the headquarters of His Catholic Majesty to Valladolid." The Emperor demands immediate compliance with his orders!

FAREWELL TO MADRID

On 15 March, all of Clarke's letters arrived at once. Jourdan had been mildly urging Joseph to march; now he almost shouted his advice. Five orders, Sire! One does not play with the Emperor. The King agreed: but *Monsieur le Maréchal*, the troops are moving; we have not *really* disobeyed. Joseph knew, however, that it was a moot question. *Hé bien!* Give the order to march! On 17 March he left for Valladolid, his guard shepherding a sizable convoy of carriages which carried three ministers, selected councillors and members of the royal household . . . and Madame Nancy Derrieux.

"The King, our *Señor*, has departed to visit the lines of the armies," announced the *Gaceta de Madrid* the next day. No one believed that. The Army of the Center had departed ahead of the King; the bulk of the Army of the South was following him. The *Joséfinos* were packing, and detachments of troops were scouring the city for vehicles to transport the hospitals and depots.

The King's feast day, 19 March, was celebrated riotiously, all the same. The evening before a hundred-gun salute was fired; it was repeated three times on the day itself. There were parades, free bullfights, and free food and wine for revelers in the streets. In the evening the opera, theaters, embassies, and palaces were illuminated; there were fireworks to entertain the masses and balls for the elite. The *afrancesados* had their last fling, and Ferdinandist assassins took advantage of the confusion to murder a dozen of them.

On the morrow they beseiged General Hugo, commandant of Madrid, to ask for escort to Valladolid. Joseph, anticipating the request, and unwilling to put them in real danger, had assigned General Laval, with 10,000 troops (from the Army of the South) to guard convoys. Within days, the King's followers, a few hundred at a time, were taking the route north.

COURT OR HEADQUARTERS?

"I have seen practically everybody since I arrived in Valladolid . . ." reported La Forest on 14 April. Josephist Madrid had moved to the new capital—the government, court, embassies, and their hangers-on. The city of 20,000 had been inundated by thousands of civilians and soldiers, and there were more troops in the environs. Housing was short, food was short, everything was short but words. The city buzzed like a beehive; no one was happy, and everyone blamed the King for his misfortunes.

Joseph had reached Valladolid on 23 March, where more letters from Clarke soon found him. The harassed minister had repeated Napoleon's orders four more times before he finally got Joseph's response to his 4 January letter. The King justified his behavior in a long dispatch: he had not received the orders until 17 February; he had obeyed as quickly as possible. He still disagreed with the Emperor's decision, however:

I add only an observation. [In the provinces we have abandoned] the people are neutral or for us. . . . The north, on the contrary, is a furnace fed by its own inhabitants. It seems to me that, if the principal inhabitants were reassured as to the future [of Spain] . . . if half the troops here were put at my disposition; if I were free to administer the country as I like and to conduct this *interior war* as I like; I could soon pacify the [whole] country. . . .

If not very clearly, Joseph was suggesting that someone else deal with Wellington, while he devoted himself to the pacification and governance of Spain. His views had not changed in five years; he still felt he could deal with his people if Napoleon, or someone else, would fight the war. He still felt that the brutalities of the generals had spawned guerrilla bands among potentially loyal subjects. Now additionally he was convinced that the Spanish were increasingly angered by the presence of the British, and that if Wellington could be held at bay, he could consolidate the Spanish behind him. Perhaps, if Napoleon had returned to the Peninsula in 1810 or 1811 and won the war, Joseph could have made good his hopes. Thereafter, the question had become academic.

At Valladolid, as at Madrid, Joseph was the rope in a tug-of-war between the army and the court. Send the civilians to France, said the military; they get in the way, they complain, they gobble food which ought to feed soldiers! It is our right to be with Your Majesty, said the civilians; you are our only protection. You are the *King*, not merely a general. What hope for Spain is there without you? Jourdan urged Joseph to concentrate his troops and march against Wellington, if not to engage him, to keep him from seizing the initiative and interfere with his preparations. The court held for occupying as much territory as possible, and, though they had left the capital, holding it as a token of good faith.

Joseph tried to please everybody. The courtiers stayed. Madrid was held, not evacuated. He shifted the bulk of the Army of the South to the line of the Tormes and the Army of Portugal behind the Duero. The Army of the Center was between, but he did not consolidate his forces. All the armies were widely extended, and Gazan still had men in Madrid and other posts far to the south, while Reille, with headquarters at Palencia, had a garrison at Burgos.

Joseph still hoped for a revolt against the *Cortes* in Andalusia. Rumors that the British were withdrawing troops from Portugal excited him. The Spanish would break with *les Anglais* any day, he told La Forest. He was cheered by the news from Germany: Napoleon was again driving the enemy before him. He did not realize how different was this Grande Armée from that of Austerlitz and Wagram. At Dresden, Metternich would tell Napoleon the truth: "I have seen your troops. They are nothing but children. You have killed off a whole generation. What will you do when these boys are gone?"

Clarke, with strained circumspection, tried to inform Joseph on the conditions in the Empire, and goad him into action. "The Emperor orders me to declare that Your Majesty can expect nothing [additional] from him considering the circumstances in which France finds herself. . . . His Imperial Majesty orders me again to tell Your Majesty that to command an army well, one must work at it without ceasing." The Emperor asks why the armies lie in "complete inactivity," giving the English complete freedom. It was of *"Plus haute importance"* to "keep the English in check, menace Portugal."

Despite Clarke's urging, however, Joseph kept his armies dispersed. In his defense, it must be said that the minister put undue emphasis on destroying the guerrillas and maintaining communications. Still, as late as 16 May, the King had no plans to meet an Allied offensive. As in every similar situation since

1809, the court, by playing on his sense of duty and guilt over the whole Spanish tragedy, had doomed him to military failure.

Wellington was already on the move. He was now commander-in-chief of all the Spanish armies, as well as British and Portuguese forces on the Peninsula, and felt strong enough to depart (cautiously), from his "Cautious System," and go over to the offensive.

"THE PEER" ADVANCES

In early May, Lord Wellington had sent General Graham, with 40,000 Anglo-Portuguese, across the Duero in Portugal, and into Spain along the north bank. Castaños joined him near the border with 30,000 Spanish, and Wellington's first pincer was in place. Reille (Army of Portugal), on the line of the Duero, was outflanked. (See map, p. 231.) On 26 May Wellington himself, with 30,000 British, forced the Tormes, flanking Gazan (Army of the South). Scattering light French detachments before him, "The Peer" pushed on to the Duero, crossed, and on 4 June joined Graham and Castaños. His army, 100,000 strong and screened by uncounted hundreds of guerrillas, moved deliberately eastward, threatening to envelop Valladolid on the north.

Joseph learned on 28 May that his armies were outflanked, and that he was outnumbered. Unless he wanted to give battle soon, his position at Valladolid was untenable. If he remained passive, he would, at best, be cut off from Clausel (Army of the North), his only source of help, and from France. His solution was to march toward Clausel. He ordered the Armies (Portugal, South, and Center) to concentrate on Burgos, fifty miles to the north, and signaled Clausel to reenforce him there. Marshal Jourdan rode ahead to examine the fortress of Burgos, on which the King hoped to hinge a strong defensive position where he could hold until Clausel arrived. The chief-of-staff returned in a few days to report that the fortress was a shambles, and indefensible, but Joseph let his orders stand. He could not remain at Valladolid.

The Armies of the Center and South were delayed until 2 June. Joseph had not ordered Madrid evacuated until 18 May, and the last convoy of refugees had not arrived. He would not leave his

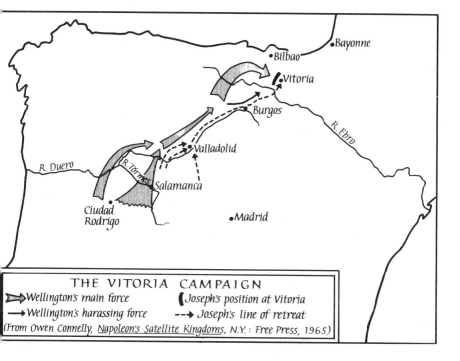

THE VITORIA CAMPAIGN
Wellington's main force   (Joseph's position at Vitoria
Wellington's harassing force   --→ Joseph's line of retreat
(From Owen Connelly, Napoleon's Satellite Kingdoms, N.Y.: Free Press, 1965)

people to be captured by guerrillas (or, if they were lucky, Wellington). This convoy, which included the carriages of the Marquise de Montehermoso, and other caravans carrying the civilians from Valladolid, made rapid, orderly retreat impossible.

On reaching Burgos on 9 June Joseph found that the fortress was indeed useless, and Clausel was nowhere in sight. He decided to retreat behind the Ebro, to Vitoria. The depots and artillery parks of his armies had been at Burgos all along. They were put on the road first, together with the mass of refugees. Pressed by Allied units, Joseph ordered the armies to march on 12 June, though the roads were still jammed. The next day the last of his troops, after making a stab at destroying what remained of the depots, moved out, the cavalry fighting a rear guard action. In the confusion, the arsenal of the fortress was blown up before it was cleared, killing some three hundred soldiers.

Joseph was already beaten, but he did not know it. The months spent in Madrid could not be recovered, nor could those at Valladolid, when he could have been shaping his army into a solid, coordinated mass, and doing some planning. The paraphernalia of government, families, and plunder, which should have been abandoned, now added to his troubles. Madrid had been evacuated too late. No staff work had been done, and the generals vied with each other over the routes of retreat. Units of armies and corps became mixed on the roads. Orders were carried out in a haphazard fashion or not at all.

Wellington, meanwhile, detaching units to keep pressure on the French rear, swung the bulk of the Allied army north, toward the headwaters of the Ebro. By 15 June he had most of his troops across the river, and they began marching in columns, along parallel routes, down the north bank, in the direction of Vitoria.

PRELUDE TO DISASTER

At Vitoria on 14 June, Joseph determined to make a stand, though no reenforcements had arrived from Clausel. The French were strong enough to fight, and perhaps win. Though the King had allowed two divisions to march with convoys, he had 70,000 men, almost all French. Wellington reached the battlefield with some 90,000, discounting *guerrilleros*, but his force was heterogeneous, and he was uncertain how the Spanish would perform, especially since many of them had recently been guerrillas. The French army was better equipped and armed than the Allied force, though neither lacked anything essential. Joseph had two hundred cannon which he did not even use, and there was no shortage of ammunition, either for artillery or small arms. French soldiers were well equipped personally, well fed, and, by the time of the battle, well rested.

The French had everything except that which was most needed —a commander. It is difficult to divine what Joseph was thinking, or to excuse him. In the days before the battle he allowed the generals to make most of their own dispositions. Jourdan, ill and tired, posted Reille on the Bilbao road, but gave little attention to the other forces, which arranged themselves loosely on the heights behind the Zadora River, southwest of the city. No overall scheme was imposed to lock the defenses of the three armies together, or even the positions of corps within armies.

At headquarters all was lethargy and confusion. No concerted attempt was made even to clear the streets of the city. Miot tells us that the convoy carrying he Marquise de Montehermoso "unaccountably" did not leave until 20 June—"The city was jammed with carriages and coaches." Many civilians were still in Vitoria on 21 June, the day of the battle, including Nancy Derrieux, who was rather unhappy with the King for spending time with the Marquise. The artillery park was allowed to spill over onto the major route to France.

The King behaved as if he did not believe what was happening. And according to Miot, an air of unreality pervaded the whole city and encampment:

... 20 June passed in irresolution and inaction ... No new disposition [of troops] was made, no order given which would have forecast the events of the next day; at such silence, at such immobility, one was given to suppose for a moment that the march of the enemy had been stopped, and one could believe that he was *dans la plus grande securité.*

Marshal Jourdan kept to his room. The King went nowhere near the lines until four the next morning, when it was much too late to shift troop units.

THE BATTLE OF VITORIA

On the morning of 21 June, in fog and light rain, the Allied army debouched into the hilly lowlands before Vitoria. General Graham attacked along the Bilbao road, General Hill along that from Madrid. Wellington commanded the center in person. As the Allied forces drove in the French outposts they found that all seven of the bridges over the Zadora were intact. The French central command had taken no decision to destroy them.

At Vitoria the French fought well, but, with the exception of Reille's army, only, at best, in corps, most of which were out-flanked and battered at right angles to their line by British cavalry. In the very center, late in the morning, the English found the bridge of Tres Puentes unguarded. It lay between two French corps. Skirmishers went across, then the whole 15th Regiment of Hussars, without losing a man or firing. Minutes later they were attacking through the rear of the French infantry lines. Such incidents continued through the day.

A mighty French army, rudderless, floundered and milled in confusion. At one o'clock in the afternoon Joseph, seeing that his center was crumbling, ordered his reserve to retreat on Vitoria. He then gave the order for the army to retreat by stages, depending on Reille to support the withdrawal by holding fast on the Bilbao road. It was the signal for the breakup. Still fighting well as individuals and in small units, the French forces withdrew in wild disorder toward cluttered Vitoria. Says Napier:

At six o'clock the French reached the last defensible height, one mile in front of Vittoria [sic]. Behind them was the plain in which the city stood, and beyond the houses thousands of carriages, animals and non-combatants, men, women, and children, huddling together in all the madness of terror; and as the English shot went booming overhead, the vast crowd started and swerved with a convulsive movement, while a dull and horrid sound of distress arose: but there was no hope, no stay for army or multitude. It was the wreck of a nation.

As the darkness fell, the Allies reached Vitoria itself. Reille's rear was partially overrun. He was forced to withdraw and open a free passage across the Zadora in his sector, the only one which had been held. In chaotic flood, the French mass took the roads to the north, British cavalry and Spanish *guerrilleros* in hot pursuit. Nancy Derrieux was captured, but quickly rescued by a young cavalry officer and his men. The Duchess de Gazan (wife of the commander of the Army of the South) was taken and led to Lord Wellington, who gallantly sent her back to her husband.

For a major battle, French losses in killed and wounded were small—some six thousand: Allied casualties were about the same. But Joesph lost all his artillery, stores, and even his treasury. In a typical last act, he had the chests opened, and invited the soldiers to take what they wanted, but few could take advantage of the opportunity. The King's personal carriages and baggage had to be abandoned. He, like his generals, lost everything except the clothes on his back. Says Napier: ". . . the soldiers were not half beaten, and yet never was a victory more complete."

THE NIGHTMARE ENDS

Fired on at close range, Joseph was saved by a Spaniard of his guard, who shielded the King's body with his own. "I die for my King!" On horseback, he fled precipitously northward, protected doggedly by the cavalry of his guard. Beset by English hussars, barely rescued, galloping across rough country in the dark, the King's party, which included Miot, Jourdan, O'Farrill, and others, got separated. But most of them reached Salvatierra by midnight, Miot as Joseph was about to have supper in the village inn, Jourdan as they ate. "Well, we wanted to have a battle," said the marshal, saluting airily with his baton, "and we lost it!" The King motioned him to a chair, and all ate in silence.

The next day he went on to Pamplona, where he began re-establishing contact with commanders, and he and Jourdan prepared reports on the battle (but not before Joseph had written Julie). Moving on, he joined first one army and then another, and when they finally halted to reorganize, he crossed the French border and set up his headquarters at Saint Jean de Luz. From there he sent Miot to Napoleon with a personal report.

The Emperor would not see his brother's emissary, and, for once, coined no bitter sarcasms. Wearily, he ordered Marshal Soult off at all speed to take over Joseph's armies, and sent instructions to the King to seclude himself, at a place of his own choosing, near the border.

When Soult arrived at Saint Jean de Luz, on 12 July, Joseph refused to see him. But he gladly relinquished command, and went off, with a great sense of relief, to Château de Poyanne, in the beautiful Adour River country. There he and his suite rested and Joseph applied himself to helping the *afrancesados*, many of them total strangers to France and some in desperate need of funds. After two weeks permission arrived for him to travel, incognito, to Mortefontaine.

Adopting the title Count de Survilliers, after one of the farms of his estate, he set off for home, the chateau in the peaceful countryside he loved, where Julie and his children waited. His mind ran on the quiet paths of the gardens and woodlands, the sweet comfort of being amid the leatherbound volumes of his library, of the circle of his friends who would soon gather, and yes, the Marquise—Amalia would be in Paris, not far away.

The nightmare of his Spanish reign was over.

GOOD INTENTIONS

Technically, Joseph still had his title, and the French armies would fight other battles, but Spain was lost. The blow of Vitoria would eventually prove fatal. Nor did the battle affect only events in Spain. In Vienna, jubilation reigned; the Austrian Emperor, made hesitant earlier by Napoleon's limited victories over the Prussians and Russians, prepared to desert him for the Allies. Reflecting the mood of Napoleon's enemies, overt and covert, all over Europe, Beethoven celebrated Vitoria with his gloriously noisy *Wellington's Victory*, wherein *Rule Britannia* drowns out *Malbrouck s'en va t'en guerre* amid cannon blasts, rifle volleys, and bugle calls.

Joseph failed at Vitoria. Generally, his record as a soldier is not good. But to condemn him too much is to forget that Napoleon, who knew he was not a commander either by training, temperament, or inclination, gave him armies to lead, and then complicated his task by ordering his subordinates about and veritably encouraging them to disobey him. His lassitude (sense of doom?) before Vitoria could have resulted from the feeling that he was not really in control of his commanders, especially Clausel. When, as in 1809, he had shown signs of becoming a soldier, Napoleon had responded by condemning him the more. Vitoria was Napoleon's failure as well as Joseph's.

At all times, Joseph was trying to do his duty both to Napoleon, and by his lights, the Spanish. If he did not succeed, it was because he was too good to abandon one or the other. Treason would have been easy and profitable (as Murat proved before the year was out) for one with fewer scruples, or, alternately, betrayal of his people for the sake of France. Joseph could do neither. He failed, but he failed nobly.

Joseph continued to do what he could for the *afrancesados* exiled in France. After Napoleon's abdication, he received a letter from O'Farrill and others which he always treasured:

We are Spaniards; Your Majesty was also when he was in Spain. He defended the national integrity and independence like a Spanish prince. . . . [Eventually] enlightened men will pay [just tribute]. . . . The memory of the good intentions of Your Majesty toward our country and the benevolence he has for us, is all that our hearts could desire.

History, they said, would show the error of opinions formed during "tumultuous movements." They were right. Ferdinand VII, who returned in 1814, destroyed the rebel *Cortes* in a stroke. His repressive policies quickly destroyed the image rebel propaganda had wrought of the prince of light imprisoned by the godless French. Very soon the Spanish felt pangs of regret and guilt over the fate of their Bonaparte King. Many of his former enemies, when they could safely do so, expressed respect for him, some in memoirs and histories. In our century, no reputable Spanish historian denies that he was a man of great heart, enlightenment, and "good intentions."

☙

CHAPTER XIV

Lieutenant General
of the Emperor

NAPOLEON AT BAY

"**Y**OUR Majesty can count on us as on the guard!" shouted Napoleon's underage draftees of 1813. Dwarfed by man-sized uniforms, their greatcoats dragging the ground, weighted with seemingly gigantic packs and rifles, they followed their Emperor into Germany with the enthusiasm, pathetic in the circumstances, of boys taken on men's adventures. They could not replace their brothers and fathers who had perished in the snows of Russia, however, and the veterans who marched with them, and their commanders, were jaded and spiritless. Victorious in the spring of 1813, Napoleon signaled weakness by agreeing to a truce, during which the news of Joseph's defeat at Vitoria arrived. When hostilities resumed in August, Austria joined the Allies, Bavaria followed suit, and after the fatal "Battle of the Nations," at Leipzig (16–19 October 1813), Napoleon's German allies deserted him *en masse*. The Grande Armée retreated into France. Meanwhile, in the south, Wellington had crossed the Pyrenees and opened a second front on French soil.

The number of persons on whom the Emperor could depend dwindled. At Naples Murat and his own sister Caroline were in the process of defecting to the Allies. The marshals were moody and privately talked of negotiated peace. Within a few months even the Mameluke Roustan, for fifteen years the fierce, turbaned shadow of his imperial master, would disappear. Not strangely, Napoleon turned to Joseph for support.

A Gesture for the Spanish

Buried at Mortefontaine, ignored by the Emperor completely for four months, Joseph was suddenly summoned to the Tuileries in late November—in secret and at night. Napoleon greeted him warmly. There could be no more thought of "foreign domination," he said. It would be enough to protect the "ancient boundaries" of France. Joseph brightened. Then surely the Allies will make peace? Napoleon brushed off the question.

You must abdicate the throne of Spain. "I will give Spain to Ferdinand [VII]; I will give him to the Spanish on the sole condition that they respect the French border, and place themselves between the English and ourselves." What of the thousands of Spanish who followed me into exile? Joseph asked angrily. Legally, they will become rebels against their king—your ally. How can they have any future in France, much less Spain? No. I will not abandon them. He left, resolved to live in "philosophic indifference" at Mortefontaine.

Joseph's followers knew he had taken his stand for the sake of honor alone. They, however, were free to urge that he do what was practical. Azanza, O'Farrill, and others came to argue that he could best do his duty to them by serving Napoleon, on whom all their futures depended. For them to say what he knew to be true, but could not aver himself, satisfied his honor. He offered to do whatever the Emperor wished—in the interest of the "tranquillity and well-being" of France and Europe.

Despite Joseph's cooperation, the plan to restore Ferdinand failed. Though the Bourbon Prince cooperated eagerly, the *Cortes* would not take him as a gift from Napoleon. (He returned on his own terms in 1814.) Joseph's defiance had startled and impressed his brother, however. He returned to the Emperor's service not as a penitent (Napoleon never blamed him, to his face, for the loss of Spain), but as head of the Clan, freely giving his support.

In January 1814, Joseph was named lieutenant general of the Emperor, charged with protecting the Empress-Regent and the little King of Rome and commanding the defense of Paris. As adviser to Marie Louise and member of the Regency Council, he was effective head of the government while Napoleon fought his brilliant but fruitless campaign in northern France. Busy always, he spent his happiest hours with the imperial heir, a precocious blond three-year-old.

Together, they reviewed the troops, the little King grave and rosy in his grenadier's uniform, saluting in imitation of "dear Papa," so excited afterward he could not sleep. They played war games, crawling about on the floor, moving toy soldiers and cannon, shouting and trumpeting happily. The doting uncle let his charge enter rooms alone and hear himself announced: "His Majesty the King of Rome!" The boy was being spoiled rotten, said the severe Madame de Montesquiou, his governess. Joseph knew it; he could not help himself.

Napoleon's instructions, at first mostly military, began to show concern for his wife and child as the Allies, despite his victories, slowly closed in on Paris. "I order you to do, for the Empress and the King of Rome . . . whatever the circumstances indicate," he wrote on 8 February. "If Talleyrand wants to keep the Empress in Paris, in case our forces are evacuated, it is treason." If Paris cannot be defended, he commanded, take the Empress and King southwest, toward the Loire. "I would prefer having my son's throat cut to seeing him brought up in Vienna, as an Austrian prince." On 16 March he repeated the order to take his wife and child away from Paris "if resistance becomes impossible." And he made positive that Joseph was to leave also: "Do not leave my son, and remember that I would prefer to have him in the Seine than in the hands of the enemies of France."

In February, when the Allies had offered Napoleon peace if he would accept the French frontiers of 1792, Joseph had urged that he do so. "It appears to me that true glory is in preserving what one can of his subjects and territory." Unlike Louis, however, whose yen for peace verged on treason, Joseph was loyal. "If you do not make [peace] you must perish with resolution, like the last Emperor of Constantinople. . . . In that case, Your Majesty can count on me fully for everything . . . and I will do nothing to dishonor him or myself." Napoleon chose to fight, and Joseph, true to his word, carried out his instructions.

On 29 March, one hundred thousand Allied troops were before Paris, twice the number of the defenders, who were mostly national guardsmen. Joseph sent the Empress and little King to Rambouillet, safely away from the city, but where he could easily recall them or go to take them toward the Loire. The King of Rome went unwillingly, kicking and screaming, clinging to door jambs and furniture. "Papa is not here! I am in charge!" The next day the Allies attacked, and Joseph, after a half-day at his headquarters atop Montmartre, judged the city would fall. Dashing off authorization for Marmont and Mortier, his commanders, to make terms with the enemy, he rode for Rambouillet, accompanied by Jérôme, whose Westphalian kingdom had been overrun the previous fall. A few days later most of the Bonaparte Clan was assembled at Blois.

Napoleon, arriving near Paris in the dawn hours of 31 March, learned that Marmont had surrendered the city. "Joseph lost me Spain and now he has lost me Paris! he stormed. "And the loss of Paris means the loss of France." The Empire was dead, and the Emperor blamed his favorite scapegoat, who had been guilty only of following his orders.

From Blois, Joseph tried to reach Napoleon at Fontainebleau, where, deserted by his marshals, he negotiated with the Allies. The way was blocked by enemy troops. On 6 April, the Emperor abdicated in favor of his son, then, on 11 April, unconditionally. Meanwhile a Russian general appeared at Blois with Napoleon's authorization to take custody of Marie Louise and the little King. Joseph saw them safely to Orléans, then, his duty done, he fled to Switzerland. Julie declined to go with him. She and their children took refuge instead in Paris with Désirée, whose husband, Bernadotte, since 1810 crown prince of Sweden, was among the Allied commanders.

Louis XVIII de Bourbon returned to the French throne. Napoleon was dispatched for Elba. Marie Louise was designated Duchess of Parma. The King of Rome was destined for the fate Napoleon had most feared. Taken to Vienna, he was reared at the Austrian court; history would know him later as the Duke of Reichstadt.

PRANGINS

Joseph leased the Château de Prangins, on Lake Geneva, and there lived the life of a country gentleman. Madame de Staël, the actor Talma, and other friends visited. The French ambassador, Auguste de Talleyrand, cousin of the arch-traitor to Napoleon, had spies watching his every move, and though he found scant evidence that Joseph was involved in any anti-Bourbon plots, finally got him ordered expelled from Vaud canton (though not Switzerland). Both Joseph and the Swiss authorities, who were fond of him, took the order casually, however. When he did leave, it was for Paris.

While spies watched Joseph in Switzerland, Eugène in Munich, Jérôme in Trieste, Madame Mère and Louis in Rome, etc., and seized and read the letters of all the Bonapartes, Allied surveillence over Napoleon had been deficient. On 26 February 1815, the Emperor of Elba had sailed calmly for France. Rallying troops as he marched northward from Cannes to Paris (Where is the man who would fire upon his Emperor?) he was in Paris on 20 March.

Joseph arrived two days later, again ready to serve his brother. The Allied leaders, at Vienna, had ordered him seized and imprisoned in the Austrian fortress of Gratz. They acted too late. Joseph had been in communication with Napoleon all along, knew of his escape before they did, and was out of their reach. Jérôme appeared in Paris also. And so did the black sheep Lucien. He had enjoyed the notoriety of being "the brother who stood up to Napoleon," but the Emperor's downfall had paralyzed him with guilt.

"France does not want the Bourbons," Joseph had written Napoleon before his abdication in 1814. "She would prefer eternal war." He hoped the throne would be saved for the King of Rome by his grandfather, the Austrian Emperor. To encourage the other Allies to accept Napoleon II, and rally the French people, he proposed that a policy of peace be proclaimed, the independence of Italy (the only non-French territory still at Napoleon's disposal) be guaranteed, and a "truly monarchal" constitution be proclaimed—that is one for France alone, which would be a pledge that she would no longer disturb Europe. "France wants peace, a liberal monarchy." He suggested also promises to abolish conscription, war taxes, and pardon all political offenders.

THE HUNDRED DAYS

Napoleon gave Joseph no credit for inspiring him, but he proclaimed a policy of peace and non-aggression in 1815, and put Joseph and Benjamin Constant to work on a new constitution. France, wrung easily from the rotten grip of the Bourbons, was willing to believe Napoleon had been born again. The Allies, however, were not. Murat, turncoat in 1814 and still King of Naples, strengthened their skepticism by attacking the Austrians in Italy.* "He absolutely ignored the position of the Emperor," the French foreign office signaled Vienna. Unimpressed, the Allied leaders declared Napoleon "an enemy and disturber of the peace of the world."

The armies began to deploy for battle. Napoleon, badly outnumbered, struck north into the lowlands, hoping to defeat the British and Prussians before other armies could reenforce them. His campaign ended, however, almost before it had begun, at Waterloo.

His new-formed army in rout, the Emperor made for Paris. Before he arrived, on 21 June, the legislative chambers, under the leadership of Lafayette, had voted to ask him to abdicate. "Return to the army," Joseph advised, "and let me fight the cham-

---

* Murat was not really fighting for Napoleon. He hoped to become King of a united Italy. His Queen, Caroline Bonaparte, tried again to put Naples on the Allied side to strengthen their credit with the powers, who had become hostile in the past year. She was convinced that if Napoleon maintained his throne, he would destroy them.

bers." Napoleon, however, had lost heart. On 22 June he abandoned his crown. In the Chamber of Peers, Lucien and others secured a vaguely worded resolution declaring the King of Rome had succeeded to the throne as Napoleon II. It meant nothing. Fouché, who' had control of the ministry and chambers, was ready to throw his support to Louis XVIII as soon as Allied armies appeared.

Joseph went to the Tuileries, where Napoleon wandered about listlessly, and led him to a window. Look at them! He pointed to the crowds below cheering for the Emperor. Take control! Rally Paris! Rally the army! Napoleon stared dully ahead. He was finished. His superhuman energy had finally been exhausted.

Joseph made for Rochefort, where he intended to charter a vessel and escape to the United States. Napoleon overtook him at Niort; he was accompanied by a suite of some fifty people, including Generals Bertrand, Gourgaud, and Montholon and the Count de Las Cases, whose writings at Saint-Helena would make them famous. They went on together, arriving at Rochefort on 8 July, where Napoleon went aboard a French frigate, the *Saale*, whose path to the sea was blocked by the British warship *Bellerophon*, commanded by Captain Maitland. Joseph remained in Rochefort while a local lawyer, Pelletreau, undertook to find a ship for him.

NAPOLEON DECIDES

James Caret, Joseph's American interpreter, was quizzed for hours by Napoleon about the United States. There was a French colony in northern New York, Caret told him. Too close to the English! I would prefer Baltimore. They talked about cities, roads, the government, banks, and businesses. Joseph pressed Napoleon to accompany him to the United States; an American ship would soon be ready to sail.

No. Not that way. He would go, he said, if he could sail out in the *Saale*, under the French flag. It was beneath his dignity to sneak away. He sent two generals, under a flag of truce, to Captain Maitland. The Emperor desires to repair to America, they announced. Will you allow his ship to pass? With great courtesy, Maitland said he was unable to "grant that request."

Lady Bertrand and Las Cases urged Napoleon to surrender to the English. See the treatment they gave Prince Lucien! No people are more civilized. Joseph agreed that if surrender it must be, the English were surely preferable to others. The Emperor, pale and sick, decided to give himself up to Captain Maitland. It was the first step toward exile and death on Saint-Helena. Later, in the United States, says Ingersoll: "Joseph often blamed himself for having contributed to that option, by the opinion of the English which his admiration of Lord Cornwallis led him always to entertain and impress his brother with."

IMPERIAL STAND-IN?

On 14 July Napoleon and his party went to the Isle of Aix, in the harbor, preparatory to going on board the *Bellerophon*. Joseph, plagued with doubt about the move, risked a last visit. Let me take your place, Joseph pleaded. You are ill; I can remain in bed a few days. The English captain, even if he comes ashore, would not know that I am not the Emperor. We look alike; he has never seen either of us. You can get away to the United States on the ship I have chartered. Napoleon refused; he considered the ruse beneath his dignity. And he would not have history record that *Joseph saved him*.

Joseph stayed until nightfall on the island. When it was time to leave, Napoleon went to the door with him, the two arm-in-arm, as they had walked as children in the streets of Ajaccio. They embraced, the pudgy little Emperor, his face white and lined, his taller, more robust brother, tears rolling down their cheeks. Among the onlookers—generals, nobles, and ladies—there was not a dry eye.

The brothers were never to see each other again.

⚜

CHAPTER XV

That Peaceable Gentleman

"King Joseph; or that peaceable gentleman, Mr. Bonaparte
. . . lives near Bordentown, in New Jersey."
—NILES' REGISTER, July 1825.

ESCAPE TO AMERICA

THE Lily Banner had not replaced the Tricolor over Rochefort, and the people were friendly. Bourbon officials
were expected any day, however, and Joseph knew they would
pay heavily for the distinction of delivering him to the Allies,
who surely had plans for him (exile in Russia, he later learned).
He therefore went into hiding at a country house, while his
secretary, Louis Mailliard, Louis's son Antoine, and Caret prepared for the flight. Already, Pelletreau had sent his son to
Bordeaux, where he secured passage for the party to New York
on the American brig *Commerce*, out of Charleston, Captain
Misservey. Another local lawyer, Dumoulin, helped make arrangements, and as acting American consul in the area, obligingly
stamped the party's passports. (Joseph's read Count Surviglieri,
an Italianization of Survilliers, the title he had used after Vitoria
in 1813.) On 24 July, the *Commerce* dropped anchor off Royan,
at the mouth of the Gironde. Caret, who was waiting at a hotel
in the town, tells the story:

M. Dumoulin showed her to me, and we agreed that a shallop should
be ready at midnight to take us on board. . . . I sent an express to
King Joseph, who arrived in the night on foot, quietly, accompanied
by M. Edward Pelletreau, M. Unzaga [Joseph's physician] and young

Mailliard. At twelve o'clock the bark had not yet come. We spent two or three hours of painful expectation. The [new Bourbon] commandant was in a room near us; the Prince might have been recognized by some of the officers who were going and coming in the house; we were relieved from a great weight when they informed us that the bark was waiting. . . . The weather was beautiful; the moon shone for our embarkation, which was made cautiously. The tide being favorable, the anchor was raised and the sails spread.*

They were away. There were heart-stopping moments on 25 and 26 July, when British warships brought the *Commerce* alongside. In neither case, however, did boarding officers search the cabins. After that it was smooth sailing. The passengers, with "Count Surviglieri" the center of attention, entertained each other, and occasionally the ship's officers. Caret remembered the voyage with pleasure.

The Prince . . . [recited] French and Italian poetry equally well, his memory stored with effusions of literature in both languages. Having passed five years of my early youth in Italy, I could appreciate his perfect pronunciation, when he recited the flight of Herminia, and other stanzas of Tasso, his favorite author. The most dramatic passages of Corneille's and Racine's fine tragedies were the ones he preferred, with which his voice assumed extraordinary power. With so lofty a political career, what he taught us of men and things was also very remarkable. The Captain formed a high opinion without knowing him. . . .

Misservey, who had been paid 18,000 francs to sail early, without his cargo, knew he was carrying someone of importance. He guessed it was Lazare Carnot, the most brilliant Frenchman he knew of. His passenger's true identity never occurred to him, since the British and American press had always pictured Joseph as stupid, lazy, and inept.

The *Commerce* sighted New York on 18 August and lay offshore overnight. As she made for port next morning, two British frigates bore down on her, but a harbor schooner reached her first, and put aboard a gleeful American pilot: "Do you see those damned English . . . hoping to stop our way. But let me alone;

---

* The two Mailliards, Caret, and Unzaga sailed with Joseph; Pelletreau did not.

the breeze is in our favor, and I will hug the land so close you will soon see them change their course." He was right, the warships, fearful of running aground, gave up the chase. In an hour Joseph was on American soil, where he would remain for eighteen years.

PROTECTION AND HOSPITALITY

Joseph took rooms at a boardinghouse in Park Place, signing the register "M. Bouchard." He could not long remain anonymous, however. The New York *Evening Post* reported the arrival of a mysterious Frenchman, thought to be Carnot. (Captain Misservey had been talking.) A former French soldier recognized him on the street, bellowed "Your Majesty," and to Joseph's acute embarrassment, knelt down and tried to kiss his hand. Commodore Jacob Lewis appeared at the boardinghouse to visit his son, and rushed up to recall their meeting in Paris. When the mayor of New York showed up to pay his respects to "Monsieur Carnot," Joseph gave up the game and confessed who he was. New York was agog; to get some privacy, he fled to Commodore Lewis's home in New Jersey.

The ex-King was concerned over his legal status. Did he not need a passport? In France one could not travel across Paris without one. The commodore assured him that he didn't (immigration laws had yet to be thought of; America was open to all). Joseph still thought it would be prudent to visit President Madison and ask permission to live in the United States. In September, he and Lewis set out for Washington.

The President had troubles enough without appearing to take sides in French politics. He wrote Richard Rush, the attorney general, to have Joseph stopped. "Protection and hospitality do not depend on such a formality." Rush sent Edward Duvall, of the Navy Office, who knew Commodore Lewis, to head off the travelers. "He is here on the mere footing of hospitality and protection which the laws hold out to all, without discrimination, whom choice or misfortune may bring us." If the Count de Survilliers merely intended to pay his respects, "[The President] would prefer declining at this time." Joseph turned back.

Official Washington was being very careful. (James Monroe,

then secretary of state with presidential aspirations, would not deign to meet Napoleonic generals, much less a Bonaparte.) Americans, however, took Joseph to their hearts. Passing through Philadelphia, he encountered Henry Clay, whose party occupied most of the Madison House Hotel. The gaunt Kentuckian offered him his personal suite and would not take no for an answer. In Pennsylvania and New York, while he scouted for land and a house in the country, farmers invited him into their homes, treated him to homemade cider, and found him (to quote one) "a very plain and agreeable man"—not the royal jackanapes they had expected. They liked him. Joseph now signed himself consistently "Comte de Survilliers," but was usually called "Mister Bonaparte," which offended him not in the least.

He urged Julie to join him with the children, but not unexpectedly, she refused. Her health was poor; she was afraid of the voyage and of the New World. Further, she reminded Joseph, the girls would soon be of marriageable age—Zénaïde was sixteen, Charlotte fifteen. Should they be buried in the "wilderness" of America? Unwelcome in France, Julie moved to Florence, where she would live out her life. Joseph did not see her for twenty-five years. His daughters, however, came to visit him, as we shall note shortly.

POINT BREEZE

Exile presented Joseph, though in an unexpected setting, with the opportunity of fulfilling a lifetime dream—to live the life of a country gentleman. Because he had managed his personal finances well, multiplying Julie's fortune and investing his income wisely (he had robbed no one), he could afford to do so. He had brought little money with him, but he did have precious stones that could be turned into cash. (Mailliard, who had carried them from Europe sewn in his clothing, went to Switzerland in 1817 and recovered more, which they had buried in the forest at Prangins.) Moreover, in view of his properties in Europe (Mortefontaine, its four farms, and other holdings in France, Corsica and Italy) he could easily obtain credit.*

---

* The French properties were in the name of Joseph's sister-in-law, the Countess de Villeneuve.

Stephen Girard, Philadelphia's elegant, nationally powerful French-American financier, became Joseph's banker and business adviser. As legal counsel, Joseph retained Charles J. Ingersoll, United States District Attorney, former congressman from Pennsylvania (later reelected), sometime journalist and historian. Both men, in time, became his fast friends. With their help, he began searching for a suitable estate.

In the spring of 1816 he bought Point Breeze, on the Delaware River near Bordentown, New Jersey, and began remodeling the three-story mansion built by the former owner, Stephen Sayre, onetime High Sheriff of London. Agents and friends shipped hundreds of crates of furnishings, paintings, and objects of art from Europe. Joseph, happy as he had not been in decades, supervised the workmen and movers in person, often working by their sides. He was conforming "to the manners of the country," reported *Niles' Register*, whose informant had seen the ex-King helping unload furniture. "To a person who said something about sending for other hands, he said 'No—everybody worked here.' "

Soon the mansion rivaled in splendor the rich châteaux of France. "With the exception of the president's, in Washington, it is the best I have seen [in America]." wrote an English visitor. Its treasures, however, surely outshone those of the White House—and would today. More than two hundred paintings graced its walls, including seven Murillos, five Rubens, two Canalettos, and one each by Leonardo da Vinci and Velasquez. Among the dozens of busts and statues were seven of the imperial family by the great Canova, the only talent of the period whose work has been compared to that of the Renaissance masters. Guests were confronted in the foyer by David's *Napoleon Crossing the Alps*. In the central salon, on walls hung in blue Merino, were paintings by Gérard of Napoleon, Joseph as King of Spain, and Julie and the children, seascapes by Joseph Vernet, and Neapolitan landscapes by Denis.*

---

* For the benefit of those who might assume Joseph had looted the galleries of Naples and Spain, it is noted that no government or individual ever challenged that the art works were his legally acquired, private property.

The original estate, which comprised only two hundred and eleven acres, was expanded to seventeen hundred, and turned into a park, after the French fashion, combining disciplined gardens, hedges, and rows of shrubs with "natural" stretches of timber and tangle. Using the waters of Crosswick's Creek, Joseph built an artificial lake, stocked it with waterfowl, including swans from Europe, and equipped it with boats.

Point Breeze was a working farm as well as showplace, however. The press, eager to show that the ex-King was adapting to the environment, played up the fact. "The last account I had of him, he was cultivating cabbages and potatoes . . . much respected by the neighboring people, for his mild and friendly qualities," wrote one editor.

In 1820 the mansion burned. The citizens of Bordentown turned out to help Mr. Bonaparte, and saved almost all of his priceless artworks and many of the furnishings. Joseph, grateful, and not a little astonished that there had been no looting, wrote Judge William Snowden, the town's leading citizen, to thank the people for their help.

The Americans are, without contradiction, the best people I have ever known. . . . This event . . . shows that men, in general, are good, when they have not been perverted in their youth, by a bad education; when they maintain their dignity as men and feel that true greatness is in the soul, and depends upon ourselves.

The letter was reproduced in newspapers all over the country, with comments on Joseph's "philosophy," which seemed to editors altogether "American." It endeared him further to Bordentowners, and promoted general sympathy. Public wrath turned on a Russian lady diplomat, who lived nearby. The story circulated that she had had the fire set either because (a) Joseph had neglected her or (b) she wanted to burn letters unfavorable to her Czar. Mr. Bonaparte, however, quieted the rumors, though he himself half believed them true.

Joseph built a new mansion in another location, and put a belvedere on the hilltop site of the old one—"The count's observatory," as many visitors called it. Near the lake, he put up a three-story guest house, the Maison du lac, which from the first was steadily in use.

VISITORS

The local people found Joseph the best of neighbors. Their children made his estate a playground, using the iron deer, dogs, and lions in the gardens as hobby horses, playing hide-and-seek among the marble gods and goddesses, to whose nudity they adjusted more quickly than their elders. In winter, the lake swarmed with skaters, children and adults. Joseph often gave candy and small coins to the youngsters and brought baskets of fruit for the skaters—oranges and tangerines shipped in from Florida or Spain, the like of which most people could not afford except perhaps for one or two for a child's stocking at Christmas. Farmers and tradesmen found the Count ready to show them about, listen to their advice, and give them a glass of French wine. Visitors, expected or not, were received with gracious informality—French exiles, American politicians, travelers—everyone.

None came away more enthusiastic than the ladies. "He is a *very* good looking man," reported the beautiful Julia Rush, sister of the attorney general, adding that he was "urbane and polished," a good talker, and that all his servants loved him. She and a party of babbling Philadelphia socialites had appeared unannounced of an August morning, stayed for champagne, a mid-day dinner of several courses and hours of conversation. Frances Wright, an aristocratic English authoress, began an account of their meeting dispassionately, but warmed to her work:

Count Survillier [*sic*] . . . soon came to us from his workmen, in an old coat, from which he had barely shaken off the mortar, and,—a sign of the true gentleman,—made no apologies. His air, figure, and address, have the character of the English country gentleman—open, unaffected, and independent, but perhaps combining more mildness and suavity. . . . His face is fine . . . it was difficult at the first glance to decide which of the busts in the apartment were of him, and which of Napoleon. The expression of the one, however, is much more benignant [*sic*]; it is indeed exceedingly pleasing, and prepares you for the amiable sentiments which appear in his discourse.

[Walking in the park] He gathered a wild flower, and, in presenting it to me, carelessly drew a comparison between its minute beauties and the pleasures of private life; contrasting those of ambition and power with the more gaudy flowers of the parterre, which look better at a distance than upon nearer approach. He said this so naturally, with a manner so simple, and an accent so mild, that it was impossible to see in it attempt at display of any kind.

He is particularly attentive to sufferers of his own nation . . . is careful to provide work for the poorer emigrants; and to others, affords lodging, and often money in considerable amount. His kindness has . . . been imposed upon . . . though he does not suffer his humanity to be chilled. This I learned from his American neighbours. I left Count Survillier [sic], satisfied . . . that fortune had rather spited him in making him the brother of the ambitious Napoleon.

Men were impressed also. "I was introduced & took *the hand* of King and Prince," wrote John Fanning Watson, the Philadelphia historian. With typical ambivalence toward royalty, he had come to be awed and astonished, but proceeded to judge the King by American standards. He was not disappointed. Joseph, he recorded with satisfaction, was "free from arrogancy [sic] and pride," soft of manner, "of good size," and not even "foreign looking." "The King . . . would not have been noticed as *uncommon* . . . in mix'd comp'y." Watson was not sure he approved of the dinners at Point Breeze—seventeen courses, some "disguised" so as to be unrecognizable. He reacted to the paintings at the Maison du lac in touchingly Early American style. "The largest was the Escape of Europe [actually the "*Rape* of Europa"] —drawn in great spirit, but with little regard to female modesty." About Joseph himself, however, he had no reservations; he liked him.

More sophisticated Americans were equally taken with Joseph, for example Francis Lieber, editor of the *Encyclopaedia Americana*, born in Germany, and widely traveled. "He must be 'truly good' as [Czar] Alexander so often declared him to be," Lieber wrote after his first encounter with Joseph. "He is loved by everyone for he is accessible to all and always glad to help others." After an interview in Philadelphia concerning the article on Napoleon for the *Encyclopaedia*, he came away convinced that he had seen history through the eyes of a great man. "I felt so bewildered I scarcely knew where I was when I reached the street. . . . I shall never forget that afternoon."

THE LADY "DRYS"

In the endless procession of visitors, one delegation went away breathing outrage—the ladies of the American Society for the Promotion of Temperance. Offered wine! They say he has breakfast at *eleven o'clock,* and drinks *champagne!* (It was true, but Joseph began the day hours before, with coffee or tea.) He keeps a cellar full of wine and awful spirits! Their pamphlets damned French immorality in general and Mr. Bonaparte, the ex-King, in particular.

In that era liquor was fifty cents a gallon (for native corn) . If every man could not live like a King, he could get "drunk as a lord," and considered it his God-given right. Only a little earlier, Washington's whiskey tax had brought bands of angry men from the frontier, ready to fight for the "natural rights of man." Americans drank rivers of whatever they could afford. Both Joseph's friends at the local tavern and his more affluent acquaintances in Philadelphia, therefore, shared his amusement at the "drys."

Still, the prevalent puritanism of the churches had made most Americans feel a little guilty about using "strong spirits." Charles J. Ingersoll, surely no provincial, undertook to excuse Joseph in an article in the *American Quarterly Review,* and later in his history of the War of 1812:

I never saw, I may add, a person—not even a lady—more abstemious of drink than Joseph Bonaparte, who always took a little wine both at breakfast and dinner, but very little, and that little even champagne diluted with water. . . . According to my notion, it would have been more wholesome for him . . . to eat less meat and drink more wine.

The attitude of apology forecast the later triumph of the "drys." Fortunately for the "wicked" Count de Survilliers, however, the days of the saloon-smashing Amazons of the Women's Christian

Temperance Union were far in the future. Otherwise he might have had to arm his servants and fortify his wine cellar.

MINA

Not all the visitors to Point Breeze considered Joseph's political career at an end. In early 1817 an incredulous but still shaken Louis Mailliard announced the arrival of General Xavier Mina. It was "The Student"—the most famous of all the Spanish guerrilla chiefs who had fought against Joseph. Backed by a frightening delegation of Spanish and Mexican revolutionaries, he begged an audience with "His Majesty, the King of Spain and the Indies."

Joseph, puzzled, received the group. The handsome Mina, still in his mid-twenties, fell on his knees, and the others followed suit. Embarrassed, Joseph got them on their feet. Your Majesty, said Mina, we are here to recognize you as King of the Indies. We shall win the crown of Mexico for you. More will follow! The crown of Mexico? Joseph asked softly. No. No. No more crowns. Surely not in America.

Nothing is more flattering to me than to see men, who would not recognize me in Madrid, search me out in exile. . . . But I cannot believe that the throne which you wish to reestablish will promote your happiness. Each day I spend on the hospitable soil of the United States convinces me anew of the excellence of republican institutions for America: guard them, therefore, as a precious gift of Providence; settle your internal quarrels; imitate the United States, and find among yourselves a man more capable than I to play the great role of Washington.

The decision was practical, though made on other grounds. Mina was destined to die in an attempt to overthrow the viceroy of Ferdinand VII. As Joseph hoped, Mexico would, in the end, become a republic, though over the opposition of a nephew he never understood, the Emperor Napoleon III.

THE CUP OF POWER

Others had plans for Joseph. In Kentucky, the French exile Joseph Lakanal dreamed of making him King of Mexico and the Indies—and of rescuing Napoleon from Saint-Helena and installing him as Emperor of South America. The stocky, wavy-haired Lakanal, who looked twenty years younger than his fifty-five, was a professor who had seen an hour of glory under the Republic—voting to execute Louis XVI and masterminding a revolutionary public education program in the Convention, and organizing the Institut for the Directory. An *ideologue* and republican, he had fared badly under the Empire, but he detested the Bourbons. And as he wrote in his diary: "When a man has drunk a long time in the cup of power, it is very difficult for him to enter again into the class of citizens." What irony if the colonies of the Spanish Bourbons became a base for the overthrow of their cousin, Louis XVIII of France! He busied himself with contacting French exiles of all ranks.

In mid-1817 he sent one of his men to Joseph with a packet of letters and documents announcing the imminent invasion of Mexico. "Deign, Sire, to transmit to me your orders, as speedily as it may please Your Majesty . . ." read one letter. Others requested that Joseph send money, and as King of the Indies, grant land, titles, and medals to encourage his followers, including Lakanal. "This new mark of your gracious favor will give me a degree of political importance in the eyes of your Mexican subjects." Academician that he was, Lakanal included a twenty-three-page report on his "Napoleonic Confederation" and conditions in Mexico and the adjacent Louisiana Territory, a list of Indian tribes, a vocabulary of Indian languages, and a sort of code to be used in correspondence.

Joseph, forewarned of Lakanal's machinations, refused to accept the packet. Some days later, in Philadelphia, the messenger lost (or sold) it to agents of Hyde de Neuville, the French ambassador, who turned it over to John Quincy Adams, then secretary of state. Aware that Joseph had been visited by scores of former Napoleonic soldiers, including Marshal Grouchy, Generals Henri and Charles Lallemand, Clausel, and Lefebvre-Desnouettes, the ambassador was really alarmed, not so much over the threat of the exiles themselves as the possibility that they might really rescue Napoleon. "Where will we be if that prodigious man arrives in Mexico?" Luis de Onis, the Spanish ambassador, soared red-faced and frantic to Secretary Adams to second Neuville's demand for an investigation. Henry Clay, who was all for the exiles as long as they didn't try to take United States territory, thought the ambassadors' dance riotously funny. The government, however, could not ignore their protests.

President Monroe put William Lee, former consul at Bordeaux and intimate of many French exiles, on the case. Lee reported Lakanal still in Kentucky; his invasion army was mostly imaginary. He discovered, however, that Charles Lallemand and others had been in contact with Mexican revolutionaries. Lallemand was president of the "Society for the Cultivation of the Vine and Olive," to which Congress had voted land on the Tombigbee River in Alabama, and Lee suspected the society was, in part, a front for a Mexican expedition. Joseph, he said, had contributed, innocently, to the proposed agricultural colony, but was not involved in the Mexican venture, and had written to General Galabert (who was) ". . . urging him not to enter into the wild and extravagant projects of these French fugitives, & offering him a means of settling himself in Pennsylvania."

Secretary Adams, in his direct New England way, called Lallemand to Washington and asked him what was going on. He did not even know Lakanal, the general swore, and he was not planning anything contrary to United States interests. As for Joseph, he was in "perfect retirement," and "should not be held responsible for letters written to him, which he had refused to receive."

President Monroe, with some relief, ruled Joseph innocent. As for Lakanal, why bother with him? He was a friend of Henry Clay, and what harm could he do? Life in the young republic had its beauties. (Lakanal, before returning to France in 1836, served as president of what became Louisiana State University, and helped organize higher education in Alabama and South Carolina.) The President's one concession to the nervous Hyde de Neuville and Onis was to set a watch on the Tombigbee settlers, who were assembling in Philadelphia for a voyage to Mobile, Alabama. Nothing was done to stop them, however. In December Lallemand sailed ahead of the rest—in a ship loaded with muskets, sabers, kegs of gunpowder, and six cannon—via Mobile, but for New Orleans.

CHAMP D'ASILE

The Tombigbee settlement was made in earnest (though it was doomed to complete failure), but not by Lallemand's expedition. In April General Charles and his less dashing brother Henri, uniformed as generals of imperial cavalry, cut a swath through New Orleans society, gathered up more settlers and supplies, and sailed on to the camp of the pirate Jean Lafitte, on Galveston Bay, in Texas territory disputed between Spain and the United States.

A supply ship sank en route to Galveston. The spring was unusually cold; few of the four hundred colonists, half of them women and children, had any experience with the wild frontier. The mere sight of Lafitte's men was enough to discourage faint souls. The suave buccaneer, however, controlled his men, donated some supplies, and got the settlers across the bay (though some drowned when boats capsized). They pushed inland to a site on the banks of the Trinity River, and established *Champ d'Asile* —the Field of Refuge.

Lallemand proclaimed that the colonists would live in peace, but refused to recognize the Spanish governor of Texas (or any other authority). Spanish troops moved in from San Antonio. The French, well armed but few, without expected help from Mexican revolutionaries, and short of food, withdrew to Galveston. There a hurricane swept their camp, leaving many dead and destroying their remaining possessions. Lafitte took some of the survivors to New Orleans. The rest made their way overland to United States soil.

William Lee had long since reported to President Monroe from New Orleans that the expedition was a failure, and would best be ignored. The President tried to take his advice. The French and Spanish ambassadors insisted, however, that Lakanal's "Napoleonic Confederation" had been born, wedging a state between the United States and Spanish Mexico. The British minister called on Adams to state that ". . . if there was a Bonaparte concerned in it, his government would of course consider it deserving of high attention." Monroe assured them all that Joseph was not involved, cited Lee's reports, and waited. The miniature crisis was short-lived.

The *Champ d'Asile* disaster finished the exiles' hopes of transplanting the Empire, or some bit of it, in the New World. No one was gladder of it than Joseph Bonaparte.

BLACK RIVER

During his flight from France, Joseph had left with Count Le Ray de Chaumont silver and other valuables worth some $40,000. In exchange he received land on the Black River in upstate New York, part of 350,000 acres bought after the American Revolution by the Count, who had hoped to found a French community.

The Count de Survilliers got around to surveying his backcountry domain in 1818, and liked what he saw. Virgin forest covered the hilly countryside, the valley was broad and beautiful, the river clear and deep, and there was a lake, which he called "Lake Bonaparte," the name it still bears. He added more land, bringing his holdings to 150,000 acres, built paper and cotton mills and a forge (largely to employ fellow refugees). On a promontory overlooking the lake, he put up a hunting lodge, of logs, but huge by local standards, and comfortably furnished.

In the early years many old friends had land nearby—Marshal Grouchy and his two sons, the Count Réal, ex-councillor of state and imperial policeman, and a clutch of generals. A little later, Lucien Murat, the huge rawboned second son of the marshal, came also (buying in with his American wife's money and staying solvent on loans from Joseph). Most of the "lords" visited the area only occasionally, and often traveled up from Philadelphia or New York in groups, partying as they went. In their cups, they were a raucous and sometimes destructive crew. Read a bill from a Mohawk Valley innkeeper to Joseph:

"To Making in Mine House one Big Fuss—$200"

After Joseph had left America, marvelous tales were told of him in the Black River country. The King, they said, was wheeled about in a magnificent coach drawn by six white horses. He was rowed along the river to his estate in a six-oared gondola; he hunted in a green costume trimmed with silver, and much more. Actually, the Count Réal, who built the curious "cup and saucer" house on Cape Vincent, cut much more of a figure. (He voiced about that the place was for Napoleon, whom he intended to bring in via Canada.) Lucien Murat had a much more lordly style, occasionally applying a giant boot to the backside of a servant or tradesman, running up debts, drinking and wenching, galloping through the villages to show off his horses. Joseph came quietly to inspect his enterprises, rest, entertain a hunting party for a few weeks, or seclude himself with a lady friend. Mailliard or some other agent usually made advance preparations and servants went out to make local purchases. Mr. Bonaparte was seldom seen by the local people, and then frequently passed unrecognized.

As other prominent refugees lost interest in building up the remote Black River area, so did Joseph. (Marshal Grouchy returned to France in 1820; Clausel preferred the Tombigbee project; Lucien Murat's ambitious colonizing scheme came to nothing; and so it went.) Joseph came to prefer summer excursions to Saratoga for the baths, races, and good company. Otherwise he spent his time at Point Breeze, or Philadelphia, where he bought a town house, and infrequently, New York City. After 1828 he never went to Black River; in 1832 he sold his holdings there.

Yet today, Joseph is better remembered in the Black River country than in New Jersey. This is because he left there the beautiful Annette Savage and the daughter she had borne him.

ANNETTE SAVAGE AND CAROLINE

By family tradition, the blood of Pocahontas flowed in her veins, and looking at Annette Savage, one could believe it. Small, light of foot and graceful, black haired and olive skinned, her somewhat heavy features were balanced by huge, dark eyes, luminous and willful, which gave her face a regal loveliness. Joseph met her in Philadelphia, where her Quaker family, though of modest means, was well respected. The ex-King was smitten, and Annette, in turn, awed, fascinated, and finally in love also, though Joseph was thirty years her senior. Over the shocked protests of her parents, she began visiting him alone, and soon went to live in a house he took for her near Bordentown. Her father and mother begged that she and the Count de Survilliers be married, at least by a justice of the peace, and to save their feelings, she told them they had been.

In 1822, shortly after Joseph's daughter Charlotte arrived from Europe for an extended visit, Annette gave birth to a baby girl, whom they named Caroline. For discretion's sake, Joseph took the mother and child to his Black River estate, and later built a house for them near Watertown. At first, "Mrs. Bonaparte," who seemed eminently respectable, if withdrawn, was accepted by her pioneer neighbors. But her relationship with Joseph deteriorated, he visited her less and less frequently, and her position became very awkward.

Uneasy in conscience, Joseph found a very French solution to their problem. He arranged a marriage between Annette and Charles Delafolie, a fellow exile, and set them up in a new stone house (a mansion by local standards) at Theresa. He also gave them property in Watertown and LeRay, and thousands of acres of timberland. There was gossip about the marriage, but Annette and Caroline gained a normal place in society. When her husband died, a few years later, Annette moved to Watertown, where she reared Joseph's daughter as Caroline Bonaparte Delafolie.

Caroline became a beautiful woman, much resembling Joseph's sister Caroline, after whom she was named, though she was more lovely and lovable than her hardminded aunt had been. At seventeen, she married the elegant Colonel Zebulon Howell Benton, of Oxbow, New York, who counted among his relatives Thomas Hart Benton, the renowned Senator from Missouri, and James Fenimore Cooper. Joseph could not be present, but he sent Caroline a dowry, and enabled her to have the most elaborate wedding Watertown had ever seen.*

---

* Annette Savage married again, and moved away from Watertown. Caroline had seven children by Benton, of whom five, three boys and two girls, grew to adulthood. In the heyday of the Second Empire, she was received by Napoleon III, officially recognized as a legitimate Bonaparte,

THE DEATH OF NAPOLEON

In August 1821, at Saratoga, Joseph received word of the death of Napoleon on Saint-Helena. He returned to Point Breeze, and for weeks would see none but his most trusted friends. Often before he had brooded over the contrast between his pleasant life and the harsh existence of his brother, confined in a shabby house on the jungle-ribbed rock of Saint-Helena. Twice he had offered to join Napoleon. Now he was wracked with guilt. Had he failed Napoleon in Spain? In Paris in 1814? Had his admiration of Lord Cornwallis shaped Napoleon's opinion of the English—made him trust them—sent him to his death?

Letters came from Generals Montholon and Bertrand, who had been with the Emperor to the end. "He spoke of the volunteers of Corsica, of his old uncle Lucien, of his youth, of you, of all the family." The family . . . much of the family. Joseph *could* live in the United States, if he wanted to, Napoleon had said. But what of his daughters? Suitable marriages could be more easily arranged in Europe ". . . however there are several families such as the Washingtons, the Jeffersons, etc.; he would be able to have a president of the United States in his family." Rome is best. Ally with all the princely families ". . . who have produced popes and who have commanded the consciences of the whole universe." Joseph could not imagine his brother lying, as the letters described him, skeletonal, wasted, gasping for breath. Napoleon was force, motion. . . . The old spirit broke through occasionally, flippant, bold, profane. "One has to kiss the —— of the Pope, but he kisses the —— of nobody and no family." Joseph had to smile—and to weep. Command the consciences! Command. Even at the end! Oh, but Napoleon did love the family. His will distributed substantial property, but

---

and provided an income on which she lived in France for almost a decade. After 1870, she returned to New York, taught French in Watertown and Richfield Springs, wrote for magazines and newspapers, and published one book, *France and Her People*. She died in 1890, more respected than her husband, who survived her. (A notoriously bad businessman, Colonel Benton had lost most of his wife's inheritance before she went to France.) Her grave is in the old Presbyterian cemetery at Oxbow, New York.

also gave Joseph and others personal items, most of little value, even shabby, but things Napoleon had kept near him, used, or worn—snuffboxes, an antique sword handle, pieces of clothing. Sentimental gifts! Joseph was deeply touched.

For Napoleon's son there was the sword of Austerlitz, and via Bertrand the admonition: "He must always glory in being born French . . . he must never do anything to alienate or injure the French." One day he will govern France! I charge my *brother and friend*, Joseph, to advise him when to return; I charge my son to obey him. The little King of Rome! The golden-haired, demanding, irresistible little King with whom Joseph had spent such happy hours in 1814. Now he was almost eleven. They were making an Austrian Prince of him! Visitors said he was taught nothing of his father—but that he *knew*, he knew.

Napoleon! Napoleon! For all that he had done evil, he did not deserve this!

Even the cause of the Emperor's death seemed in doubt. Reading the descriptions of his suffering, Joseph's anger rose. He had been treated at first by his own physician, whose potions made him scream and retch until he refused them, then by an English surgeon who eased his pain, but could not diagnose his trouble. Poison? No. No government would be so stupid. But the climate! Napoleon had complained of it; Montholon wrote of its "disastrous influence." Saint-Helena had killed Napoleon! The English had killed him!

Joseph wanted to believe that, but doubts lingered. Despite the pain they caused him, he returned to the accounts of his brother's agony again and again. He could not but remember his father in his last weeks, writhing from stomach pains, unable to keep down food—finally not even liquids—looking pitifully small and fragile under his coverlet. Had the same disease claimed Napoleon? Was it the Bonaparte curse?

Joseph decided that if *he*, the elder brother, were suffering from stomach disease, he could believe Napoleon had died of it. He called in his friend Dr. Benjamin Morgan, who declared him in perfect health, but to ease his mind, sent him to specialists in Philadelphia and Baltimore. None of the examinations showed any disease, however. Joseph considered the case against the

British proved. The hurt of his bereavement had cooled some-what, however, and he would not say, as some had already, that they had deliberately put Napoleon on Saint-Helena to die. But he was outraged at the apparent indifference of the British authorities, the conditions under which Napoleon had lived, and the indignities he had suffered at the hands of Sir Hudson Lowe, his "jailor."

The climate of Saint-Helena has since been ruled "salubrious" by dispassionate experts; though it was not pleasant to Napoleon, it probably had little to do with his death. And Hudson Lowe, though not the most compassionate or tactful of men, was no monster. He had a prisoner on his hands seemingly determined to be persecuted—even to die tragically and early.

As the years passed and more information appeared on Na-poleon's exile, Joseph's judgment of his brother's captors softened. But he could never see Napoleon as other than a man venge-fully tortured by his enemies, and maligned by their propa-gandists. With great honesty as to fact, but steadily, he defended the Emperor to his dying day. "It is justice . . . that I owe the man who was *mon ami*." Because he saw his brother's ultimate intentions as good, because, irrationally, he felt some responsi-bility for his downfall and "martyrdom," and because he loved him, Joseph helped build the Napoleonic legend. Selflessly, he defended the man who, at Saint-Helena, as always, had infamously depreciated his brother's abilities, and foisted on history a false image of Joseph as lazy, pleasure-bent, and good-hearted but dull.

CHARLOTTE AND ZÉNAÏDE

In December 1821, Joseph's younger daughter, Charlotte, ac-companied by Captain and Madame Sari, arrived from Florence. Sari, who had commanded the ship on which Napoleon escaped from Elba in 1814, was one of Joseph's business agents. His wife, a young French Creole from Martinique, was their patron's sometime household manager and hostess. Dark, fiery, beautiful, exuding strength like a lioness, Madame Sari normally disdained female company. The quiet, demure Charlotte had brought out her mother instinct, however. Joseph saw immediately that there would be no conflict between them, and was relieved. Charlotte! Almost twenty! She had been a child when he saw her last. Now she was a woman—and so much like Julie—like Julie as a bride —not so stern though—not so bourgeois. She was shy, as she had always been, but she wore her clothes like a Princess. Joseph was proud of her.

Showing Charlotte around Point Breeze, talking for hours, suggesting scenes for her to sketch, listening to her play the piano, Joseph stopped brooding over the death of Napoleon. She was still her father's girl—an attentive listener, boundlessly interested in whatever was on his mind, happy just to be with him if he wanted to read, write, or doze, silently sketching or knitting until he wanted to talk again.

Charlotte was with Joseph almost constantly for three years —at Point Breeze or Philadelphia, with long vacations in the summer at Saratoga, and trips to New York City when Joseph had business there or the theater offered something interesting. Occasionally Joseph felt overdomesticated, and took a trip alone. For the most part, however, he was content. One diversion was sizing up the young men who came to pay court to Charlotte and visitors who might make suitable husbands.

Jerome Bonaparte, son of Joseph's brother Jérôme by his first wife, Elizabeth Patterson, was, for a time, the favored suitor. He was warmly received by his uncle at Point Breeze and returned often. Seventeen in 1822, he had met Pauline Bonaparte in Europe the year before. The whimsical and still most beautiful Bonaparte sister had been so taken by the tall, sandy-haired and unaffected boy that she withdrew her support from another suitor and promoted a match between Jerome and Charlotte, promising to will them 300,000 francs. When he came to Point Breeze, he already had the approval of Madame Letizia and his father's wonderfully generous second wife, Princess Catherine von Württemberg, who hoped the marriage would "put Jerome in an easier relationship with me and my children."

Joseph liked Jerome, but felt that the American Bonaparte's future was in the United States, where he could have the advantage of his grandfather Patterson's connections as well as a share of his millions. The Bonaparte future (he had to agree with Napoleon's assessment) lay in Europe. Moreover, he knew that Charlotte was frightened of the United States, with its untamed countryside, sprawling, dirty, incredibly ugly cities jammed with an unbelievable mixture of grubby, noisy people who to the newcomer seemed outright dangerous, and sometimes were.

Charlotte would have to make up her own mind about Jerome, Joseph decided. She hesitated not a moment. No, she did not want to marry him. Why? Because she didn't want to. Joseph was charmed, and relieved.* Other candidates for his daughter's hand trooped in—the handsome son of Marshal Ney, the two sons of Fouché, the sons of Grouchy, exiled generals and colonels (with the French the husband's age mattered less than his family and fortune), a few Americans, and others. All were rejected. One of the last was Achille Murat, the marshal's eldest son, smaller and less flamboyant than his brother Lucien, but handsome and formidably intelligent. He later settled in Florida, married a grandniece of George Washington, became postmaster and mayor of Lipona,† a county judge, and with brief absences for adventures in Belgium, New Orleans, and elsewhere, lived out his life there. Somehow he found time to write four books and many shorter pieces about America.

Charlotte's problem was solved, to her satisfaction, in Europe. A marriage was arranged with her first cousin, Napoleon Louis, eldest surviving son of Louis Bonaparte, former King of Holland. In early 1824 Joseph saw her off for Europe.

The mousy Charlotte's place had already been taken by her sister Zénaïde, who arrived in 1823 with her husband, Charles Lucien, son of Joseph's brother Lucien. They occupied the Maison du lac, but Zénaïde soon challenged Madame Sari for control of the Point Breeze household, and won out. Small, like her mother, in coloration more like Joseph, but in will, *Napoleonic*, she disciplined servants, rearranged schedules, rewrote menus, introduced new formality into receptions and dinners.

---

* Jerome married an American girl. His son was secretary of the navy and later attorney general under Theodore Roosevelt. The line is now extinct.

† Lipona is an anagram of Napoli —Naples—the kingdom ruled by Achille's father.

The Creole icily adjusted to the new order, but took revenge on *Monsieur le Comte.* Joseph, embarrassed, soon found business for the Saris in Europe. Even before they left, however, the crisis had passed. Zénaïde, her precedence established, found plenty to occupy her at Maison du lac.

Moreover, she soon found herself with child. In February 1824, Joseph's first grandchild—a boy!—was born at his house in Philadelphia. He was christened Joseph Lucien Charles Napoléon. Probably he was the first Prince ever born in the United States. Two years later he had a sister, a little Princess, born at Point Breeze. In all Zénaïde and Charles had twelve children (the other ten born in Italy), eight of whom survived to maturity.

AMERICAN ORNITHOLOGY

Prince Charles was Napoleon's size, but wide-eyed and slightly flat-nosed like his father, with the same hot temper, independence, and perhaps more intelligence. He had lived in France and Italy as a child, and, between the ages of six and twelve, in England (where Lucien Bonaparte and family were in willing exile). He was fluent in all three languages, which he not only spoke, but could write well enough to publish. Energetic and vocal, he might have been a superb diplomat or legislator, but such opportunities were nonexistent for Bonapartes, and he had turned to scholarship.

Ornithology was his specialty. With every month he stayed at Point Breeze, the Maison du lac became more jammed with glass cases full of stuffed birds (with a few beasts thrown in), drawings and paintings of American species, and books about them. The overflow from his study pressed into the halls, parlor, and even the bedrooms. American naturalists soon involved him in their projects, as the editor of *Niles' Register* noted in May 1825, taking the occasion to thumb his nose at Europe, pay tribute to Joseph, and demonstrate a deep affection for commas:

AMERICAN NATURAL HISTORY. A splendid work in the subject is about to be published. . . . It is written by Dr. John D. Goodman . . . Professor Say, Drs. Dekay, Mitchell and Harlan, and Messrs. G. Ord and Charles Bonaparte. It is hoped that the association of the latter in this great work, will not offend the "holy alliance." [The European powers] . . . may be assured, though, the movement of a Bonaparte, from one village to another, is a matter of grave and serious consideration in Europe, that Mr. Joseph Bonaparte and his family are very quiet and orderly people, and much respected by all. . . .

In 1825, Charles published the first volume of an independent work, *American Ornithology*, which he finished after his return to Europe in 1828. Exulted *Niles' Register*, "Mr. Bonaparte's exceeds in magnificence . . . [all similar] publications."

Already, Joseph and Charles had been elected members of the American Philosophical Society (as of April 1823), which had received the Count de Survilliers informally for years, and to which he had lent paintings for exhibits, and done other favors. No similar American groups could boast so distinguished a membership as this Philadelphia-based organization "for promoting useful knowledge." Its first president had been Benjamin Franklin, its third Thomas Jefferson. If Joseph's friendship with Robert Patterson, the fifth president, Charles Ingersoll, and others influenced Charles's quick acceptance, he soon became a valued member on his own. He introduced to the society, among others, John James Audubon, whose masterful paintings of American birds are classics of the genre.

Charles, by 1828, had also been elected to the Academies of Natural Science of Philadelphia and Baltimore, the College of Natural History of New York, and the Columbian Institute of Washington. The American bodies thus set an example later followed by the Berlin Academy, the French *Institut* (*before* the rise to power of Louis Napoleon), and many others. Joseph took great pride in his son-in-law's distinctions; he himself, now approaching sixty, felt sufficiently honored to belong to the American Philosophical Society, the most prestigious of all.

THE GOOD LIFE

Many French immigrants were far from happy in America. Wrote one:

Living in the finest house here, surrounded by generals, majors, colonels, chevaliers of the Order of Cincinnati,—that is, lodged in a

wretched hut, with titled neighbors who drive their own teams, cultivate and very badly their own fields, wear poor clothes, entertaining
some visiting Indians, who prefer Frenchmen to Americans, since the
latter can never cultivate the arts.

Joseph agreed more with another famous resident of his
adopted hometown, Tom Paine: "I would rather see my horse
Button eating the grass of Bordentown than to see all the pomp
and show of Europe."

Mr. Bonaparte had been fully accepted—and more. He was
a prominent citizen. His closest American friends were Charles
Ingersoll and Stephen Girard, the first and best, and his witty
and humane physician, Dr. Benjamin Morgan, for whose death,
in 1827, Joseph mourned as if he were a brother. Frequent visitors
were his neighbors Admiral Charles Stewart, who had commanded
the famed *Constitution* of the War of 1812, and Judge Joseph
Hopkinson, a former congressman, whose lovely daughter considered Joseph a foster-uncle, and corresponded with him for
years, even after she married and moved away. Nicholas Biddle,
the Byronesque Philadelphia *litterateur*, financier and president
of the Bank of the United States, was a member of Joseph's
circle, as was Senator Richard Stockton, of Princeton, at whose
home he met Daniel Webster, and Dr. Nathaniel Chapman, later
first president of the American Medical Association.

Several times in the 1820s, the legislature of New Jersey was
entertained in a body at Point Breeze. Joseph enjoyed the visits
and always boasted afterward about how many bottles of wine
the solons had drunk. Old friends from Europe stayed for months
at Point Breeze (Miot de Melito for better than a year); Americans for shorter periods. Charles Ingersoll described the hospitality offered:

A cup of coffee, or tea, as you chose, brought by a servant before you
were out of bed in the morning; a meat breakfast, between ten and
eleven o'clock; a good library; the host's prolonged and unceasing
historical and biographical narrative; horses and carriages, for excursions
in the vicinity; shooting, fishing, or whatever pastime you desired, till
evening; dinner between six and seven; a drive round the grounds; a
game of billiards, or some other amusement, after dinner, till an early

bed-time, seldom, if ever, later than ten o'clock, were commonly the day's routine.

On Sundays and holidays crowds came by steamboat from Philadelphia and other points to see the house and grounds. All the paintings and sculpture were on view, and the "King" often appeared to greet visitors, and sometimes to hold forth on the history and merits of his treasures. His unblushing lectures on the beauties and allegorical significance of the female nudes gave the ladies a delightful shock. Some quietly scurried away, others stayed "out of politeness," but all had something marvelous to tell their friends at home. To Joseph, the great wonder was the orderliness and honesty of his guests, who never, over almost two decades, took or damaged anything.

The private joys were many. In the early years, before the exiles began returning to France, there were many gatherings. Fitz-Greene Halleck describes a French wedding party in New York where Joseph blew a paper trumpet while Marshal Grouchy sang military songs and General Lallemand crawled about playing horse for a little boy. "They romped and played like children. . . . [It was] the raciest and most amusing night I ever passed." Later there was the happiness of having his daughters near him, and of watching his grandchildren grow. It was hard to see the boy go when his parents returned to Europe. He was four, precocious and destructive, but wonderful.

Joseph was pleased also to see the cultural life of the country improving. He was present in 1825 at the first performance of an opera in New York City, by an Italian company, and in 1827 at the first ballet, by a French company he helped sponsor. The response of the audience to the latter left something to be desired. At the first pirouette, recorded Achille Murat, skirts whirled and ballerinas' *limbs* were seen. The ladies "screamed for shame" and left. "The gentlemen remained, crying and laughing at the very fun of the thing." Joseph was appalled, but, as always, tolerant of his "countrymen."

Occasionally, he did indirectly express some homesickness, as in a letter of 1827 to Mrs. William H. Keating, a good friend who was in France with her husband. Achille Murat, he told her, had been at Point Breeze for a month with his wife (Catherine Willis Gray), and her family had also stopped in. "[Catherine] . . . is *jolie*, gentle, and gay, but she doesn't speak a word of French. . . . Her sisters are pretty, and well brought up, they belong to the family of Washington, but none of them speak French." Momentarily, Joseph seemed a querulous old man, pouting that there was no one who could *really* talk to him. Perhaps he was thinking of the loneliness he would feel when Zénaïde and her family left him.

For the most part, however, Joseph was established and content. His adopted country had given him a good life, and he was respected even in the White House. "Mr. Hopkinson spoke to me of the desire of the Comte de Survilliers that his son and daughter might have passage in our ship-of-the-line *Delaware*, which is soon going out to the Mediterranean," recorded President John Quincy Adams in October 1827. Return Charles, Zénaïde and family to Italy on an American battleship? The answer was *yes*. They sailed in early 1828. Joseph was saddened at their going, but he did not intend to follow. "I regard myself as having arrived in port," he wrote in 1830.

The Bonaparte Cause

Nevertheless, Joseph had never been able to ignore that there were Bonapartists in France, or that popular nostalgia for the Empire was promoted by Napoleon's "martyrdom," and grew with every year of Bourbon oppression. He had adopted a watch-and-wait attitude, however, since he, like most French politicians, did not believe the powers would tolerate a Bonaparte restoration, even after Britain wrecked the "congress system" in 1822. Naturally, there were always those who wanted him to take positive action.

In 1824, the Marquis de Lafayette, on a triumphal tour of the United States, called at Point Breeze. Touched by what seemed purely a gesture of personal regard, Joseph received him warmly, and found him the same—affable but dignified, at sixty-seven more portly, like his host, but still vain of his appearance—as was evidenced by the careful set of his impressive mane of curly hair. He avoided discussing politics, assuming that Lafayette, though a liberal and opponent of Bourbon policies, was still a legitimist. To his surprise, his guest took him aside and said he could deliver the French throne to Napoleon II (the King of Rome, now Duke of Reichstadt) if Joseph would contribute 2,000,000 francs to the cause.

Joseph refused, pleading lack of funds. Actually, he could have raised the money, and would gladly have given his whole fortune to restore Napoleon II, but he did not believe it could be done. Even if the French cried out for it and the powers declined to oppose, would Austria release the Duke of Reichstadt? He thought not. Moreover, he did not trust Lafayette as a politician. The "Hero of Two Worlds" was personally the soul of honor, but he had deserted Napoleon "on principle" in 1815, and might justify betraying his son on the same basis. Lafayette visited Joseph again before he left for France in 1825, but they made no deal regarding Napoleon II.

Joseph did not believe, in any case, that Napoleon II should be restored by intrigue, but by the will of the French people. Only then would the Bonaparte dynasty be permanently installed. He did not doubt that Napoleon I had been the choice, to the end, of the French people and the champion of the masses of Europe against the tyrannies of the Old Regime. If this were clearly understood, it seemed to him inevitable that the French would recall his son, and that other peoples would approve their action.

He set himself the task, therefore, of telling the *truth* about Napoleon. The Allies, he wrote Francis Lieber, sacrificed "legal equality, constitutional liberty, religious liberty, and permanent peace" to the interests of nobles and priests imbued with "the gothic prejudices . . . of the middle ages." His view was reflected by the *Encyclopaedia Americana*. The Baron Méneval, who had been his secretary and later Napoleon's, placed unsigned articles for him in French journals. He used Felix Lacoste's *Courrier des États-Unis*, founded with his money and published in New York, to refute the statements of authors he considered in error. His letters to authors whose views he hoped to change and friends who might publish his opinions ran into the hundreds.

He deplored the fact that Sir Walter Scott "wrote for the English government," questioned if Philippe de Ségur's history and memoirs were not meant to ingratiate him with the Bourbons, and rebuked Madame de Staël's son for publishing her *Ten Years of Exile*, pointing out that her opinion of Napoleon had changed by 1815, when she supported him. Few memoirists got his complete approval, though Méneval and Miot de Melito came close. Savary was sent cordial regards, but apprised of inaccuracies; Thibaudeau excoriated for saying that Napoleon had "reversed the course of the Revolution." Soult, said Joseph bluntly, had written an incredible fabric of lies about events in Spain, himself, and Napoleon. (The sometime bane of Joseph's existence had received back his marshal's baton from Louis XVIII, and would later be minister of Louis Philippe.) Joseph collaborated with Lamarque, Belliard, and others to refute the errors "voluntary or involuntary" of Bourrienne. In June 1827 he published an article in the *American Quarterly Review* defending his performance in Naples and Spain. Anti-Napoleonic works, like Montbreton de Norvins's history, he treated scornfully, while approving the more laudatory ones like Count Bonacossi's *Commentari di Napoleone* and Baron Bignet's history.

Joseph was too honest, however, to praise untruth, even if favorable to Napoleon. Were the Emperor's half-formed thoughts ". . . to be transmitted to posterity as if they were legislative acts?" he asked Emmanuel de Las Cases after reading his *Mémorial de Sainte-Hélène*. Scholars have since confirmed that Las Cases rewrote history to suit Napoleon, who even supplied him with a few false documents. Neither would Joseph tolerate calumnies against his former enemies in Spain. "I have the conviction," he wrote a well-meaning defender, "that the Duke d'Infantado . . . and Cevallos himself, took the oath to me at Bayonne in good faith. . . . I must say, to tell the truth, that I authorized Cevallos . . . to remain at Madrid [in 1808]. The Duke d'Infantado was also disposed to follow me if I had insisted."

It is evident from Joseph's letters and articles that he must have plowed through no less than a thousand heavy volumes between 1824 and 1831, inch-by-inch, spinning out hundreds of thousands of words of analysis and commentary. It was a labor of love, but hardly pleasure. To his visitors and casual acquaintances, he seemed to have unlimited time to talk and play, and struck many as lazy, as had been the case all his life. They did not see him at his literary work, or consider that he had farms to manage, and properties and investments in Europe and America to watch over. Joseph wanted it that way. He was brilliant, worked fast, and had chosen competent secretaries and agents whom he knew how to use. Time was left to play the carefree country gentleman. It was not by accident, however, that while his guests drank deep, the Count de Survilliers sipped, and while they kept what hours they liked, he was in bed by ten or eleven. There was work to do the next day.

In April 1830, Joseph began writing his memoirs. He was vain enough to record his own successes, but he did not write to glorify himself. "Napoleon was still more a . . . friend of men . . . still more a good and just man, than a great warrior and a great administrator. . . . Today I can better appreciate what the causes . . . were which forced him to give himself a false character, a character which made him feared by [the men and nations] . . . he had to employ . . . [to fight against] the oligarchy [which] had declared war on the principles of the revolution."

The memoirs were never finished. In July 1830, revolution shook Paris, and Joseph was soon occupied with the cause of Napoleon II.

THE EAGLET

News of the flight of Charles X, and the appointment of the Duke d'Orléans, Louis Philippe, as lieutenant general of France, reached Joseph in early September. The Duke, whom the liberal monarchists wanted to make King, and Lafayette, the republicans' choice for president, were cooperating to restore order. No permanent government had been established, however.

Perhaps the parties could compromise on Napoleon II, whose government would be both monarchical and "revolutionary." Surely no more attractive Prince could be found than "The

Eaglet"—the Duke of Reichstadt. Now a tall, blond soldier of nineteen, with wide blue eyes and a look of melancholy maturity, he was disciplined, educated, and had a precocious knowledge of men and affairs. Combining the studied informality of an Austrian Prince with the grace of a French courtier, he moved with the assurance of one who had won respect even as a child by refusing to deny his heritage.

Joseph wrote Lafayette first. "You remember our conversation [in the United States] . . . my sentiments and my opinions were the same as yours. . . . Everything for the French People! . . . I cannot forget that my nephew, Napoleon II, was proclaimed by the chamber which, in 1815, was dissolved by the bayonets of foreigners." He urged the Marquis to dissociate himself from Louis Philippe (after all a Bourbon) and let the French people decide on their government. Napoleon II, he insisted, was legally King, since the chamber had acted under a constitution approved by three million voters. "The nation alone has the right to destroy its own work."

He went to New York, where the mail boats from Le Havre put in, to await further news, and began preparations to leave for Switzerland or the Low Countries if reports were favorable. Meanwhile, he wrote to Jourdan, Ménéval, Belliard, Lamarque, and other friends in Paris pleading that at all costs they defeat Louis Philippe. "You will be accountable to your children, the nation, to posterity [if] you surrender them to new calamities." He predicted (rightly) that if the Bourbon became King another revolution would soon come—" . . . another 14 July [storming of the Bastille], another 10 August [overthrow of Louis XVI]."

When the next mail showed the situation still unsettled, Joseph sent off appeals for the freedom of the Duke of Reichstadt, whom he asked to be allowed to escort into France. With the skill of the lawyer he was, he begged the ex-Empress Marie Louise, for the sake of ser son, France, Austria, and Europe, to use her influence with her father, the Austrian Emperor. "[Napoleon II] . . . has only to show himself to the French, his mere presence will reestablish the throne." To Metternich he touted the value to Austria (a family alliance) and in maintaining his European system. "Napoleon [II] will prevent republican ferment from developing in France, Italy, Spain, and Germany." His letter to the Emperor Francis played on his personal feelings, self-interest, and fears: Would he deny his grandson his heritage? Would he withhold from the French ". . . the only prince who can give them internal peace, and assure the tranquillity of Europe?" Could the Emperor not trust him, Joseph, whose moderation he had praised in writing and had even recommended for the throne of Italy? Did His Majesty not realize that *even a republic* might be founded in France if Napoleon II did not appear?

On 20 September Joseph heard the worst—Louis Philippe had been named King by a rump of the chamber of deputies. He protested to the chamber itself. "Napoleon II was proclaimed by the chamber of deputies in 1815. . . . Since the nation has not adopted another [constitution] . . . legally and voluntarily accepted by the people [Napoleon II is Emperor]. . . ." Only the nation could reject him. "Until then, monsieurs, you have a duty to Napoleon II." He, Joseph, would share that duty, accompany the young Prince to France, and see that he knew ". . . the last dispositions of his father, dying a victim of the enemies of France on the rock of Saint Helena."

Joseph decided, however, to postpone his trip to Europe, and returned to Point Breeze. During the winter of 1830–31 there was much to discourage him. The Austrians refused to release Napoleon II. Louis Philippe invited most of the Napoleonic exiles to return, but maintained the ban against the Bonaparte family. Joseph's message to the French chamber was not read to the deputies, and the King prohibited its publication. And belatedly, Lafayette wrote that despite their friendship, he had not and could never support the return of the Napoleonic system" . . . which was bright with glory, but tinged with despotism."

"Napoleon," Joseph replied, "was forced into war by the English, by war into dictatorship; these four words are the history of the Empire. . . . He expiated at Saint Helena the crime of turning all institutions to the good of the people. . . . The French nation will do him justice . . . [as will] the European masses." He was not ready to give up. There were too many indications that France was unhappy with Louis Philippe.

Bonapartism and Recall to Europe

Lafayette's republican followers were the first to be disillusioned with the July Monarchy. The Marquis's decision for Louis Philippe finished his political career, begun almost fifty years before when he returned to France wearing the laurels of the American Revolution, one of surprising eminence, considering that his every major decision had been wrong. French workers turned sullen: the peasants apathetic. It early became apparent, as Joseph wrote Ingersoll, that the new government served only "the rich bankers and merchants of Paris." At home there was stagnation, repression, and corruption in high places; in foreign affairs France was a nonentity. Before 1830 was out Metternich had bluffed Louis Philippe into a do-nothing policy by, among other things, threatening to "turn loose" Napoleon II in France. France laughed bitterly. What could one expect from the "bourgeois King" with his black suit and umbrella? France was unhappy, and what was worse, for her, France was *bored*.

The market boomed for tales of past glory, and Bonapartism grew apace, buoyed by the Napoleonic legend, on which magnificent talents were at work. Victor Hugo, once a legitimist, had signaled a change of heart with his poem *"Lui"* ("Him") in 1827, and produced more in the same vein every year. Gérard Labrunie (Gérard de Nerval) tore at French emotions with his verse-epics *L'Ile d'Elba*, *Waterloo*, and *Sainte Hélène*. And in 1828 the work of the incomparable romanticist Pierre Jean Beranger began to appear:

> Long, long, will they talk of his glory
> Under the thatched roof;
> In fifty years the humble dwelling
> Will know no other history
>
> Children, through this village
> I saw him ride
> Followed by kings.

It was heady stuff for patriots, even non-Bonapartists. For the more sober-minded, there were the convincing writings of the Emperor's loyal defenders, led by Joseph, the flood of books by returnees from Saint-Helena—Las Cases, Montholon, Gourgaud, and others, including the Irish surgeon Barry O'Meara, whom Napoleon had totally captivated—and the admiring histories, for which Baron Bignon's set the style.

Pierre Louis Roederer, General Lamarque, and many more old friends, had advised Joseph to come to Europe even before 1830. After the July Revolution, letters came by the score. Come! Head up the cause! France is closed to Your Majesty (the royal style again), but there is Switzerland—Belgium—England. Joseph hesitated. The situation was unclear; the most positive encouragement came from those outside France, like Achille Murat, who had accepted a commission in the Belgian army (but soon lost it, when Louis Philippe protested to the Belgian government). Méneval, Miot, and others, in France, were inhibited by police surveillance.

The outbreak of revolutions in Italy, with Charlotte's husband Napoleon Louis and his brother Louis Napoleon among the leaders, dismayed him. They were operating in the Austrian north and the Papal States; he sensed disaster, discredit to the Bonapartes, and feared for his nephews' safety. Rightly so. An Austrian army made short work of the rebels. At least, however, the young Bonapartes escaped.

Word came shortly, however, that Napoleon Louis had died suddenly of a mysterious malady. Joseph's heart went out to Charlotte. Her marriage had been far from happy, but she was devoted to her husband. Perhaps if he went to Europe she could join him. But the triumph of Austria—of Metternich and reaction—in Italy made him hesitate to go.

Late in 1831, however, Joel Poinsett returned from France with the opinion that the nation seemed ready to receive Napoleon II. He brought a clutch of letters, the most moving from Victor Hugo, begging Joseph to return. Poinsett had not seen Méneval, who, fearing arrest, had left Paris, but a message soon arrived from the Baron recommending that Joseph come to Europe. Shortly after, M. Peugnet landed in New York with his dance troupe and hurried to Point Breeze with a list of Bonapartists in the French chamber and the prediction that the deputies would at least open France to the Bonapartes.

In December 1831 Joseph sold his Black River property and prepared to leave for England (Poinsett had brought a note from Lord Grey stating that the Count de Survilliers was welcome there). It was hard to leave, however. He had been in America sixteen years; Europe's struggles seemed somewhat unreal, while the United States became more familiar and friendly by the year. Then too, Joseph, though he was loath to admit it, was growing old—in January 1832 he turned sixty-four. Still handsome, though portly, still a lion among the ladies, though now more fatherly (Madame Sari's eyes were beginning to rove), he moved a little slower and took decisions with more difficulty than before. He temporized, waiting for some positive sign— above all a vote of the French chamber which would allow him to enter France.

In June 1832 he visited Washington, and was received by President Andrew Jackson, with whom he got on famously. Jackson, it was evident (unlike Madison in 1815), didn't give a damn if Joseph *did* get him involved in European politics. In July, however, Joseph felt his hand was forced. Colonel Collius, a Belgian who had earlier been aide-de-camp to General Exelmans in Spain, appeared at Point Breeze, avowing that his brother, who held a position at the Austrian court, guaranteed that it was time to press the cause of Napoleon II. Joseph decided, recalled Ingersoll, "that as the eldest of the Emperor's family, it was his duty to afford his adherents the opportunity, which they nearly all assured him was good, for restoring the Bonaparte authority."

On 20 July 1832, he embarked from Philadelphia for Liverpool, accompanied by Louis Maillard, Captain and Madame Sari, and others of his retinue. Wrote Ingersoll: "Alarming accounts were in the public journals of the extreme illness of the Duke of Reichstadt, which I was about mentioning to his uncle . . . but I checked myself. . . . He was in excellent spirits and health, hopeful, though not sanguine, of a prosperous voyage."

From the tomb, Napoleon called once more on his faithful brother, who, against his better judgment, sailed away from the United States, which he loved, to do his best for the Emperor's tortured son, who, unknown to him, was dying in Vienna, and would breathe his last two days after Joseph sailed.

Though short of cash, the Count de Survilliers had left behind his annual Christmas contribution for French refugees in New York, and another for the Spanish. He was still taking care of "his people."

⚜

CHAPTER XVI

The Reluctant Pretender

"A SENTIMENT OF DUTY"

ON 16 August 1832, off Liverpool, Joseph learned from the pilot who came aboard that the Duke of Reichstadt had died, of a respiratory infection, in Vienna, where he had already been entombed. Even in death "The Eaglet" remained a prisoner, another god-martyr for the Napoleonic pantheon.* Thunderstruck, Joseph was saddened the more because *he* was now Napoleon's heir.† At sixty-four the last of his wishes was to be Emperor. But if France called . . . ? He could have but one answer. He went on to London and took up his role as Bonaparte pretender, first at a house on Park Crescent, then one with spacious grounds in Morden Park.

Joseph hoped at least to be admitted to France as a private citizen, since his whole life testified that he was no revolutionary. He hoped to build a party and achieve power peacefully. If France would not receive him, then he planned to work through friends until there were enough Bonapartists in the chamber of deputies to repeal the law that barred him. His supporters could reach him in London with relative ease, and he could direct a

---

* The remains of Napoleon II were finally returned to Paris in 1944 by Adolph Hitler in a futile effort to cultivate French friendship.
† Napoleon had been expected to adopt one of his brother Louis's sons, but had abandoned the plan after the birth of the King of Rome (Napoleon II). Thus the succession ran to Joseph and his male heirs (he had none), then Louis and his male heirs.

press campaign, for which, in time-honored French fashion, he invested in the Paris *Globe, Capital,* and other newspapers. So far, freedom of the press was being maintained.

Bonapartism was booming, all the while, on its own. The French wept over Victor Hugo's "Napoleon II," fed their nostalgia from the tales of the old soldier in Balzac's *Le medécin de campagne,* and stormed the booksellers' even for the most artless Napoleonic literature. Louis Philippe felt compelled to pronounce Napoleon a "great Frenchman," and the chamber voted to replace the statue of the Emperor removed from its column in the Place Vendôme in 1814.

Most practical politicians remained attached to various monarchical or republican factions, but Joseph believed they would eventually have to "join the people." Many, he thought, were deterred only by the fear that the powers would oppose a Bonaparte restoration, and on that score, he hoped for benefits from the British Reform Bill of 1832. Surely more popular governments would now appear, and in favor of letting Frenchmen choose their own rulers.

Disappointments came thick and fast, however. In October 1832 Joseph's old enemy, Marshal Soult, became first minister of Louis Philippe. The Reform Bill wrought no miracles. The most impressive visitors from France were republicans who wanted the Bonapartists to join *them,* not vice versa. And some of the most vocal Bonapartists were displaying ambivalent attitudes. Victor Hugo, for example, wrote Joseph a beautiful letter in February 1833, addressing him as "Your Majesty" and praising his love of liberty. "I would be very fortunate, Sire, if I could come to London, and there shake the royal hand that so often pressed that of my father." But he also said: "In truth, we are marching more toward a republic than [a new Empire] . . . but to a sage like yourself, the exterior form of the government is of little importance."

Joseph's feelings were mixed too. Despite himself, he often wished for some positive sign that his cause was hopeless, so that he could return to the "peace of Point Breeze." As early as January 1833, he had written Ingersoll that he hoped to be in the United States before the end of the year. Nothing, he said, could hold him in Europe, "but a sentiment of duty." The sentiment was strong, however, and he stayed on.

"THE YEAR ENDED WITH RAIN . . ."

If nothing else, Joseph kept expecting to be allowed to enter Italy and visit his mother and wife, perhaps for the last time. Letizia was past eighty; Julie ill. Charlotte came to live with him, hoping they could travel to Rome and Florence together. But it was not to be. The participation of Bonaparte Princes in the recent revolutions had hardened the hearts of Italian rulers, even the Pope, to whom, indirectly, Louis Napoleon owed his life. Sadly, Joseph could not even keep Charlotte with him. Her unhappy marriage and the death of her husband had aged her, and her health was poor. He decided she needed the sun of Italy, and after a year sent her back alone.

Prince Louis Napoleon, twenty-four, visited for six months. Third in line of succession (after his father, Louis) he had plunged into the Italian revolutions like a schoolboy off on a hike, pursued by his adoring mother, Hortense de Beauharnais, who had dragged him away in the nick of time, and gotten him out of Italy with the aid of churchmen. In London he was mannerly and deferent to his uncle, and showed intelligence, but he could not conceal his ambition, impulsiveness, love of intrigue, and romantic nature. Joseph could not make him understand that Napoleon had depended on no "star of destiny," for all his talk of it, but careful planning and grinding work. He feared that this odd-looking Bonaparte, with his stubby arms and legs, massive head, beaked nose and small eyes, this moody gamecock of a man, would get himself killed. He did not suspect that Louis Napoleon (the future Napoleon III) would become the bane of his declining years, but the boy made him uneasy. He was glad to see him go.

Generally, Joseph's personal life was not too unpleasant, however. His brother Lucien installed himself in London, and they were frequently together. Old friends from imperial days, and their sons and daughters, came to call. He found the British slower to accept him than Americans, but cordial, and a few became fast friends, notably Barry O'Meara, the bluff ex-naval surgeon who had served Napoleon at Saint-Helena and been expelled for protesting his treatment. But he was not *at home*. "I have nothing but praise for the English of all classes," he wrote Madame Mère's secretary, "but how can I live here indefinitely? In America, all is good and right for me, I have there friends of twenty years."

By the fall of 1833, he was ready to go back to Point Breeze, but his health broke, and he could not. Winter found him confined to the drafty mansion in Morden Park, able to receive few visitors, and passing the evenings, when he was not in bed, playing lotto with Louis Mailliard. *"Triste"* (sad) the secretary scribbled again and again in his diary.

Mailliard had been with Joseph thirty years. They were old friends who lived a single life, making decisions, writing letters, sizing up "their" young relatives together. Touchingly, Mailliard never presumed equality with his master, to whom he invariably referred, even in his private diary, as "M^r" [*Monsieur*], *"Le Comte,"* or *"Le Patron."* Yet when Joseph's interest was involved, he could be stern with him.

Monsieur must call in physicians, the secretary insisted. Joseph did, one after another, until a veritable international medical convention was assembled. In late December four doctors—English, Irish, German, and Italian—operated on Joseph to relieve an intestinal condition. After that he was bedridden for some weeks.

On the last evening of 1833, after a day of watching over his master and gazing out at the dreary countryside, Mailliard poured their feeling of futility into one laconic line: "The year ended with rain. . . ."

Waiting for a "moment of light"

As Joseph's health improved, he again prepared to return to Point Breeze. In April 1834, however, workers revolted in Paris and Lyons. The Orleanist government defeated them handily, but with much bloodshed, and in July, Soult was ousted from the ministry. In Britain, Lord Melbourne, a liberal, became Prime

Minister. Less encouraging, Britain and France allied to support the "Constitutionalists" in the Spanish civil war which had followed the death of Ferdinand VII. To Joseph, they had chosen the less evil of two sides—that of the late King's daughter, Isabella II, against his absolutist brother, Don Carlos. But he was sure Louis Philippe fought for *legitimacy*, not constitutionalism, and foreign interference in Spain smacked of the old Metternich system.

Nevertheless, Joseph decided to stay on in England, though he was far from optimistic. "I am more than ever disgusted with Europe," he assured Ingersoll, "and if I could hope to snatch from it my mother and wife, without fearing to lose them both on the way, you would not be delayed in seeing us all on your happy shores." He would wait another year, he said, "in the hope that . . . there will be a moment of light in politics, to allow me to go and say a last farewell." This would have satisfied the wish of his heart, but not his sense of duty. It was the faint hope of a greater "moment of light" which held him.

Friends, Relatives, and Parasites

Bonapartists were presented with an "old pretender," Joseph, who rejected unconstitutional methods or violence and a "young pretender," Louis Napoleon, who was too boyishly eager for action to inspire confidence. Bonapartism flourished, but a Bonapartist party failed to appear. In the end the Napoleonic legend, and the truth of Napoleon's efforts for the European masses, which Joseph patiently propagated year after year, would make possible Louis Napoleon's leap to power in 1848, not the latter's own juvenile efforts. But for the moment, neither had much political influence.

Joseph, however, had achieved immense personal stature. French patriot, friend of the masses of all countries, sage and man of heart, he compelled respect and affection. "My attachment for King Joseph is so profound, so true, so old, so founded on bases that can never crumble," wrote Laure Junot, aging and unable to travel, "that I would give days of my life just to talk with people who love him as I do. . . . For me, to see him for just a moment is now the most ardent of my desires." General Francisco Espoz y Mina, the elder of the ex-guerrilla chiefs, sought an introduction through O'Meara, and vowed that if Joseph had had a free hand in Spain, he would have supported him. Robert Walsh's *Biographical Sketch of Joseph Napoleon Bonaparte*, Louis Belmontet's *Joseph-Napoléon jugé par ses contemporains*, and other works on the "philosopher-king," attracted readers in England and America as well as on the continent.

When Soult mouthed "columnies" in the chamber of deputies, the London *Herald* printed Joseph's reply. Sir Gore Ouseley, adviser to the King and distinguished Orientalist, sought the Count de Survillier's friendship. The poetess, Lady Emmeline Stuart, came to talk for hours, and commanded that Monsieur go with her to the theaters and opera. He should get out more! (Her father went also, however. He trusted no French Prince, even one of sixty-five.) The Irish MP, Daniel O'Connell, "The Liberator," became his friend, and later roared eloquently for the return of Napoleon's remains from Saint-Helena. There were many more. Those who knew no more knew of his goodness. One such left a baby on his doorstep.

Mailliard and the Saris moved the household to Denham, near Uxbridge—in the country—where Joseph could have peace to write for the papers, review the ever multiplying histories and memoirs, and lodge his visitors. Invitations to London were frequent, however. Joseph dined with Lord Brougham, who had championed the Reform Bill and whose new cause was abolition of slavery in the colonies, with Nathan Meyer Rothschild, and with the famed jeweler Hamlen. The jeweler's daughter, Mailliard recorded, asked Monsieur to a more private dinner, which, however, he refused "for the most sage reasons." Life was not bad. But the political clouds did not break, and again, there were personal disappointments.

Prince Léon, Napoleon's natural son by Élénore Denuelle, presented himself. Struck by his resemblance to Napoleon, even to his voice and manner, Joseph received him as a son and recommended him to O'Meara's care in London. Mailliard was skeptical: "Léon left content from M^r, who gave him £100." Letters of warning came from Ménéval, in Paris: Léon was a drunkard and gambler; he had abandoned his wife, squandered his inheritance, lived on the charity of whores, and had recently been in prison. Joseph still gave him a chance—and more money—but for Léon not enough. He slandered his uncle before O'Meara, who turned him out. Joseph, presented once too often with his gambling debts and reports of his brawls, had to disown him. Breathing malevolence, he left for Portugal, hopefully to sponge off other relatives.

Brother Jérôme, and his son, Jérôme (by Catherine of Westphalia), appeared, looking like brothers. Slender, handsome, with *chercher la femme* as a law of life, they meant more trouble, and more expense. Jérôme's debts had reached almost a million francs. His solution to the problem was to find a rich husband for his daughter, which he did, some years later—the Russian Count Demidoff. Meanwhile, the long-suffering Joseph fed him loan after loan.

Most shattering, brother Lucien fell into an affair with Madame Sari. The household was disrupted. "Oh *les Femmes*!!!" scrawled Mailliard after a trying day. "S [Sari] would like to send her to Turkey!!!!" Lucien made no secret of the business; Joseph drove him out with "You were always the Emperor's enemy!" Madame Sari loved every minute of it. She went off to London and had her portrait painted; Lucien bought it—for half what the artist asked. The artist screamed; Captain Sari shouted about a duel. Joseph decided the Saris must go. He offered them 50,000 francs, payable in Paris, or American land worth 100,000. Madame Sari was for Paris; her husband for America. In the spring of 1835 they went off to Paris. "We do not miss them at all," wrote Mailliard, with positively English understatement. Joseph and Lucien were reconciled, but neither could forget their quarrel.

Even Joseph's beloved Charlotte gave him hurt. She had become involved with a young artist, Léopold Robert, of whom she wrote rapturously, if somewhat impersonally. Her father was worried, but her life had been so sad that he did not object. Then suddenly, in the summer of 1835, in Venice, Léopold, protesting drunkenly to his friends that Charlotte would not give herself to him and life was useless, cut his throat with a razor, and died writhing in a pool of blood on his studio floor. Lurid newspaper accounts drove Charlotte, who had only wanted friendship, into hiding, and her father to despair.

Heartsick over his family, Joseph also had financial worries. Life in England, wrote Mailliard, "eats money." And in France, the Duke de Broglie, the new premier, had initiated repressions worse than Soult's, culminating in the "September laws" of 1835, which legalized arbitrary arrest and imposed press censorship. No longer could Joseph present his views to the French people. Here was the fruit, he wrote Ingersoll, of the Revolution of 1830, ". . . the great political crime, the usurpation, by a few . . . of the popular power, raising to the throne an individual not voted by the people." Joseph determined to go home—to escape "the grave that encloses Europe." In September 1835 he sailed for the United States.

HOME

Niles' Register heralded Joseph's return:

The count Survilliers (Joseph Bonaparte) was received at his residence in Bordentown, we are informed, by the citizens of that place, with every mark of esteem and regard, and gratification at his return. The urbanity and politeness which this distinguished individual has always exhibited in his intercourse with our citizens, his liberal enterprise and open-handed benevolence to the necessitous [needy] have secured him a strong hold upon the affections of the community . . . and it is their ardent desire that he may again take up his permanent abode with them, and be favored with the enjoyment of a long life of health and happiness.

The reception moved Mr. Bonaparte to tears. Almost sixty-eight now, his wishes, with almost desperate intensity, matched those of his townsmen. Before he was rested from his journey, however, he knew he would have to return to England.

In January 1836, Madame Letizia died at Rome—"a prisoner of state, yes, a prisoner of state," she had written. To compound the tragedy, the family set to squabbling over her sizable legacy. Caroline made things awkward by bringing suit in Paris. The family prevailed on Joseph to come and set matters straight. Caroline! "The slut that ruined us all!" said Joseph in a rare venomous moment, thinking of how she had led Murat to betray Napoleon in 1814. (In the end Joseph satisfied her by sacrificing part of his share of the estate.)

Joseph also found his income from investments in America disastrously reduced by bank and business failures. President Jackson's assault on the Bank of the United States, speculation by state banks with federal funds he shifted to them, especially in western lands, had softened the dollar and disrupted the economy. To recoup, Joseph needed to sell from his Point Breeze gallery—and there was little market in America. (That fall, in London, fourteen of his masters went for $114,000, enough to cover his expenses, and those of relatives and hangers-on, for about a year. Today the same paintings—by Murillo, Leonardo da Vinci, et al., would be worth millions.)

"My losses of every kind are such as to occasion my departure from the land which has become my second *patrie*," he wrote his brother-in-law, Prince Bacciochi. He was also influenced by pleas from Lucien, still in London. Louis Adolphe Thiers, who had republican if not Bonapartist sympathies, had become premier of France. If Joseph could come and make contact with him personally, said Lucien, perhaps they would all get passports to Paris.

Joseph doubted that Bonapartist fortunes would change. He assured his old friends Charles Ingersoll, Joseph Hopkinson, and Dr. Nathaniel Chapman that he would soon be back. But duty and necessity called. In late August 1836, he was back in London.

NAPOLEON THE LITTLE

In September 1836, Thiers gave way to the Count Molé, but remained a power. Joseph sent agents to him with letters, and there seemed some hope he would help. All possibility was swept away in October, however, by the comic-opera performance of the man Hugo would later call "Napoleon the Little."

Louis Napoleon, in the uniform of a Swiss colonel and a cocked hat, descended upon the garrison of Strasbourg, his confederate, Colonel Vaudrey leading the troops in shouts of "*Vive l'Empereur!*" One officer, however, shouted "He is an impostor!" and another, "He is Colonel Vaudrey's nephew!" The troops looked again; the little man resembled Napoleon not at all. Laughing sheepishly, they hustled him off to prison. He expected to be shot, as Louis Philippe's cousin, the Duke d'Enghien, had been in 1804. Instead he was shipped off to Rio de Janeiro, trembling with relief but a little insulted not to be taken more seriously. When Brazil refused to take him, he was dropped at Portsmouth, Virginia, and went from there to New York. "My enterprise miscarried, it is true," he wrote Joseph, "but it announced to France that the family of the Emperor is not dead yet." The letter closed "Your tender and respectful nephew."

Joseph was disgusted. "He behaves as if his uncle and father were dead," he told Lacoste. Nevertheless, when Louis Napoleon presented himself in London the next summer, en route to Switzerland, where his mother was dying, Joseph forgave him. The "young pretender" in turn, promised to listen to his elders in the future, which he had no intention of doing.

Chances of reentering France ruined by Napoleon the Little, Italy still closed to him, Joseph stayed only long enough to settle Madame Letizia's estate and reorder his own finances. In September 1838, he was again in the United States.

"To see the sun . . ."

"It is said he comes to America to see the sun, being tired of living under the lugubrious and lurid sky of England, in the midst of fog and rain . . ." wrote Samuel Breck, after meeting Joseph on a Philadelphia street. The clouds had followed him, however. Joseph was ill, tired, and feeling his seventy years. Breck, uncomprehending, observed that the Count looked seedy, and wondered why one of his nine servants hadn't "brushed his hat." Dr. Chapman, frightened by his feebleness, made him spend the winter in Philadelphia, where he could be near in case of need. His friends tried to revive his spirits, but found him "taciturn and grave." Fate worked against them.

In January 1839, Cardinal Fesch died in Rome. In April, Charlotte died suddenly of a brain hemorrhage at Sarzana, Italy. The shock erased the beauty of the returning spring at Point

Breeze. Charlotte! What a life for one so quiet and kind—an unhappy marriage, a husband dead at twenty-seven, the bloody suicide of Léopold Robert. . . . Again he felt he must draw nearer to his family. The Bonapartists were again optimistic, now over the proposed return of Napoleon's remains from Saint-Helena. Perhaps at least he could reach Italy this time and see Julie, Zénaïde, and his grandchildren. In November 1839 he was again in London.

Before he left, he asked that Ingersoll, who was again preparing to run for Congress, propose that the government grant him lands in exchange for the art collection of Cardinal Fesch. It was by far more magnificent than his own; he hoped, in a stroke, to furnish the United States with a national gallery to rival the great European collections. Ingersoll, aware that many Americans considered display "undemocratic," opposed any opulence at the White House, and even the beautification of Washington, refused. He later regretted it, and well he might. It would be more than a hundred years before the capital boasted anything to compare with the Fesch collection. The small portion of it which Joseph gave to Corsican galleries gave them a permanent claim to prominence.

No Rest for Monsieur

Joseph found Louis Napoleon in London, deep in intrigue with his cronies, Colonel Vaudrey, General Montholon, and others. The busiest was Jean Fialin, who called himself the Viscount de Persigny; he had masterminded the Strasbourg coup, and still didn't see why it hadn't succeeded, which boded ill for the future. The "young pretender's" associates were introduced to Joseph, but they kept "the old man" ignorant of their true plans. Persigny did make bold to propose that Joseph make Louis Napoleon head of the family and raise twenty million francs for the cause (he could borrow it). They were at dinner, however, and much wine had flowed into Persigny, so Joseph laughed.

He was not so blind as not to have suspicions. When he cautioned Louis Napoleon, however, the Prince protested that he would *never* make any move without seeking his uncle's advice. Montholon gave Joseph hints, but did not tell all he knew. Meanwhile, Joseph had much to occupy him.

Charles Bonaparte, at odds with Zénaïde and in debt, challenged Cardinal Fesch's will. Occupying one of the Cardinal's residences in Rome, he refused to move, claimed the furnishings and artworks, for months threw out Joseph's agents one after another, and generally *"fait le diable à quatre"* as Mailliard kept saying. Louis Napoleon's social life got Joseph involved in paying off irate ex-mistresses (or their fathers), supporting him in property damage suits, and the like. Lucien, ill, had returned to Italy, but Jérôme was back, as extravagant and more poverty-stricken than ever.

Then there was Léon. The bad penny turned up at Joseph's door in early 1840, and was sent away. At Louis Napoleon's he got the same treatment. Angry, he accosted the Prince on the street. Who is the fellow? said Louis Napoleon, and walked on. Léon challenged him to a duel. They met on the foggy morning of 3 March. Léon arrived late to find Louis Napoleon nervously whipping a rapier about. No swords! said Leon. Choose your weapons, said Louis Napoleon, encouraged. Léon preferred to hurl insults, which the Prince returned in kind. Before they finished shouting, London police galloped up on horseback and hauled them off to jail, each under £500 bail. Joseph put up the money for Louis Napoleon, who emerged swearing Léon had been sent by Louis Philippe (!). *Punch* and the newspapers kept London laughing for weeks over the hot-air war of the bantam Princes.

A ghost from Joseph's own past rose up—Madame Delafolie —Annette Savage, now aging and grown vicious. Ingersoll wrote from Philadelphia that if Joseph didn't pay her $20,000 she intended to publish her memoirs. Madame "of-the-folly" wrote herself, to the same effect. "That is one devil of a woman!!!" Mailliard kept writing in his diary until they finally settled with her.

There were pleasant times, if few. The American Bonaparte, "M. Jérôme de Baltimore," came from Italy with news of the family. Lucien Murat, happy and loud as ever, stayed a few days before taking the *Great Western* for New York. The Countess de

Merlin visited—Mércèdes de Jaruco, who had married General Merlin in Spain—her hair still a billow of black, her complexion, to dimming eyes, unlined and fair. What memories she stirred!— of her beautiful mother, of Amalia de Montehermoso, of palace balls, gleaming candelabra, jewels on soft hair, swirling silks, uniforms, gold and silver epaulettes. Merlin! What a man! What a jealous bull! "What if the King should . . . ?" "Kill him, Sire!" All so long ago! They forgot Mércèdes's handsome son, an officer of engineers, who listened indulgently.

It was increasingly difficult, however, for Joseph to enjoy anything. He was ill during the Countess's stay, and could return her calls only with great effort. "M^r gets feebler every day," wrote Mailliard in May 1840, "the climate does not suit him." He did not like to admit that Monsieur's aged body was crumbling under the multiplying strains and worries. There seemed no end to the blows to his spirit.

With the return of Napoleon's remains agreed upon by the French and British governments, Joseph thought it fitting that the sword of Austerlitz be presented to the French nation. Intended for Napoleon II, it had been entrusted at Saint-Helena to General Bertrand, who was living in France. Joseph commanded him to take it to Marshal Moncey, Governor of Les Invalides, to be placed at the Emperor's tomb. "[Napoleon's] . . . sword will be carried to you by his grand marshal . . ." he wrote confidently to Moncey, "Make, I pray you . . . all arrangements to give to its return all the solemnity appropriate to souvenirs of such grandeurs, of so much French glory!" He reminded Moncey that the Emperor had called him "*le chevalier sans peur et sans reproche.*" In whom could he put more trust?

Moncey and Bertrand sent their apologies. Louis Philippe had ordered the sword delivered to him! *He* would have it placed at the tomb. Joseph was appalled at such pettiness.

At the same time, the chamber voted a mere one million francs for the *retour des cendres* of the Emperor. Joseph offered a million of his own, plus a million for the veterans of the Grande Armée. The money, however, was in treasury bills issued by Napoleon in 1815, repudiated by Louis XVIII, and worthless— unless the chamber accepted Joseph's offer, in which case he had two millions more with which to fight Louis Philippe. It seemed a good joke on the Bourgeois King of France—but it backfired. The British newspapers cried "for shame," and in France, even the republican journals, normally friendly, thought the proposal dishonorable. "That was . . . the first time when Joseph was ever charged with the duplicity often imputed to Napoleon," wrote Ingersoll.

A Brush with Death

Joseph heard little of the public censure, however. In mid-June he was stricken with paralysis, and for a week lay at death's door. Louis Napoleon sent his physician, Dr. Conneau, but did not come himself until the British surgeon, Sir Henry Halford, outraged at the Prince's callousness, called on him and ordered him to see his uncle. Conneau, meanwhile, insisted on sleeping at the house, and muttered ominously that the other doctors were too optimistic. He frightened Mailliard, who thought him capable of doing his master harm. Ill and sleepless, the secretary remembered that mystery had surrounded the deaths of Napoleon II and Napoleon Louis, and taking no chances, threw Conneau out.

Joseph was soon taking tea and eating American biscuit, which he loved. In a month he was up, but very weak, and still partially paralyzed in his left arm and leg. The doctors recommended he go to the baths at Wildbad, in Württemberg, whose King, after many delays, agreed to let him enter on an American passport. The United States minister, Andrew Stephenson, a good friend, immediately supplied the papers. On 26 July 1840, Joseph, supported by Mailliard and an English physician, Dr. Granville, boarded a steamer for the first leg of the journey. Louis Napoleon, suppressing his glee, waved soberly from the dock. The old man was out of the way!

The Flight of the Vulture

Nine days later the paddle steamer *Edinburgh Castle* decked out for a pleasure cruise, moved slowly down the Thames. Tied to the mast was a ruffled and unhappy looking vulture, masquerading as an imperial eagle, while sprawled beneath him, on deck, eating sandwiches and drinking wine, were Louis Napoleon and fifty followers, masquerading as Napoleon and his gallant band, returning from Elba.

In the dawn hours of 6 August the jolly crew landed on the French coast near Boulogne, uniformed and laden with imperial banners, placards, and pamphlets. At eight-thirty that morning they were all prisoners.

France waited in frenzied anticipation to receive the remains of Napoleon the Great (returned in December 1840). She was not ready for Napoleon the Little. Tried by the Chamber of Peers, he was locked away in the fortress of Ham, where he would languish for six years.

Death Comes to Monsieur

Joseph heard of Louis Napoleon's landing at Wildbad. Barely settled, just told of the death of his brother Lucien, so ill already that Mailliard had to help him at the baths, he found himself unwelcome in Germany. His arrival seemed to have been coordinated with his nephew's return to France. Refused permission to go to Switzerland or Italy, too weak to attempt a voyage to America, he returned, by stages, to England.

Ingersoll, Chapman, and Hopkinson sent the wish that he would be able to return to "tranquil America, near us." Mailliard had to answer for Monsieur, who was very sick. "How we regret [not having] the quiet of Point Breeze and excellent Dr. Chapman, to reestablish his precious health," he told Ingersoll. "By leaving the United States . . . he sacrificed himself to his relations."

Housed comfortably at the country estate of Lord Denbigh, Joseph was better by Christmas, and began thinking of crossing the Atlantic. But from Italy, the relatives begged that he come to them. When, with Louis Napoleon safely jailed, the powers agreed to permit it, their call became irresistible. In April 1841, Charles Bonaparte and his son came to take Joseph "home" to Julie. In late May he sailed, warmed by the farewells of Lord and Lady Denbigh, the country folk, who remembered his small kindnesses, waving children mustered to thank him for his Christmas gifts to their school and charity, and a host of friends at the London dock.

At Genoa, a great crowd cheered him as he came ashore, and his English ship's captain fired a royal salute with his little cannon —a marvelous gesture. Zénaïde appeared shortly, with a swarm of children, to travel with him to Florence. In mid-July he and Julie were reunited after over twenty-five years. He found her grayer and more subdued, somehow tinier, but much the same, and seemingly in better health than he.

Life moved on in comfortable monotony, broken by the visits of Joseph's children and grandchildren, his brothers Jérôme and Louis, and others. Joseph, more than ever, gave and gave—to Mailliard his house in Philadelphia, to Corsican cities hundreds of paintings, to France Napoleon's grand collar, cordon, and plaque of the Legion of Honor, to relatives and friends paintings and objects of art, commemorative medals, personal items of his or Napoleon's. In his old age, giving was his greatest pleasure.

Death hovered over Joseph continually, however. The stroke he had suffered in 1840 had deprived him partially of the use of one arm and leg. At ever shorter intervals total paralysis returned, and between, his body gave way to lesser ills. Physicians visited almost daily. Julie, hovering over her husband, suffered also. "The Queen is ill, feeble, and sad," wrote Mailliard in 1842; she would survive Joseph by only a few weeks. Both sank lower in 1843 and 1844, but neither feared death. Joseph was completely tranquil after he completed his will, giving most of his property to Zénaïde and his grandchildren, but leaving generous sums to all who had served him, from his housekeeper to the caretaker at Point Breeze, and personal tokens to dozens of friends. Joseph Hopkinson and Louis Mailliard were his executors; Ingersoll their counsel and custodian of his letters and papers.

On 28 July 1844, death came to Joseph Bonaparte, quietly, as he slept, with Julie and Mailliard at his bedside, and his daughter and grandchildren nearby. On 3 August he was interred. "The thirty bells of Saint Nicholas waked us at an early hour . . ." began Mailliard in a trembling hand as he recorded the events.

The clergy of Saint Nicholas preceded the funeral carriage, drawn by four horses and escorted by two companies of grenadiers of the Grand Duke of Tuscany. The route was lined by people of Florence, out by thousands to pay their respects, as had hundreds of friends and dignitaries of all nations while he lay in state. At the Church of Santa Croce, the coffin was received by the monks of the chapter, who, after the service, carried it in genuine sorrow to a crypt in the Chapel of the Medicis.

About Joseph's neck, at his request, had been placed the Order of the Golden Fleece—the highest decoration of Spain. In death he made a final pledge of love to "his people." But France was his nation. His will charged his daughter and grandchildren to find a final resting place for him there—not "on the banks of the Seine," as Napoleon had asked dramatically, but simply "on free soil," when France was again free.

Epilogue

O N a sultry morning in June 1862, at mid-course of the Second Empire, Joseph's remains were brought to Paris. His family considered his last wish fulfilled, but there was much of which he would have disapproved in the France of Napoleon the Little. His quiet reception would surely have pleased him, however.

The Abbé (later Cardinal) Lucien Bonaparte, Joseph's grandson, had brought his casket from Florence. At the Lyons Station it was met by another grandson, granddaughters and their husbands, great-grandchildren, and a swarm of other relatives. Louis Mailliard, leaning on the arm of the young Count de Cambacérès, wept openly. He could not but relive the day of Monsieur's death, he said—an "inexpressible sensation."

In "sad and modest convoy," flanked by a few imperial guardsmen, the *cendres* were borne along the tree-lined, sun-blotched Champs Élysées, and on to Les Invalides. There the tricolordraped bier was received by clergy and official delegations headed by the Count Walewski (son of Napoleon and Marie Walewska) and a distinguished Corsican soldier, Marshal Ornano. Napoleon III was not there. "He should have been for his Uncle Joseph," wrote Mailliard indignantly. But perhaps the man who was sponsoring an alien Emperor in Mexico knew better.

Joseph was interred in one of the crypts ringing the sarcophagus of Napoleon, as was Jérôme, and much later, Napoleon II. But the ornate well beneath the dome of the Church of Saint

Louis was not a shrine to the Bonapartes, but the military heroes of France. There lie, among others, Turenne, Marshal of the Sun King, Foch of World War I, and Leclerc of World War II.

It is a strange resting place for Joseph. He is honored and yet dishonored in the halls of glory, overshadowed in death as in life by Napoleon, who was many things, but above all a conqueror. A monument to peace and human betterment would be a fitter place for the bones of the Gentle Bonaparte. He might have preferred a country churchyard near Mortefontaine or Point Breeze.

Bibliography

BIBLIOGRAPHY

I. Manuscript Sources

American Philosophical Society: *Minutes, 1823* and *1826.* Fifteen Joseph Bonaparte letters.

Archives des Affaires Étrangères, Espagne: Volumes 679–687.

Henry E. Huntington Library and Art Gallery: Forty-seven Joseph Bonaparte letters. Account of Francis Lieber's visit to Joseph Bonaparte.

Historical Society of Pennsylvania: One hundred and two Joseph Bonaparte letters.

Library of Congress: *The William Vans Murray Papers.*

Yale University: *The Journal of Louis Hypolite Mailliard, 1815–1869,* 6 v. [English title, French text].

II. Printed Primary Sources

Adams, John Quincy, *Memoirs Comprising His Diary from 1795 to 1848,* 12 v. Ed. by E. F. Adams (1874–1877).

Barante, Baron de, *Souvenirs du Baron de Barante (1782–1866), de l'Académie Française,* 2 v. (1890).

Barkhausen, Georg Heinrich, *Tagebuch eines Rheinbundoffiziers aus dem Feldzug gegen Spanien und wahrend spanischer Kriegsgefangenschaft* (1900).

Beauchamp, Alphonse de, ed., *Collection des mémoires relatifs aux révolutions d'Espagne,* 2 v. (1824).

Beauharnais, Eugène, *Mémoires et correspondance*, 10 v. Ed. by A. du Casse (1858–1860).

Bertrand, Général, *Cahiers de Sainte-Hélène, 1815–1819*, 3 v. Ed. by Paul Fleuriot de Langle (1949–1959).

Bigarré, Auguste Julien, Baron de, *Mémoires du Général Bigarré, aide-de-camp du Roi Joseph, 1775–1813* (1899).

Blaze, Marie Sébastien, *Mémoires d'un apothicaire sur la guerre d'Espagne pendant les années 1808 à 1814*, 2 v. (1828).

Bonaparte, Hortense Beauharnais, *Mémoires de la Reine Hortense*, 3 v. 12th ed. (1927).

Bonaparte, Jérôme, *Mémoires et correspondance du roi Jérôme*, 7 v. Ed. by Baron du Casse (1861–1866).

Bonaparte, Joseph, et al., *Bourrienne et ses erreurs volontiares et involontaires*, 2 v. (1830).

Bonaparte, Joseph, *Mémoires et correspondance du Roi Joseph*, 10 v. 2d ed., Ed. by A. du Casse (1854).

——, *Lettres d'exil inédites (Amérique—Angleterre—Italie) (1825–1844)* (1912).

——, *Lettres inédites ou éparses de Joseph Bonaparte à Naples (1806–1808)*, Ed. by Jacques Rambaud (1911).

Bonaparte, Louis, *Documents historiques et réflexions sur le gouvernement de la Hollande*, 3 v. (1820).

Bonaparte, Lucien, *Mémoires* (1818).

Bonaparte, Napoléon, *Correspondance de Napoléon Ier, publiée par l'ordre de l'Empereur Napoléon III*, 32 v. (1850–1855).

——, *Recueil des décrets, ordonnances, traités de paix, manifestes . . . de Napoléon et des membres du gouvernement française dupuis 18 brumaire . . . jusqu'à . . . 1812*, 6 v. Ed. by Lewis Goldsmith (1813–1816).

——, *Napoléon, Recueil par ordre chronologique de ses lettres, proclamations, bulletins, discours*, 4 v. Ed. by M. Kermoysan (1853–1865).

——, *Lettres inédites de Napoléon Ier*, 2 v. 2d ed., Ed. by L. Lecestre (1897).

——, *Lettres inédites de Napoléon Ier*, Ed. by Léonce de Brotonne (1898).

——, *Dernières lettres inédites de Napoléon Ier*, 2 v. Ed. by Leonce de Brotonne (1903).

——, *Inédites Napoléoniennes*, Ed. by Arthur Chuquet (1913).

——, *Correspondance inédite de Napoléon Ier, conservée aux Archives de la Guerre*, 5 v. Ed. by Ernest Picard et Louis Tuetey (1912–1925).

——, *Mémoires pour servir à l'histoire de France . . . écrits à Sainte Hélène*, 9 v. (1829–1830).

——, *Ordres et apostiles de Napoléon* (1799–1815), 4 v. Ed. by Arthur Chuquet (1911–1912).

——, *Lettres de Napoléon à Joséphine et lettres de Joséphine a Napoléon* (1959).

——, *Lettres de Napoléon Ier à Marie Louise écrites de 1810 à 1814* (1960).

Bourbon, Marie Caroline de, Reine, *Correspondance inédite de Marie-Caroline, reine de Naples et de Sicile, avec le Marquis de Gallo*, 2 v. (1911). .

Breck, Samuel, *Recollections of Samuel Breck with Passages from his Note-book (1771–1862)*, Ed. by H. E. Scudder (1877).

Casse, Albert du, Baron, *Les rois frères de Napoleon Ier* (1883).

Catherine de Westphalie, *Correspondance inédite avec sa famille et celle du roi Jérôme* (1893).

Chaulanges, M., et al. (eds.), *Textes historiques, l'epoque de la Révolution, 1789–1799: L'epoque imperiale, 1800–1815*, 2 v. (1960).

Dallas, George Mifflin, *Life and Writings of Alexander James Dallas* (1871).

Damas, Roger de, Comte, *Mémoires*, 2 v. Ed. by J. Rambaud (1912–1914).

Desboeufs, ——, *Souvenirs du Capitaine Desboeufs* (1901).

Dumas, Mathieu, *Souvenirs du Lieutenant Général Comte Mathieu Dumas, de 1770 à 1836*, 3 v. (1839).

D'Urban, Sir Benjamin, *The Peninsula Journal of Sir Benjamin D'Urban . . . 1808–1817*, Ed. by I. J. Rousseau (1930).

Fée, Antoine Laurent Apollinaire, *Souvenirs de la guerre d'Espagne, 1809–1813* (1856).

Férussac d'Audebard, Baron de, *Diario historico de los sitios de Zaragosa* (1908).

Fouché, Joseph, *Mémoires de Fouché*, Ed. by Louis Madelin (1947).

Fririon, Baron de, *Journal historique de la campagne du Portugal . . . (du 15 septembre 1810 au 12 mai 1811)* (1841).

Gachot, Édouard, ed., *Mémoires du Colonel Delagrave, campagne du Portugal (1810–1811)* (1902).

Gallo, Duca di, "Memorie," *Archivo Storico Napolitano* (1888).

Gille, L. F., *Les prisonniers de Cabrera, mémoires d'un conscrit de 1808* (1892).

Girardin, Stanislas, *Mémoires, journal, et souvenirs*, 2 v. (1829).

Godoy, Alvarez Manuel de, Príncipe de la Paz, *Memoirs of Don Manuel de Godoy*, 2 v. (1836).

Gonneville, Aymar Olivier le Harivel de, *Souvenirs militaires* (1895).

Gordon, Alexander, *A Cavalry Officer in the Corunna Campaign, 1808–1809* (1913).

Gourgaud, General Baron, *The St. Helena Journal of General Baron Gourgaud—1815–1818* (1932).

Gouvion de Saint-Cyr, Laurent, Marquis de, *Journal des opérations de l'armée Catalogne en 1808 et 1809*, 2 v. (1821).

Grolmann, Ludwig von, Major, *Tagebuch eines deutschen Offiziers (in Spanien im Jahr 1808)* (1814).

Grouchy, Emmanuel, Marquis de, ed., *Mémoires du Maréchal de Grouchy*, 5 v. (1873–1874).

Hauterive, Ernest d', *La police secrète du premier empire: bulletins quotidiens adressés par Fouché à l'empereur*, 5 v. (1909–1923; 1963–1964).

Howitt, E., *Letters written during a tour through the United States during the Summer and Autumn of 1819* (1820).

Hugo, Joseph Léopold Sigebert, Comte, *Le Général Hugo, 1773–1828, lettres et documents inédits*, Ed. by Louis Barthou (1926).

——, *Mémoires de Général Hugo*, 3 v. (1823).

Jollivet, Maurice, *La Révolution française en Corse; Paoli, Bonaparte, Pozzo di Borgo* (1892).

Jomini, Henri, Baron, *Vie politique et militaire de Napoleon, recontée par lui même*, 2 v. (1841–1842).

Jourdan, Jean Baptiste, *Mémoires militaires (Guerre d'Espagne)*, Ed. by Vicomte de Grouchy (1899).

Jovellanos, Gaspar Melchor de, *Mémoires politiques de Gaspar de Jovellanos* (1825).

Junot, Laure-Saint-Martin (Permon), Duchesse d'Abrantès, *Mémoires de Madame la Duchesse d'Abrantès*, 3 v. 4th ed. (1837).

La Fayette, Marquis de, *Mémoires, correspondance et manuscrits du général de La Fayette*, 12 v. (1838).

Las Cases, Emmanuel, *Mémorial de Sainte Hélène*, 8 v. (1823–1824).

Levasseur, A., *Lafayette en Amérique en 1824 et 1825 ou journal d'un voyage aux États-Unis*, 2 v. (1829).

L. F. L. H. [Heritier de l'Ain], *Le Champ d'asile, tableau topographique et historique du Texas, publié au profit des Refugiés* (1819).

Lieber, Francis, *The Life and Letters of Francis Lieber*, Ed. by Thomas Sergeant Perry (1882).

Long, Robert Ballard, *Peninsula Cavalry General, the Correspondence of Lieutenant General Robert Ballard Long* (1851).

Manière, ———, *Souvenirs d'un canonnier de l'armée d'Espagne, 1808 à 1814* (1892).

Marbot, Baron de, *Mémoires du Général Baron Marbot*, 3 v. (1892).

Marmont, Auguste Frédéric Louis Viesse de, Duc de Raguse, *Mémoires du Duc de Raguse*, 5 v. (1857).

Masséna, André, Prince d'Essling, *Mémoires de Masséna*, 7 v. (1848–1850).

Massin, Jean, *Almanach du premier empire: du 9 thermidor à Waterloo* (1965).

Mina, Espoz y, Francisco, *Breve estracto de la vida del General Mina* (1825).

Miot de Melito, André François, Comte, *Mémoires du comte Miot de Melito*, 3 v. Ed. by General de Fleischmann (1858).

Mollien, François N., *Mémoires d'un ministre de trésor public, 1780–1815* (1845), New ed. by Charles Gomel, 3 v. (1898).

Montholon, C. J. T., *History of the Captivity of Napoleon at St. Helena* (1846).

Moore, Sir John, *The Diary of Sir John Moore*, Ed. by General Sir J. F. Maurice (1904).

Murat, Joachim, Maréchal, *Lettres et documents pour servir à l'histoire de Joachim Murat*, 8 v. Ed. by Paul Le Brethon (1908–1914).

————, *Lieutenant de l'Empereur en Espagne, 1808, d'après sa correspondance inédite et des documents originaux* (1897).

Nellerto, Juan [Juan Antonio Llorente], *Mémoires pour servir à l'histoire de la révolution d'Espagne*, 3 v. (1814–1819). Published in Spanish as *Memorias para la história de la revolucion Española* (1814–1816).

Neuville, Hyde de, *Mémoires et Souvenirs du baron Hyde de Neuville*, 2 v. (1890).

Ney, Michel, Duc d'Elchingen, Prince de la Moskowa, *Mémoires du Maréchal Ney, Duc d'Elchingen, Prince de la Moskowa*, 2 v. (1833).

Nicola, Carlo de, "Diaro Napolitano, 1798–1825," *Archivo Storico Napolitano* (1939).

O'Meara, B. E., *Napoleon in Exile*, 2 v. (n.d.).

Parquin, Denis Charles, Captaine, *Souvenirs, 1803–1814* (1892).

Pignatelli-Strongoli, Francesco, *Memorie intorno alla storia del Regno di Napoli dell' anno 1805 al 1815* (1820).

[Pococke, Captain], *Journal of a Soldier of the Seventy-first Regiment, Highland Light Infantry, from 1806 to 1815* (1822).

Porter, Sir Robert Ker, *Letters from Portugal and Spain* (1809).

Pradt, Dominique G. F. de Riom de Prolhiac de Fourt de, *Mémoires sur la révolution d'Espagne* (1816).

Rémusat, Claire E. J. G. de Vergennes, Comtesse de, *Mémoires, 1802–1808*, 3 v. Ed. by Paul L. E. de Rémusat (1870–1880).

Richelieu, Duc de, *Lettres du duc de Richelieu au Marquis d'Osmond*, Ed. by S. Charléty (1939).

Roederer, Pierre L., Comte, *Autour de Bonaparte: Journal: notes intimes et politiques d'un familier des Tuileries*, Ed. by Maurice Vitras (1909).

————, *Oeuvres du Comte Pierre Louis Roederer*, 8 v. (1853–1859).

Roguet, François, Comte, *Mémoires militaires du Lieutenant Général Comte Roguet*, 4 v. (1862–1865).

Savary, Anne Jean Marie René, Duc de Rovigo, *Mémoires du*

Duc de Rovigo, pour servir à l'histoire de l'Empereur Napoléon, 8 v. 2d ed. (1829).

Schumacher, Gaspard, Capitaine, *Journal et souvenirs* (n. d.).

Sébastiani, François Horace Bastien, Comte, "Opérations du 4e corps d'armée d'Espagne (1809–1811) d'après la correspondance du Général . . . Sebastiani." Communiqué par le Vicomte E. H. de Grouchy et publiée par P. G. M. Guitry. *Carnet de la Sabretache* (1902).

Ségur, Philippe-Paul, Comte de, *Histoire et mémoires*, 7 v. (1873).

Sherer, Joseph Moyle, Captain, *Recollections of the Peninsula during the Late War* (1823).

Sommer, Frank H., "America's First King," *Winterthur Newsletter* (1963) [John Fanning Watson on Joseph].

Soult, Nicholas, Maréchal Duc de Dalmatie, *Correspondance politique et familiere avec Louis-Philippe et la famille royale*, Ed. by Louis et Antoinette de Sainte-Pierre (1959).

———, *Mémoires du Maréchal Soult: Espagne et Portugal* (1955).

Staël, Madame de, *Dix années d'exil*, 2d ed. (1904).

Stille, Arthur Gustav Henrik, *Dépêches Suédoises de Cadix en 1808 et pendant les années suivantes*. Extracted from *Las Publicaciones del Congreso de la Guerra de la Independencia*, II (1907).

Suchet, Louis Gabriel, Duc d'Albufera, *Memoirs of the War in Spain from 1808 to 1814*, 2 v. (1829).

Thibaudeau, Antoine Claire, Comte, *Mémoires . . . 1799–1815* (1913).

Thiébault, Paul Charles F. A. H., Baron, *Mémoires*. Ed. by Robert Lacour-Gayet (1962).

———, *Relation de l'expedition de Portugal, faite en 1807 et 1808 par le Premier Corps d'Observation de la Gironde* (1817).

Tomkinson, William, Captain, *The Diary of a Cavalry Officer in the Peninsula War and Waterloo Campaign* (1894).

Vigo-Roussillon, Colonel, "La guerre d'Espagne, fragments des mémoires du Colonel Vigo-Roussillon," *Revue des Deux Mondes* (1891).

Villargennes, Doisy de, *Souvenirs militaires de Doisy de Villargennes*, Ed. by M. G. Bertin (1900).

Wagré, Louis Joseph, *Les adieux à l'île Cabrera* (1833).

Wellesley, Arthur, Duke of Wellington, *The Dispatches of Field Marshal the Duke of Wellington . . . from 1799 to 1818*, 12 v. Ed. by Lt. Col. Gurwood (1837–1839).

———, *Supplementary Dispatches and Memoranda of Field Marshal Arthur Duke of Wellington, K. G.*, 15 v. Ed. by his son, the Duke of Wellington (1858–1872).

———, *Military Memoirs of Field Marshal the Duke of Wellington*, 2 v. Ed. by J. Moyle Sherer (1833).

Wilson, James Grant, *The Life and Letters of Fitz Greene Halleck* (1869).

Wright, Frances, *Views of Society and Manners in America during the Years 1818, 1819 and 1820* (1821).

Yung; Rouargue; Lalaisse, et al., *Album des mémoires du* [about] *Roi Joseph* (1856–1858).

III. Secondary Works

Acton, Harold, *The Bourbons of Naples* (1956).

Alcázar Molina, Cayetano, *El Madrid del dos de mayo* (1952).

Almagro, Melchor Fernández, "Del antiguo régimen a las Cortes de Cádiz," *Revista de Estudios Políticos* (1962).

Anderson, J. H., *The Spanish Campaign of Sir John Moore* (1905).

Andrés, Diego Sevilla, "La Constitución de 1812, obra de transición," *Revista de Estudios Políticos* (1962).

Arteche y Moro, José Gomez de, *Guerra de la independencia; historia militar de España de 1808 à 1814*, 14 v. (1868–1903).

Artola, Miguel, *Los Afrancesados* (1953).

Atkinson, C. T., "The Composition and Organization of the British Forces in the Peninsula, 1808–1814," *English Historical Review* (1902).

Aubrey, O., *Sainte-Hélène*, 2 v. (1935).

Auriol, Charles, *La France, l'Angleterre et Naples de 1803 à 1806*, 2 v. (1904–1905).

Badía, Juan Ferrando, "Vicisitudes e influencias de la Constitución de 1812," *Revista de Estudios Políticos* (1962).

Balagny, Commandant, *Campagne de l'Empereur Napoléon en Espagne (1808–1809)*, 2 v. (1902–1907).

Baldet, Marcel, *La vie quotidienne dans les armées de Napoléon* (1965).

Barbaroux, Charles O. et Lardier, J. A., *Voyage du général La Fayette aux États-Unis d'Amérique en 1824 et 1825* (1826).

Beatty, John L., "Napoleon and the Governance of Non-French Subject Peoples." Unpublished doctoral dissertation (1953).

Bertier de Sauvigny, G., *La Restauration* (1963).

Biver, Comtesse Marie-Louise, *Le Paris de Napoléon* (1963).

Blanch, Adolfo, *Cataluña, historia de la guerra de la independencia en el antiguo principado de Cataluña*, 2 v. (1861–1862).

Bonnel, Ulane, *La France, les États-Unis et la guerre de course (1797–1815)* (1961).

Boulay de la Meurthe, *Le Directoire et l'expédition d'Egypte; étude sur les tentatives du Directoire pour communiques avec Bonaparte, le secourir et le ramener* (1885).

Butler, Lewis, *Wellington's Operations in the Peninsula, 1808–1814*, 2 v. (1904).

Cabany, Charles E. Saint Maurice, *Étude historique sur la capitulation de Baylen* (1846).

Caldora, Umberto, *Calabria napoleonica, 1806–1815* (1960).

Capella, Miguel and Tascon, Antonio Matilla, *Los cincogremios mayores de Madrid* (1957).

Casse, A. du, *Histoire des negotiations . . . de Mortefontaine, Lunéville et Amiens*, 3 v. (1855).

Chuquet, A., "La mission de Joseph Bonaparte en 1793," *Annales Révolutionnaires* (1908).

Clerc, Joseph C. A., *Guerre d'Espagne, Capitulation de Baylen* (1903).

Clinton, Herbert R., *The War in the Peninsula and Wellington's Campaigns in France and Belgium* 3rd ed. (1890).

Colin, J., Lt. Col., "Journal du Colonel Béchaud, de l'armée de Portugal, octobre, 1812," *Revue des Études Napoléoniennes* (1912 and 1913).

Colletta, Pietro, *Histoire du royaume de Naples* (1835).

Comellas, J. L., "Las Cortes de Cádiz y la Constitución de 1812," *Revista de Estudios Politicos* (1962).

Conard, Pierre, *La constitution de Bayonne, 1808, essai d'édition critique* (1910).

———, *Napoléon et Catalogne* (1808–1814), 2 v. (1910).

Corona, Carlos E., *Precedentes ideolologicos de la guerra de independencia* (1959).

Croce, B., *Storia del regno di Napoli* (1925).

Dard, E., *Napoleon and Talleyrand* (1937).

Desdevises du Dezert, G. "L'Espagne de l'ancien régime," *Revue Hispanique* (1925, 1927, and 1928).

———, "Les institutions d'Espagne au XVIIIe siècle," *Revue Hispanique* (1927).

Driault, Édouard, "Histoire extérieure du premier Empire," *Revue des Études Napoléoniennes* (1912).

———, "L'Espagne et Napoléon," *Revue des Études Napoléoniennes* (1939).

———, *Napoléon en Italie 1800–1812* (1906).

———, "Tilsit," *Revue des Études Napoléoniennes* (1913).

Duhamel, Jean, *Les cinquante jours de Waterloo à Plymouth* (1963).

Dumas, Mathieu, Comte, *Precis des événements militaires . . . sur les campagnes de 1799 à 1814*, 19 v. (1817–1826).

Evrard, F., "Le commerce des laines d'Espagne sous le premier Empire," *Revue d'histoire moderne* (1937).

Fagg, John Edwin, "The Republican Movement in Spain, 1790–1868," Unpublished doctoral dissertation (1942).

Ferrer, Victorio Piña, *Páginas de 1808, memoria de un patriota* (1889).

Fugier, André, *La junte superieure des Asturies et l'invasion Française, 1810–1811* (1930).

———, *Napoléon et l'Espagne, 1799–1808*, 2 v. (1930).

Gaffarel, P., "Deux années de royauté en Espagne, 1810–1811," *Revue des Études Napoléoniennes* (1919).

———, *Les Bonaparte à Marsielle, 1793–1797* (1905).

Galpin, W. Freeman, "The American Grain Trade to the Spanish Peninsula, 1810–1814," *The American Historical Review* (1922).

Ganière, Paul, *Napoléon à Sainte-Hélène. La lutte contre Hudson Lowe* (1960).

Garcia-Rodriguez, José María, *Guerra de la independencia (Ensayo historico-politico)* (1945).

Gavoty, André, *Les drames inconnus de la cour de Napoleon* (1805–1806) (1964).

Geisendorf des Gouttes, Théophile, *L'expedition et la captivite d'Andalousie, 1808–1810* (1930).

Glover, Michael, *Wellington's Peninsular Victories* (1963).

Godlewski, G., *Trois cents jours d'exil: Napoléon à l'île d'Elbe* (1961).

Grandmaison, Geoffroy, de, "La cour de Joseph Bonaparte à Madrid," *Le Correspondant* (1912).

———, *La France et l'Espagne pendant le premier Empire* (1899).

———, *L'Ambassade Française en Espagne* (1892).

———, *L'Espagne et Napoléon, 1804–1814*, 3 v. 3d ed. (1908–1931).

Grasset, A., Capitaine, *La guerre d'Espagne, 1807–1813*, 3 v. (1914–1932).

———, "L'Église et le soulèvement de l'Espagne," *Revue de Paris* (1923).

Groen, J. J., *La dernière maladie et la cause de mort de Napoléon* (1962).

Guillon, Édouard, *Les guerres d'Espagne sous Napoléon* (1902).

Haas, Arthur G., *Metternich, Reorganization and Nationality 1813–1818* (1963).

Hales, E. E. Y., *Revolution and Papacy* (1960).

Hamilton, Earl J., *War and Prices in Spain*, 1651–1800 (1947).

Hayes, Carlton J. H., *The Historical Evolution of Modern Nationalism* (1931).

Healey, F. G., *The Literary Culture of Napoleon* (1959).

Heckscher, Eli F., *The Continental System: An Economic Interpretation* (1922).

Heriot, A., *Les Français en Italie, 1796–1799* (1961).

Herr, Richard, *The Eighteenth Century Revolution in Spain* (1958).

———, "Good, Evil, and Spain's Rising Against Napoleon," in *Ideas in History: Essays Presented to Louis Gottschalk by his Former Students*, Ed. by Richard Herr and Harold T. Parker (1965).

Hibbert, Christopher, *Corunna. British Battles Series* (1961).

Horward, Donald D., *The Battle of Bussaco: Masséna vs. Wellington* (1965).

Hume, Martin A. S., *Modern Spain, 1788–1898* (1900).

Ibieca, Augustín Alcaide, *Historia de los sitios que pusieron à Zaragoza en los años de 1808 y 1809 las tropas de Napoléon*, 2 v. (1830–1831).

Ingersoll, Charles J., *Historical Sketch of the Second War Between the United States of America, and Great Britain* (1845).

———, *History of the Second War between the United States of America and Great Britain*, 2 v. 2d ser. (1852).

Jones, Sir John Thomas, Bart. *Account of the War in Spain and Portugal and in the South of France from 1808 to 1814* (1818).

Kemble, James, *Napoleon Immortal: The Medical History and Private Life of Napoleon Bonaparte* (1959).

Klein, Julius, *The Mesta* (1920).

Kohn, Hans, "Napoleon and the Age of Nationalism," *Journal of Modern History* (1950).

Lachouque, Henri, *Les derniers jours de l'Empire* (1965).

———, *Napoléon en 1814* (1959).

———, *Napoléon et la garde impériale* (1957).

———, *Napoleon. Vingt ans de campagnes* (1964).

La Force, James Clayburn, Jr., *The Development of the Spanish Textile Industry, 1750–1800* (1965).

Lanzac de Laborie, Leon de, "Joseph Bonaparte à Madrid (1809–1811)," *Le Correspondant* (1925).

Lecestre, Léon, "La guerre de la péninsule (1807–1813) d'après la correspondance inédite de Napoléon Ier," *Revue des Questions Historiques* (Nouvelle Série) (1896).

Lévy, A., *Les dissentiments de la famille impériale* (1931).

Locre, Jean-Guillaume, *Napoleon au Conseil d'état* (1963).

Lovett, Gabriel H., *Napoleon and the Birth of Modern Spain*, 2 v. (1965).

Lucas-Dubreton, Jean, *De qu'a vu Goya, Napoléon devant l'Espagne* (1946).

Maag, Albert, *Geschichte der Schweizertruppen im Kriege Na-*

poleons im Spanien und Portugal (1807–1814), 2 v. (1892–1893).

Maldonado, José Muñoz, Conde de, *Historia politica y militar de la guerra de la independencia de España . . . 1808–1814*, 3 v. (1833).

Martin, Emmanuel César, *La gendarmerie française en Espagne et Portugal (Campagnes de 1807 à 1814)* (1898).

Masson, Frédéric, *Marseille et Napoléon* (1920).

———, *Napoleon and his Coronation* (1911).

———, *Napoléon à Sainte-Hélène* (1912).

Mercader Riba, Juan, *Barcelona durante la occupacion francesca (1808–1814)* (1949).

———, "España en el bloqueo continental," *Estudios de História Moderna* (1952).

———, "La organización administrativa francesa en España," pamphlet of *Institución Fernando el Católico* (1959).

Mercier, Sébastien, *Paris pendant la révolution, 1789–1798 ou le nouveau Paris* (1962).

Mitchell, S., *A Family Lawsuit* (1958).

Mitchell, Sir Thomas Livingstone, ed., *Maps and Plans . . . of the British Army . . . Spanish Peninsula* (1841).

Moore, James Carrick, *A Narrative of the Campaign of the British Army in Spain, Commanded by . . . Lieutenant General Sir John Moore* (1809).

Mornet, Daniel, *Les origines intellectuelles de la révolution française*, 3d ed. (1938).

Murat, Achille, *America and the Americans* (1849).

Nabonne, B., *La diplomatie du Directoire et Bonaparte* (1948).

Naylor, John, *Waterloo* (1960).

Ollivier, Albert, *Le dix-huit brumaire* (1959).

Oman, Carola, *Britain against Napoleon* (1942).

Oman, Sir Charles W. C., *A History of the Peninsular War*, 7 v. (1902–1930).

———, *Studies in the Napoleonic Wars* (1930).

Parker, Harold T., "Napoleon's Philosophy of Governing Conquered Territories," *South Atlantic Quarterly* (1952).

Pérez-Prendes, J. M. and Muñoz de Arracó, "Cortes de Castilla y Cortes de Cádiz," *Revista de Estudios Politicos* (1962).

Picard, L., *Guerres d'Espagne, Le prologue, 1807, expédition du Portugal* (1911).

Pingaud, A., "La politique italienne de Napoléon Ier," *Revue Historique* (1927).

Pitollet, Camille, "Napoléon à Valladolid en 1809," *Revista de Archivos* (1913).

Pla y Cargol, Joaquín, *La guerra de la independencia en Gerona y sus Comarcas* (1953).

Pouzerewsky, ———, *La charge de la cavalerie de Somo-Sierra (Espagne), le 30 novembre 1808* (1900).

Prado, J. García, et al., *Guerra de la independencia: Estudios* (Institución Fernando el Católico series) (1964).

Quimby, Robert S., *The Background of Napoleonic Warfare. The Theory of Military Tactics in 18th Century France* (1957).

Rambaud, Jacques, *Naples sous Joseph Bonaparte, 1806–1808* (1911).

Ramos, Demetrio, "Las Cortes de Cádiz y América," *Revista de Estudios Políticos* (1962).

Ramos-Oliveira, Antonio, *Politics, Economics, and Men of Modern Spain*, Trans. by Teener Hall (1946).

Reeves, Jesse S., *Napoleonic Exiles in America: A Study in American Diplomatic History 1815–1819* (1920).

Renée, A., "Les Bonapartes littérateurs," *La Revue de Paris* (1840).

Robinson, C. W., *Wellington's Campaigns, Peninsula to Waterloo*, 3 v. (1905–1906).

Rodriguez, Luciano Calzada, *La evolucion instituciónal, las Cortes de Cadiz: precedentes y consecuencias* (1959).

Rollin, H., "L'Amiral Villeneuve et Napoléon," *Revue des Etudes Napoléoniennes* (1913).

Rose, J. Holland, "Canning and the Spanish Patriots in 1808," *American Historical Review* (1906–1907).

———, *Napoleonic Studies* (1914).

Rosebery, Archibald Philip Primrose, Earl of, *Napoleon, The Last Phase* (1900).

Rosengarten, J. G., *French Colonists and Exiles in the United States* (1907).

Rosselli, John, *Lord William Bentinck and the British Occupation of Sicily* (1956).

Schrandenbach, Ludwig, *Psyche und Organization des "Volkeskrieges" untersuchtam spanischen Freiheitskampf gegen Napoleon* (1925).

Shafer, Robert Jones, *The Economic Societies in the Spanish World (1763–1821)* (1958).

Shand, Alexander Innes, *The War in the Peninsula, 1808–1814* (1898).

Sieburg, Friedrich, *Napoleon die hundert tage* (1962).

Soldevilla, Fernando, *Las Cortes de Cadiz* (1910).

Solís, Enrique Rodriguez, *Los guerrilleros de 1808. Historia Popular de la guerra de la independencia*, 2 v. (1887–1892).

Southey, Robert, *History of the Peninsula War*, 3 v. (1823–1832).

Suarez Verdeguer, Federico, "Sobre las ráices de las reformas de las Cortes de Cádiz," *Revista de Estudios Políticos* (1962).

———, "Las tendencias políticos durante la guerra de la independencia," pamphlet of *Institución Fernando el Católico* (1959).

Thiry, Jean, *L'avènement de Napoléon* (1959).

———, *Le coup d'état de 18 Brumaire* (1947).

———, *Ulm, Trafalgar, Austerlitz* (1963).

Toreño, José Maria, Conde de, *Histoire du soulèvement de la guerre et de la révolution d'Espagne*, 4 v. (1835–1836) [Spanish edition, 1838].

Tulard, Jean, *L'anti-Napoléon, la légende noire de l'Empereur* (1965).

Valicourt, Charles, Comte de, *Le conquête de Valence* (1905).

Vandal, Albert, *L'avènement de Bonaparte*, 2 v. 3d ed. (1907).

———, *Napoleon et Alexandre Ier, L'alliance russe sous le premier Empire*, 3 v. (1918–1934).

Vilar, P., "Élan urbain et mouvement des salaires. Le cas de Barcelone an XVIIIe siecle," *Revue d'Histoire Economique et Sociale* (1950).

Villafranca, Don Roman Gomez, *Extremadura en la guerra de la independencia española* (1908).

Villat, Louis, *La Révolution et L'Empire*, 2 v. (1936) [bibliography and commentary].

Weller, Jac, *Wellington in the Peninsula, 1808–1814* (1962).

Welschinger, H., *Le divorce de Napoléon* (1889).

Wheeler, H. F. B. and Broadley, A. M., *Napoleon and the Invasion of England,* 2 v. (1908).

Whitridge, Arnold, "Joseph Bonaparte in America," *History Today* (1959).

Woodward, E. M., *Bonaparte's Park and the Murats* (1879).

IV. Biographies

Abbott, Jacob, *Joseph Bonaparte* (1901).

Abbott, John Stevens Cabot, *History of Joseph Bonaparte, King of Naples and of Italy [sic]* (1869).

Adalbert, Prinz von Bayern, *Eugen Beauharnais, der Stiefsohn Napoleons* (1946).

Anglesey, Marquess, *One Leg, The Life and Letters of William Henry Paget* (1961).

Armoises, O. de, *Avant la gloire: Napoleon enfant, Napoleon et ses compatriotes* (1898).

Aronson, Theo, *The Golden Bees: the Story of the Bonapartes* (1964).

Atteridge, Andrew Hilliard, *Napoleon's Brothers* (1909).

Aubry, Octave, *Le roi de Rome* (1932).

Aureas, Henri, *Un général de Napoleon: Miollis* (1961).

Baelen, Jean, *Benjamin Constant et Napoleon* (1965).

Bartel, Paul, *La jeunesse inédite de Napoléon, d'après de nombreux documents* (1954).

Belmontet, Louis, *Biographie de Joseph-Napoléon Bonaparte* (1832).

———, *Joseph Napoléon jugé par ses contemporains* (1833).

Berger, Morroe, trans. and ed., *Madame de Staël: On Politics, Literature, and National Character* (1963).

Bertaut, J., *Le ménage Murat* (1958).

Bertier de Sauvigny, G. de, *Metternich et son temps* (1959).

Bertin, Georges, *Joseph Bonaparte en Amerique (1815–1832)* (1893).

Bishop, Joseph Bucklin, *Charles Joseph Bonaparte, His Life and Public Services* (1922).

Bonardi, P., *Napoléon Bonaparte, enfant d'Ajaccio: Nabulione* (1935).

Boulot, Georges, *Le général Duphot (1769–1797), par un de ses arrière-neveux* (1908).

Browning, O., *Napoleon, The First Phase: Some Chapters on the Boyhood and Youth of Bonaparte, 1769–1793* (1905).

Cambronero y Martinez, Carlos, *El Rey intruso; Apuntes históricos referentes à José Bonaparte* (1909).

Castelot, André, *King of Rome* (1960).

Chastenet, J., *Godoy, Master of Spain, 1792–1808* (1953).

Chuquet, A., *La jeunesse de Napoléon*, 3 v. (1892–1899).

Cole, Hubert, *Joséphine* (1963).

Colomba, Hélène, *Madame Walewska* (1964).

Corley, T. A. B., *Democratic Despot: A Life of Napoleon III* (1961).

Dawson, John Charles, *Lakanal: The Regicide* (1948).

Decaux, Alain, *Laetizia, mère de l'empereur* (1959).

Defourneaux, Marcelin, *Pablo de Olavide ou l'Afrancesado (1725–1803)* (1959).

Delderfield, Ronald F., *The Golden Millstones* (1964).

Demerson, Georges, *Don Juan Melendez Valdes et son temps (1754–1817)* (1962).

Driault, E., *Le roi de Rome* (1932).

Dupont, Marcel, *Murat* (1934).

Forsberg, R. J. and Nixon, H. C., *Madame de Staël* (1964).

Garnier, J. P., *Murat, Roi de Naples* (1959).

Gaulmier, Jean, *Un grand témoin de la révolution et de l'Empire, Volney* (1959).

Gautier, Paul, *Madame de Staël et Napoléon* (1921).

Gavoty, André, *Les amoureux de l'imperatrice Josephine* (1961).

Geer, W., *Napoleon and His Family*, 3 v. (1927–1928).

Goehring, M., *Napoleon: von alten zum neuen Europa* (1959).

Guérard, Albert, *Napoleon III* (1955).

Guillemin, H., *Madame de Staël, Benjamin Constant, et Napoleon* (1959).

Hanna, A. J., *A Prince in Their Midst: The Adventurous Life of Achille Murat* (1946).

Herold, J. Christopher, *Mistress to an Age* (1958).

Hochschild, Baron, *Désirée, reine de Suède et de Norvège* (1888).

Holland, Vyvyan, *Goya: A Pictorial Biography* (1961).

Hugo, Jean Abel, "Souvenirs et mémoires sur Joseph Bonaparte, sa cour, l'armée française, et l'Espagne en 1811, 1812, et 1813," *Revue des Deux Mondes,* 2e série (1833).

Kammacher, Leon, *Joseph Fouché* (1962).

Kircheisen, Friedrich M., *Napoleon Erste. Ein Lebensbild,* 2 v. (1929).

Knapton, Ernest John, *Empress Josephine* (1963).

Labarre de Raillicourt, Dominique, *Généraux des 100-jours et du gouvernement provisoire (mars–juillet, 1815)* (1965).

Larg, David Glass, *Madame de Staël* (1926).

Las Cases, Comte Emmanuel de, *Las Cases, le mémorialiste de Napoleon* (1959).

Leon, Paul L., *Benjamin Constant* (1963).

Leproux, Marc, *Un grand Français. Le Général Dupont, 1763–1840* (1934).

Lévy, Arthur, *Napoléon intime* (1893).

Lucas-Dubreton, Jean, *Louis-Philippe* (1938).

Macartney, Clarence Edward and Dorrance, Gordon, *The Bonapartes in America* (1939).

Marshall-Cornwall, James, *Marshal Massena* (1965).

Masson, Frédéric, *Les diplomates de la révolution* (1882).

——, *Napoléon et sa famille,* 13 v. (1905–1919).

Melchior-Bonnet, Bernadine, *Le Duc d'Enghien* (1961).

——, *Un policier dans l'ombre de Napoleon: Savary, duc de Rovigo* (1962).

Missoffe, Michel, *Metternich* (1959).

Morton, John Bingham, *Marshal Ney* (1958).

Nabonne, Bernard, *Bernadotte* (1948).

——, *Joseph Bonaparte, le Roi philosophe* (1949).

——, *Pauline Bonaparte* (1948).

Oman, Carola, *Nelson* (1954).

——, *Sir John Moore* (1953).

Papillard, François, *Cambacérès* (1961).

Piétri, François, *Lucien Bonaparte* (1939).

Pomaret, Charles, *Monsieur Thiers et son siècle* (1948).

Richardson, Norval, *Mother of Kings, Maria-Letizia Ramolina Bonaparte* (1929).

Rousselot, Jean, *La Fayette* (1962).

Roux, Georges, *Monsieur de Buonaparte* (1964).

Srbik, H. von, *Metternich, der Staatsman und der Mensch*, 3 v. (1925–1954).

Stirling, Monica, *Madame Letizia* (1961).

Stoeckl, Agnes de, *Four Years an Empress* (1961).

Tarlé, E., *Talleyrand* (1958).

Tower, Charlemagne, "Joseph Bonaparte in Philadelphia and Bordentown," *Pennsylvania Magazine of History and Biography* (1918).

Valentin, René, *Le maréchal Masséna* (1960).

Vallotton, Henri, *Marie-Thérèse Impératrice* (1963).

Villa-Urrutia, Marquis de, *El Rey José Napoléon* (1927).

Waite, Richard Alfred, Jr., "Sir Home Riggs Popham: A Biography," Unpublished doctoral dissertation (1945).

Walsh, Robert, *Biographical Sketch of Joseph Napoleon Bonaparte* (1833).

Ward, S. P. G., *Wellington* (1963).

Weiner, Margery, *The Parvenu Princesses* (1964).

Welschinger, Henri, *Le Maréchal Ney* (1915).

Wertheimer, Eduard von, *The Duke of Reichstadt* (1905).

Wright, Constance, *Hortense, reine de l'empire* (1963).

V. General

Altamira y Crevea, Rafael, *Historia de España y de la civilizacion española*, 4 v. 3d ed. (1913–1914).

The American Nation, 28 v., Ed. by Albert B. Hart (1904–1918).

Artz, Frederick B., *France under the Bourbon Restoration* (1931).

Bailey, Thomas A., *A Diplomatic History of the American People*, 6th ed. (1958).

Ballesteros y Beretta, Antonio, *História de España y sus influencia el la história universal*, 9 v. 2d ed. (1918–1941).

Bignon, Louis, Baron, *Histoire de France sous Napoléon*, 14 v. (1838–1850).

Bourgeois, É., *Manuel historique de politique étrangère*, 4 v. (1892–1926).

Butterfield, H., *The Peace Tactics of Napoleon 1806–1808* (1929).

Cambridge History of British Foreign Policy, 1785–1919, Ed. by A. W. Ward and George P. Gooch (1922–1923).

Connelly, Owen, *Napoleon's Satellite Kingdoms* (1965).

Churchill, Winston S., *The Age of Revolution* (1957).

Dehio, Ludwig, *The Precarious Balance: The Politics of Power in Europe 1494–1945* (1962).

Deutsch, H. C., *Genesis of Napoleonic Imperialism* (1938).

Driault, Édouard, *Napoléon et L'Europe*, 5 v. (1910–1927).

Dunan, Marcel, ed., *Napoléon et L'Europe* (1960).

Fugier, André, *La révolution française et l'empire Napoléonienne* (1954).

Godechot, Jacques, *La Grande Nation: L'Expansion révolutionnaire de la France dans le monde*, 2 v. (1956).

Kircheisen, Friedrich M., *Napoleon I, sein Leben und seine Zeit*, 9 v. (1911–1934).

Lafuente, Don Modesto, *Historia general de España*, 25 v. (1889–1890).

La Gorce, Pierre de, *La restauration*, 2 v. (1926–1928).

Lefebvre, A., *Histoire des cabinets de l'Europe pendant le consulat et l'Empire*, 3 v. (1847).

Lefebvre, Georges, *La Revolution Française*, 3d. ed., rev. (1963).

——, *Napoléon*, 4th ed. (1953).

Madelin, Louis, *Le Consulat et l'Empire*, 2 v. (1933).

Mowat, R. B., *The Diplomacy of Napoleon* (1924).

Palmer, R. R., *The Age of Democratic Revolution*, 2 v. (1959–1964).

Pariset, Georges, *Le Consulat et l'Empire* (volume III, E. Lavisse, ed., *Histoire de France contemporaine*) (1921).

Sorel, Albert, *L'Europe et la Révolution française*, 8 v. (1885–1904).

Tarlé, E. V., *Napoléon*, 3d ed. (1964).

Thiers, M. A., *Histoire du Consulat et de l'Empire*, 21 v. (1845–1869).

Thiry, Jean, *La chute de Napoléon*, 7 v. (1939–1945).

Index

INDEX